Farmer's Diary

Charlie Allan

*Illustrations by
Turnbull*

Ardo Publishing Company
Methlick, Aberdeenshire AB41 0HR

I am grateful to *The Herald* for permission
to reproduce these articles, which first appeared
in print in that newspaper.

Published by Ardo Publishing Company, Buchan

This volume is dedicated to Sarah and Neil Purdie who have taken over my peasant's obligation to the farm of Little Ardo and to Clare and Christine Purdie to whom I shall be looking for an eighth generation of us on this hill.

F5 ALL

1059225

Foreword

AS I write I am into my tenth year of writing this Farmer's Diary and I would like to thank the editors who have put up with me for so long.

As well as my gratitude I would like to express my admiration for the way that Jim Turnbull has managed, for almost a decade, to interpret my writings with his cartoons. So many people tell me how much they enjoy them that I must confess to occasional pangs of jealousy.

The Breadwinner was too busy preparing the computers of Aberdeen for the Millennium to undertake the desk-top publishing of this volume but luckily I had a ready-made replacement in the Younger Investment. Susan Allan, who has kept her maiden name, works on the Edinburgh Evening News and put Volume Five into shape during her maternity leave whose main reason was to produce a Dividend called Elizabeth.

The Elder Investment, Sarah Purdie, read the proofs so thoroughly that I got fed up checking them. She can therefore be blamed safely for any remaining errors.

Murray Webster and the firm of BPC Wheatons fought off opposition from as far away as India to retain the printing contract and have done their usual good job.

The story so far

LITTLE ARDO is a 250-acre farm on the gently sloping north side of Ythanvale. That means it lies towards the sun which helps its second class loam to grow anything that is consistent with the climate of Buchan. It has been farmed for at least 200 years and probably many more. The Breadwinner has found several flint arrowheads in the garden.

His family having become Lord Aberdeen's tenants there in the 1830s, Charlie Allan started to contribute to the farm's history in 1946 when he helped his father plant the trees so badly needed then. It was a bare place (like so much of Buchan is still) with only 13 trees to protect the 18th century farmhouse from the hurricanes sent down from the North Atlantic.

The boy worked and played, and played at work, through a happy childhood among the cows, the corn, the neeps and the silage. In the early days when there was no use for girls, there were plenty of boys on the farm, for the staff of six were fertile. So much so that there was a football league, admittedly with only two teams, but there were real matches and a shield to be won.

One of the few frustrations suffered by the young Farmer was that when driving the tractor between the stooks at the age of seven he was made to give up the wheel when the bigger boys got home from school. I don't know what the Health and Safety Executive would have made of that but if there was one it didn't bother us much.

It was in 1976 that John R. Allan took Jean and what money there was, and left for retirement in a muse cottage in Lincoln. Then The Farmer got hold of the reins and the overdraft, and began to enjoy the suffering which is the peasant's inheritance.

But like a true peasant he embraced the falling down buildings, which had been falling down when his grandfather had bought the place from the Laird in 1920, with joy. He built three new sheds, put down an acre of concrete, stocked the place with exotic pedigree cattle from Europe and built up an overdraft described by one consultant as 'a suicide note'.

Escape was effected by taking a job with the BBC, the continuing efforts of The Breadwinner in computers, and reducing the cattle numbers from 700 to 100.

By 1986 the overdraft was

4

under control and a holiday was called for. The Breadwinner got a job in Africa and The Farmer went as her best pal.

These diaries began in 1989 when they returned to the farm. Farming had to be restarted from scratch. A successor had to be found and a retirement fundie had to be accumulated so that The Farmer could retire in comfort.

As Volume Five starts the victim has been found. He is Potions, who married the Elder Investment and who was not satisfied by life over a Chemist's shop.

This volume covers the period of the 'great sook'. The Farmer accumulates as hard as he can, skimping on maintenance and lime, to put as much as he can into the fundie. In this endeavour he exploits Potions'

uncertainty as to when he will be allowed to take over.

The lad daren't ask for wages as he must not offend The Farmer and he wants the fundie to grow as fast as possible to encourage the old man to go soon.

The series ends with The Farmer and The Breadwinner leaving the old farmhouse he and his mother came to 53 years earlier, for the new bungalow among the trees he helped his father plant in 1953.

Volume Five is subtitled The Last Laugh because there should not be another volume – "Retired Farmer's Diary" just doesn't have the same ring to it.

Charlie and Fiona Allan have been married to each other continuously for 37 years and have four married children and ten grandchildren.

Here comes Sunty

WHEN THE Farmer's sons and heirs were just changing from sweet little boys to Wasting Assets, they invited their friend Hugh to come to Little Ardo for a shoot.

They would borrow The Farmer's guns, which at that time ran to a single shot four-ten and an old double barrel twelve bore. Those were the days before The Farmer's armoury complied with the law and was securely under lock and key, so I'm not sure that they had permission.

No matter, the three boys and the two guns spent a harmless day parading the fields in a fashion so guileless that they were more danger to themselves than to any wildlife. At last however, the three, game bags (cattle-feed bags with baler twine for straps) still empty, approached the steading. The Wasting Assets with the twelve bore from the north, and Hugh with the four-ten from the south. The idea, which was sound enough, was that, in fleeing from the Assets, the game would fly straight into the range of young Hugh, and vice-versa.

It worked too. Nothing was actually shot but several black-birds and a feral pigeon were surprised by being shot at again as they fled.

But then the Assets heard a scream of terror from the other side of the steading. Hugh had thrown his gun from him in panic at his success and raced round to his friends. "There was this low-flying goose and I've shot it and it's died."

"What a success," you might think, but the Assets were not impressed.

"No no, Hugh. That goose had a name. That's one of them the bantie hen's been raising. And anither thing. They canna flee."

I think it was then that Hugh decided to emigrate, though that was an unnecessary step. Like many a hard-pressed mother, the Bantie had been glad to have one fewer to look after. It was bad enough at night climbing up on top of the one remaining goose and spreading her wings to keep it warm, and the goose five times her size, without having two to get under her wings. And I only found out what happened to that goose fifteen years later.

It came out at the Christmas dinner table. Isn't it wonderful what a healer time is? Fifteen years ago the Wasting Assets would have faced death rather than admit to that killing, and they might even have faced death if they had.

There were a few moments such as that at our table, such as what my mother said when she was eighty to her second great-grandchild. We thought her pretty demented at that time but the story shows there was a good deal of wit there yet. The three-year-old asked, "Are you old, Jean?" To which her great grandmother replied, "No, but I've been young for a very long time."

We also got a bit fed up of the jokes in the crackers. Surely we could do better than that?

But many of the jokes we like wouldn't be thought appropriate. No jokes about sex, religion, or race, for example. In the end we only could agree on one. It had the advantage of being a poem as well as a joke.

"Roses are red,
Violets are blue
I'm schizophrenic
And so am I."

The Recovery Stock was very proud of that one until the youngest Investment pointed out that you couldn't put that in a cracker in case it was bought by the family of a schizophrenic. "You're a high priest of pedantry," says The Farmer.

She fixed him with a steely stare, "PriestESS."

The Farmer missed Santa again this year. He had left out a good dram just in case he wasn't back from seeing to the cow. The Farmer made it a big one of his best malt and put in the water himself because he knows Santa hates it drowned.

The three grandchildren who are old enough to wonder, are wondering at the physical resemblance between Suntie and The Farmer. They are also suspicious at the voice which, especially when he gets annoyed, is just like The Farmer's.

They also think there is something familiar about the sharn on Suntie's wellies. But imagine the triumph of the eight-year-old when she spied something else. "Suntie, why are you wearing Granda Charlie's watch?"

"Shut up and open your presents," the old gentleman snapped, just like a real Santa.

As he was leaving, Santa gave the assembled company a salutary lesson. "To whom," he said, "do I give the invoice?"

"I thought it was for nothing," gasped the Bohemian from Edinburgh who was escorting the unmarried Investment.

Santa blew a fuse.

"Free is it? I'll give ye free. This is Christmas Day, boy, I'll have you know. Do you think if I wasna on double time I

7

wouldna be at hame enjoyin my ain Christmas wi Mrs Santa instead of dishing out presents to a puckle spoiled brats?"

Feeling the better of his outburst, Santa calmed down. "Anyway you don't have to pay it this year. This is just a dry run for next year, after we've went privatised."

January 9, 1995

New Year shoot

IT WAS just typical. Mossie didn't turn up for my shoot until the hard work had been done and we were settling in to the Stilton and port.

I'm glad he did come though, for he told us a fine story. It came out when I was telling the shooters that I had, for the second time in my life, shot eight pigeons with one shot. They had been grazing the cuffins I had brought home from the mill to encourage the pheasants to stay on Little Ardo rather than going away to feed with Lord Aberdeen's.

In the spirit of pest control, rather than in the strange name of sport, I shot into the bunch from the cab of the old lorry.

I don't think Mossie liked me getting the limelight. "Och just steading doos? That's naething. I once shot eight ducks." That did make us sit up.

The 16-year-old Mossie had been out with his father's gun when he had seen a flock of ducks among the stubble in a field neighbouring Moss-side. They were near to the edge and were all grouped together, gorging themselves on some spilt grain.

Ignoring the fact that neither the field nor the ducks were in the family, he peered over the edge of the ditch.

At a distance of no more than twenty yards he fired into the pack. Even then the ducks didn't fly off. They all ran squawking off in the direction of the neighbour's steading.

The implications of all that didn't impress the sixteen-year-old. What success! The heap of feathers on the grain spill contained no fewer than eight ducks. What a shot! What a hunter he was.

When he was selling his bag he asked the butcher what variety they were. They looked a bit like female Mallard, but where were the drakes? "Mallard!" said the butcher, "That's

8

nae Mallard. That's Khaki Campbell's ducks. They hadna been hard to shoot, laddie. Mind, they're grand layers."

When the neighbour asked Mossie if he could help solve the mystery of the eight missing ducks the lad was quite unable to do so.

Up till this year I'd have said the Little Ardo pheasants were the smartest in the world. You never see one when you have your gun. They are always missing when I have my annual shoot, and yet, come the first of February and the close season, they're everywhere. They come right up to the door and into the buildings for scraps.

My shoot is usually a disaster. Our record was last year's six. Anyway, we did better this year and shot 22. Everybody got a brace and The Breadwinner is finding out what it is to be a farmer's wife with pheasants to pluck.

I'm sad really. I much prefer to see those beautiful birds pecking around the place. All the same, most are going to die in the winter anyway and a thinning does increase the chances of those which remain.

I nearly got away without having a shoot or indeed any of the hangovers associated with the Pagan festival of New Year. A great storm blew up on Hogmanay. We were totally blocked in. A week on our own and it would all be over.

But, unfortunately, we had revellers trapped with us. So, fortified only by my sore head, I had to yoke the old snow plough. It was totally under the

9

snow, it had no pins for the three point linkage, and no top link. I could have cried by the time the frozen fingers had the old thing ready for the road.

Five hours of craning round and the road was open. By going through one field of barley we could avoid the deepest drifts and I cleared the 400 remaining yards to the road.

But, just as my New Year guests were free to go, so were all and sundry free to come in and visit us.

There was to be no peace for the poor Farmer.

I had Penny Washers the white settler to dig out as well. He is about a mile further off the road than me and thought he

was stuck for good. However I was able to plough a couple of hundred yards towards him. I explained he could take down the wires on the fence into our rape. He was ever so grateful.

But there is nothing to letting down the wires. It is only a few pulls and a few bangs with a hammer and it can be repaired in one minute. And if you stick to the tramlines there should be no damage to the fields.

BUT ... Not having a clue about living in the country, Penny Washers dismantled 100 yards of the fence ... rolling the barbed wires up neatly ... and I'll have to look at the diagonal he made through the barley till harvest.

January 16, 1995

Drowned in muck

WE CAN'T complain about 1994 and, if a farmer can't complain ... that's a good year.

But lest you think The Farmer's life is all cakes and ale, let me tell you of two accidents which have befallen me already since Christmas.

On Boxing Day, the ground being dry and the cattle on the slats being in great danger of becoming wet, I decided to put out some slurry. I've been

struggling with these slurry tanks for some time and Mossie is determined that I should do away with them. 'If you're feeding straw or silage you'll always have them solid," he says.

But the slats cost me a fortune and, with bedding going as high as £10 a bale this year, I was loath to do as he advised. Besides, I have come across a chemical called Pit-Boss which

claims to take care of the problem of the slurry going solid.

I've been trying it and it seems to work. Each six-week cycle I get more out. The last time it was a load and a half and on Boxing Day I got over three loads out of my first tank. And, do you know, slurry treated with Pit-Boss doesn't smell?

That is just as well.

I've done it before, as has every farmer, but I've never before given myself a harling like I did on Boxing Day.

The slurry tanker discharges its liquid manure from the rear. It comes flying out under pressure, and to make it spread nicely, it is sprayed onto a metal plate from which it splashes up in the air to maybe ten feet and covers the field evenly to a width of perhaps 30 feet. To increase the spraying effect there is an attachment you put on when discharging which has the effect of narrowing the pipe. This narrowed pipe can block.

And so it did on Boxing Day. To cut a long story short, instead of reversing the pump so that the blockage could be pushed in, I tried to unblock the pipe with a stick, intending to jump neatly out of the way when the slurry lake was released. Sadly my jumping-neatly-out-of-the-way days are done. An arthritic knee refused to jump and fell down under the cascade of liquid manure. They say it is lucky.

But there is no sign of that yet, for I have had another reminder of how dangerous our job can be.

I was taking in some treated straw in case, with the promise of a thaw, the cornyard might become impassable.

The bales are stacked in threes, one above two, and I was taking all three at once. It is a balancing feat I do always and which landed a young neighbour in hospital last summer.

Of course, he didn't have a safety cab. I was quite safe, or so I thought.

I was struggling so hard to get wheelgrip on the icy ruts that I failed to notice the top bale falling backwards towards me until it was too late.

I didn't feel the least bit threatened. But I should have.

The five foot bale had come down onto the digger's exhaust chimney. When I lowered the loader to let it down the pipe went further in. And when I lifted the loader up it jammed the bale onto the front of the cab. To lift the bale clear of the lum I would have to smash the cab. I was stuck but I still wasn't unduly worried until I realised that the blue stuff wasn't exhaust fumes but smoke from burning straw.

I switched the engine off but it was too late. The pipe was too hot. I tried to smother the flames with my jacket and seemed to have succeeded several times but always the flames started again.

It looked as though my poor digger was doomed to have a quarter of a tonne of straw burn out on top of it. I set out to limit the damage by dismantling the bale with my pen knife though I could see that would let air in and I would be engulfed.

At last I noticed that the chimney had snapped. I was then able to pull it out of the way. That left the bale resting on the lift arms of the loader. With the strength given by panic, the thought of my neighbours seeing what a state I was in, and the nagging doubts about what was covered by the insurance (and if the insurance was paid up), I managed to shoulder the flaming mass off.

The total damage was a few fire blisters on my hands, one bale of treated straw demolished and a slight dent in the roof of the cab. To set against that, I won't have to go to the barber for ages.

I have learned two lessons. Two bales at a time is plenty and carry a small fire extinguisher in your tractor. Only time will tell if I will take the lessons but they are quite clear.

Of course I'm not the only one who has had fun with the weather. The Irishman who bought Mossie's outfarm was quite unprepared for the wild horizontal snow which filled the roads level with the dykes. Luckily, after Mossie's stewardship, the dykes weren't that high, but it was a far cry from the gentle Irish snow.

"There was nothing about this in the particulars," he protested.

"Na, na. We tended to stress the good points. But you can mention the snow when you're selling," said Mossie, helpfully.

A Dog Called Honda

WHAT A huge country Scotland is. Little Ardo is 230 miles from the north coast. And yet, after driving 285 miles south, I was still 240 miles from the Border. That was last week when I went down to Campbeltown to address the Annual meeting of the Kintyre Branch of the National Farmer's Union of Scotland.

I had been there before though on much sadder business.

It was about 1975 that I sold a fine looking Simmental bull to Mr William McKerral of the Bleachfields at Campbeltown. He cost about 1900 gns, which was no mean trade at that time. And he was looking well. One of those light coloured Simmentals who stood tall, he was well fleshed and big boned. Had he not been a little bit straight of his back legs I would have fancied that bull for a champion, and so would Mr McKerral.

But it was not only his back legs that were less than perfect. After three weeks the cows he'd seen to all came back. Another three weeks and he might have settled one. Tests were done. They showed that our fine looking bull was firing not fewer than 93 blanks out of 100.

That was bad. I was setting myself up as a breeder of fine bulls and here they were all show and no go.

But if it was bad for me it was a potential disaster for my client. His calves were late and getting later by the day. I had two young bulls and an old float so the answer was obvious.

I loaded them up. I would

13

start early, arrive at dinner-time and drive back in the afternoon.

That was a fine plan except that by closing time that night I had only got as far as Inveraray. In the old Albion float it was a two-day journey to Campbeltown, never mind back.

What a contrast last week. In the Jaggie it took five hours.

I must say they've got their Union well organised. The annual meeting was held in a suite of two rooms; a very small meeting room and a very large bar. Those proportions were ideal for those members who found they had to remain in the bar until the formal business was over and the real business could begin.

And the real business was enhanced by the announcement from the chair that this was in fact Auld Eel (January 6). It is some years since I enjoyed that excuse for another seasonal refreshment but we all stuck in with a will.

It was a very jolly occasion which emphasised to me once again that farming folk are much the same wherever you meet them. There were many fine stories of farming life on Kintyre.

I can only remember one.

It reminded me of the time that the Red Rooster was shot at a shoot in Aberdeenshire. At the end when the game was laid out for the count, the Rooster lay down between the pheasants and the hares, a little trickle of blood running from a pellet below his eye.

My friend from Kintyre would cap that with the story of the famous shoot for which 400 pheasants had been put down. The bag had been disappointing though, amounting to only 23 pheasants, seven rabbits and a greenhouse. I have had many's the happy moment since I was told about that, thinking about what they could have said to the greenhouse owner. I once kicked a football through the side of one and that was bad enough, but shooting a greenhouse is, as they will say nowadays, something else.

I liked Kintyre. It reminded me of when I was a boy and Aberdeenshire was an agricultural community. Now the land here is for living in rather than working on. But driving around on Old New Year's Day, with local President Donald Taylor, was like the old days driving round with my father. He would know nine tenths of the people he met whereas I will be lucky if I know one in ten.

The dog population is changing though.

I used to think I was very clever to think of using Honda my fourwheeled dog for herding the cattle, but I find everyone in this stock and dairy country has one. Typically a farmer who once had three dogs now has two and a motor bike.

One dog on the front, one on the back and a driver make the perfect modern team for herding. It is a breakthrough, though it can be dangerous. One eager collie jumped off and was killed by a passing car. The farmer braked, sending the other flying off, whereupon he ran it over himself.

And the four wheelers can be dangerous for the men as well. The trouble is that you get excited when the chase is on and you forget that all this speed is coming from a machine, and that there are limits to its stability. I heard horrendous tales of shepherds trying to turn after a rogue on a steep slope and the bike going somersaulting down the hill.

Thank goodness I didn't get Honda when I was young. With the timidity of age I am in little danger.

And how good she is. My cattle know they cannot win. As often as they break for the bottom of the field so will I be there waiting for them, and not even out of breath. They know that now and they hate Honda so much for it, that, as soon as we start to circle them, they bolt for the gate.

January 30, 1995

Feed the pigeons

THE WOOD-PIGEONS are back feeding on the rape. They haven't bothered us for the last two years. We thought they had so much setaside to feed on that they weren't bothering.

And yet they are back feeding in their thousands. I only had to go away for two days and they had cleaned all the foliage off two of my six fields.

That has been something of a talking point among the boys at the Salmon Inn. The Irishman has had three acres cleaned up. He presumed they were lost and wanted to know how to avoid losing his remaining hundred acres.

We were quick to put his mind at ease. "It won't do it the slightest harm. As long as it is well-rooted the rape will come on strong in the spring. It might be a few days later at harvest but it won't affect the yield. In fact it may help your disease control. If there are no leaves in winter there is no need to spray with fungicides. The only dis-

15

advantage with the doos is if they only eat one bit so that it ripens unevenly and you can't get it all cut at once."

"The Irishman's will all be ready at the same time. I know, because I'm cutting it," says Mossie.

"But should I not be getting a banger?" says the Irishman. We put a stop to that idea. The bangers are completely effective for an area of about ten square yards round the gun so you need about five hundred guns to the acre.

Mossie remembers the time he found a bird's nest in one of his gas guns. In fact almost nobody bothers with them nowadays. They are the worst possible publicity for the industry and they don't work.

All this was explained to the Irishman. What we didn't explain was that pigeons can't be in two places at once. As long as they were eating his crops they couldn't be eating ours.

Anyway, the Irishman was fly enough not to take the advice and has managed to keep most of the doos flying. That, I supposed, was the reason they had all landed at Little Ardo.

Mossie had another theory.

As you know he has been giving me his second-best advice on spraying my crops. The banker could (if we still had such a thing rather than just a hole-in-the-wall connected by red tape to a bank of computers) testify to the fact that this advice has been a considerable improvement on what went before it. By way of reward Mossie would accept a day's shooting at the joint expense of myself and Her Majesty.

And so it was we landed at Auchmacoy. It is only the second time I've been to a shoot when the laird was at home.

I brought the soup, the sandwiches, the Stilton and the port and was determined to do right by my guest. But if I ever get cornered into such an expense again I'll just do the paying and let him do the shooting.

I am a good hunter. If I decide I want a pheasant for the pot or a hare to make soup for the gods, I can go out with my gun and be back very quickly with my mission accomplished. But there's something about standing freezing in line looking like one of the Virgin Soldiers, that doesn't suit me.

I did shoot a partridge on the first drive and a pheasant on the second. I'd have had a third kill had Mossie not hit it again before it reached the ground.

After that I suffered humiliation upon humiliation. When I go hunting in my own wood no one sees me miss. But out there in the open no error goes unaccounted.

My greatest disaster was at

a patch of game crop. I had the prime spot at the end of the field and the whole effort was designed to funnel the game down to me. Beaters and dogs in front of me and eager guns to the left and right, I waited.

The strategy was a great success ... except that all the birds decided to fly at once. One broke and came low. "Game over," shouted the Red Rooster. "Too low," screamed Mossie, as I swung my gun at it. I let it through and missed with one shot. I would reload. But that was the signal for about twenty pheasants to fly straight out at me. There was no time to reload. I would fire off my remaining cartridge. I took too long aiming and then ... nothing. I hadn't put the safety catch off. By the time I had fired and reloaded I couldn't have hit a barn door with a shovel.

And that gave Mossie his theory about why ten thousand pigeons are so keen to graze on Little Ardo this year. "They ken they're safe. They saw you sheetin at Auchmacoy."

The emigrant's farewell

WE HAD a party on Monday night to say goodbye to the latest from this hill to seek a new life in what used to be called the Empire. The fact that the émigré was a granddaughter, was called after him and was only seven years old, gave The Farmer a meaning to the words, "parting is such sweet sorrow".

Charlie Jean has been spending school terms with her father, the Recovery Stock, in his new family at Fraserburgh and her holidays in Edinburgh with her mother.

She likes the farm and indeed is the only one of her generation to show any interest in livestock. She likes to feed the cattle with handfuls of cake from the bag, and there is no anthropomorphic nonsense about her. When I showed her the little piggies gambolling in the straw she asked eagerly, "Can you eat them?" If we had her for longer we could help her avoid the hazards of vegetarianism.

Of course, we're used to sending our best abroad. I have told you of my great-grandmother in 1909 watching the last of her three sons setting off for the Empire. She never saw any of them again and is said to have complained only once. Then, she told of her longing to hear from Jimmy before she died. He had never even managed a letter.

My grandfather's siblings stayed in Scotland but my mother had a cousin Sandy who planted tea in Ceylon, and cousin John, who went to Canada and became the boss of Long John (from which he got the inevitable nickname Whisky Johnny) before climbing to the top of the American booze tree as Chairman of Schenleys.

That was my mother's side. In a pattern which was once familiar in these parts, my father's father went to California when the baby was announced and his mother left soon after he was born. That way I got seven aunts in California and an aunt and two uncles in Canada. And two of my father's uncles followed their little sister to the Americas.

So Charlie Jean stood in a proud tradition when she embraced her family on Monday.

There was her uncle, the Wasting Asset who realises that the thing he is wasting most is the chance to produce people like her. There were her aunts; the Investments. Her two cousins were there and the half sister who she loves dearly but is as yet too young to do much loving back. She may meet that sister some day as a stranger when they are grown up. She comforted her grandmother with, "But I'll come back for your funeral, Granny."

"Damn the funeral," said The Breadwinner, "I won't see you at all if you don't come before I'm dead."

It was the Recovery Stock who said we would need to have a speech. It seemed odd to have a toast to one so young, but I agreed that it might help to give her a sense of occasion and give her another thing to remember the other half of her family by.

It was agreed that a doting uncle would be best so the Wasting Asset was chosen. After a few minutes to think about it, he decided he wouldn't manage. He is first rate when it comes to riot control at a rave, but so heart-searching a task as a farewell toast to a seven-year-old niece was too much.

So The Farmer got the job.

I'd have liked to tell her about the generations who have gone forth from here. And how, though they were scattered, there were always enough of us left on this hill for it to remain a

19

home for them all. I'd have liked to tell her about her great-great-great uncle Dod and how each year he wrote from Australia that he couldn't afford to come home yet. And how, in the hour of this country's greatest need, Uncle Dod, who never made it himself, sent a son to fight in the Battle of Britain and how that young pilot took me sledging.

I'd have liked to tell her that every few years another young backpacker appears in the village looking for Little Ardo. They are looking for their roots. And I should have told her that we would always try to be here for all those young people whose families had taken the step that she was about to take.

But all I managed was to say how lucky we were to have so many children and so many grandchildren to have a nice party with. And how we should not be selfish. With so many, we could spare another one for the new world. I told her we wished her well and looked forward to the day when she would come back to see us. Granny, far from being dead, would dance at her wedding.

Then, to our astonishment, the seven-year-old, with no mother there to prompt her, climbed onto her chair and made a wonderful speech in reply. Wearing the tartan dress which might have fitted six months ago, and looking so beautiful with her clear skin, blonde hair and sparkling blue eyes, she told her family assembled at the table; "Thank you for coming to my party. I am very excited cos I'm going to Australia. But I'll be sad as well because I'll miss all of youse."

And she didn't cry until later ...

But the Wasting Asset did.

February 13, 1995

Doodo is a Figaro

I WENT off to Perth on Wednesday to buy a replacement for poor old Argus. It's an important job because when you buy your bull you are buying half your herd. I swore I'd be careful. Now that The Breadwinner is at home doing the books she cannot be fooled. I must not go far above my limit of £3000.

I should have bought the Junior Champion for he only just beat my limit. I got bidding

constipation. It looked like a bargain. Then it looked more like a bargain. Then it was chapped out to someone else and my hands were still in my pockets.

But soon I was bidding away, trying to snatch something below three thousand. I succeeded, though I am not proud of the manner of it.

This decent-looking bull from Norfolk stuck at 1200 gns. I mentioned to my neighbour that he had a fabulous 400 day weight. He said "And he's got a top EBV." I'd never come across that one before but I was impressed.

So I bid and got half my herd for 1300 guineas.

Now my neighbour was Alan Fotheringham, a leader of that most scientific of breeds, the Limousins, so I presumed his advice was good. But on my other flank was Keith Redpath who, as a dealer, can't afford many mistakes. He kindly informed me that the figure on which I had bought my new herdsire was not the EBV but the certainty with which the predicted result would occur. On the real EBV my bull was no better than average.

But then neither was his price.

The Breadwinner was not pleased with him. It wasn't his EBV but his name she didn't like.

A bull's name should suggest he is masculine without being aggressive. You wouldn't call a bull Cyril nor would you call him Cantona. And you would call a bull Michael as in Heseltine, rather than Mickey as in Mouse. Our old bull was called Argus, suggesting an outward-looking bull going forth to multiply.

And what is my latest herdsire called? What name follows in the proud line from Columbus through Esquire and Tiberius?

Well, he's called Doodo.

I think we'll call him Dod.

Dod was not impressed by Little Ardo. He arrived in a blizzard and was stuck in a pen in an open-fronted shed with no straw. He had been dying for a drink and the water was frozen.

I soon got him a nice bed and carried water from the house. But where was his mash? And where was his fresh meadow hay? He thinks two pounds of cattle feeding nuts are a poor do. And ammonia-treated straw? He thinks I must be joking.

But the lad was over 14 hundredweights at 13 months old and he has to get into training for a summer's work. He has forty-odd cows to see to on the first of June and he'll likely get a baptism of fire on my neighbour Gowkie's braes for three weeks before that.

In last Wednesday's snow, I took The Breadwinner to see our new herdsire. I knew he would never look so well again.

Buying a bull at the bottom end of the trade seemed a long way from the days when we won the Supreme Championship at Edinburgh with Ardo Dante and followed that up a couple of years later with Figaro when they moved the big sale to Perth.

We were having a dram in Dod's honour and feeling a wee bit nostalgic when The Breadwinner let out a little squeel. Her eyes were shining. She had the catalogue open.

"He's a grandson of Figaro!"

So confused was I about EBVs and trying to see why so average a bull had stuck so far below the average price, I hadn't noticed.

But now I saw my chance. "That was my little surprise darling," I said. "We haven't had much success in recent years so I'm going back to Figaro." I didn't even blush.

Now here is a moral tale. If you feel the pressure is on us because we've succeeded in providing enough food for the country, you may enjoy it.

Once upon a time a little brown hen found some grains of wheat and asked the other animals to help her sow them.

"Too tired," said the cow. "Union rules," said the duck. "Sore back," said the horse. "No environmental impact study done," said the goose.

The hen sowed the grain, tended it and harvested it. Then she wanted a hand to make bread. "Still too tired," said the cow. "At this time of night?" said the duck. "I'll lose my dole," said the horse. "I'm applying to become a Site of Special Scientific Interest," said the goose.

So the hen baked five delicious loaves. "Give me some," they all said at once.

"No," said the little brown hen. "I've done the work. Now I'll rest a while."

"Capitalist pig," bellowed the cow. "What about the workers?" demanded the duck. "But my need is greater," said the horse. "Multi-national agent for a uni-cellular society," taunted the goose, though the little hen didn't feel very taunted as she had no idea what that meant. The others painted picketing signs and paraded round the little brown hen singing "We shall overcome."

And they did overcome. The farmer came to see what all the commotion was about. "Oh you selfish little hen," he said, "You must learn to share."

"But I worked hard for that bread."

"Exactly," said the farmer. "That is what free enterprise is. You are free to work as hard as you like. If you were on a communist farm you'd have to give up all your bread, but here you are free to share it."

So they all lived happily ever after. Especially the goose. For she got a big research grant to find out why the little hen gave up baking.

February 20, 1995

The end of the "Death House"

POTIONS IS in trouble. He and his wife were at a freebie weekend – they had sold the most toothpaste in the district or something.

One of the hotel's gimmicks was that "The Man in Black" (he's the boy in the advert who flies through hell and high water to bring chocolates to his lady friend) would deliver chocs to the guests.

The landlord donned his black mask and nipped round the rooms delivering very small boxes of chocolates to the

23

guests, most of whom were delighted.

Not so Potions. He had just returned from the bar all fired up with aggression after an afternoon watching Scotland trying to beat France at rugby. The Investment was having a quick shower when the manager appeared at the bedroom door.

Potions was confronted with this person in a woolly stocking over his head complete with eye-holes, holding out a small black object which he thought might have been a gun. With reflexes honed by an afternoon of Guinness and watching Peter Wright, he lashed out and sent the manager crashing across the hall.

Disgraceful behaviour, no doubt, but The Farmer is quite pleased. When we retire and Potions brings the Investment back to her ancestral home, he is going to need a bit of bite.

I too have been getting a bit of stick – from high places.

We were down at the Death place of Robert Burns celebrating the 200th anniversary of that sad event with the Guild of Agricultural Journalists. It was a splendid do when all those agricultural journalists who are so boring in print showed themselves to be very witty when it comes to the spoken word.

Kenny Fletcher of the Scottish Farmer gave a most original address to the haggis and Allan Wright of Farmer's Weekly's Immortal Memory was an absolute tour de force. It wasn't the usual speech-cum-lecture with three jokes, one every twenty minutes. It consisted of one side of a conversation supposed to have taken place in Dumfries 200 years ago, between one of the many who hadn't heard of the bard and one of the few who realised that we would be celebrating this man's death 200 years later.

One of the guests was Andrew Dunlop, the farmer of Mid Kelton and Chairman of the Royal Highland and Agricultural Society.

He took me to task for calling our proposed house the Death House. He is upset by the image of the ageing farmer and his squaw setting off into the Canadian wilderness with nothing to protect them but a tepee.

That may be his image but it certainly isn't mine. We plan this house to be the lap of luxury. It will have triple glazing, a wine cellar and a jacuzzi. As I see it we are more likely to die of decadence than of cold.

But as The Breadwinner agrees with Andrew I have given in. We cannot call it the Death House.

All the same it must have a name that means something. Shangri La won't do and we have several Tigh na Bruichs in the village.

We have already rejected Dunfermin, Dungraftin and its Doric equivalent, Duntyauvin. Someone unkindly suggested Dunfiddlin but we're not for that.

Andrew Dunlop put me on a better track. He suggested that one of the ideas of building a retirement house on the farm was that The Farmer could be a pain in the neck of his successor. He could continue to oversee and to criticise.

That is proper and how it has always been.

I took over, not so much from my father, as from the grieve who had run the place for over 40 years. He used to tour regularly saying, "That's wrang, that's wrang and that's aa wrang." I horrified Old Jimmy by knocking a hole in the north wall of the old byre to let the cows out to self feed silage. Jimmy feared for the roof in the next winter's gales, "I see you've got a start to tak aff the roof o' the auld byre," he said in perfect disgust.

Having gone through that there is no reason why I should let Potions off Scot free. So Andrew's suggestion of Glowerinower isn't bad. But we will be 300 yards farther up the hill, so I'll be glowering down on the young man's struggles.

Yes, that's it. Glowerindoon has a real smack to it.

When I told Potions he said he could put up with that. It wouldn't be that long before The Farmer was glowering up.

Hens on the loose

PENNY WASHERS reckons he has a contribution to make to the debate on Animal Welfare. It is very topical, because once the transport of live calves is settled the battery hen may be the next target

Penny Washers decided that it was a shame to keep hens six to a cage with only wire net to perch on, food and drinks only once an hour, being bombarded with droppings from the cage above, their eggs being whipped away as fast as they can lay them and not much room. So he liberated a whole penful. Six hens at least would enjoy the life of the Free Ranger. They might have done, but not for long.

The first night home a fox got into the old cart-shed where Penny Washers had left the old orange boxes he hoped they would nest in. Luckily he heard the squawking and was able to disturb the fox before he got at the other five hens. So free-rangeing would have to be during the day only. They would have to be shut up at night for their own protection.

The next day there was a most unfortunate accident. Penny Washers had 50 ewes in the old byre for lambing and, as it happened, none of them had seen a hen. So when the five hens came clucking up to the door of the byre, the sheep all rushed excitedly to the gate that was tied across the door.

Unfortunately Penny Washers went to the same school of gate shutters, fixers and tiers-up as me and the gate was more an act of faith than anything else. Certainly it was unable to withstand a challenge from 50 ewes. The gate fell out and squashed one of the hens flat. Penny Washers was quite affected by the sight of it lying there, wings spread wide below the gate.

For a few days the four hens squawked round freely until Penny Washers' two young labradors took a fancy to them. They didn't kill any ... exactly; they were chasing them around the yard when the vet appeared to see a sick sheep and one poor hen ran smack into his radiator and was killed.

The cat got one but thereafter the hen population of his farm seemed to have found its level.

But all was not yet well.

You see Penny Washers has been renting out a byre to a neighbour to feed 50 barley beef bulls. He comes with a 12-tonne lorryful of barley and tips it along the centre pass and that is them fed for three weeks.

This neighbour is a good farmer and very careful man. We will never know if he was joking though Penny Washers thinks not.

At any rate, the owner of the barley had just tipped another twelve tonnes for his bulls when he spied the two hens who were freely ranging over for a nibble at this mountain of grain. "That hens are eatin an awfu lot o' barley" he said accusingly.

It was the last straw for Penny Washers. He wrung the two birds' necks and gave one to his neighbour on the grounds that he'd done most of the feeding. The other made fine soup.

I tried telling Penny Washers not to be too pessimistic about the prospects for free range hens. After all, these hens, having been reared intensively, were not exactly streetwise. And again, they didn't have to be as free-range as that.

Mad dogs and Scotsmen

SO HERE The Breadwinner and I are in Kenya. We are almost entirely idle but I have done one day's work and I want to tell you about it.

I have an old Masai friend who has 2000 acres on the outskirts of Nairobi. There he keeps 200 Simmental cross cows. He's been using mostly Simmental bulls for 25 years so they are more or less pure.

He wants to register his cattle in the Kenyan herdbook so that he'll have a pedigree herd. For that they have to pass an inspection which they can do as soon as they look pure. Those are then 'foundation' stock. Their daughters are known as 'pure' and their granddaughters are accepted as 'pedigree'.

No doubt because I am far enough from home to be deemed an expert, Ole Sein did me the honour of asking me to select his foundation stock. And then the Kenya herdbook people, who remembered I had judged the beef cattle at Nairobi show in 1987, gave me the job of inspecting the cattle to see if they should be accepted.

So there The Farmer was, a lone white man with a peeling nose, out in the blazing equatorial sun, with the power of life and death over what is intended to be the biggest herd of Simmental cattle in Kenya. Meanwhile The Breadwinner sheltered under the shade of an Acacia tree and gazed lovingly at the Ngong Hills, as Karen Blixen did when she was writing Out of Africa.

I know what I like and if I am judging in Scotland and my hosts don't agree, they don't have to invite me back. But my job in the blazing sun was more complicated. I was to pick anything that was sound and looked like a Simmental for the herdbook. But the old Masai wants as big cattle as possible and some of his biggest and best really had too much of the original zebu-type African cattle in them to qualify. Then again, his adviser isn't really convinced that size is what you want under the tropical sun where drought and disease resistance, and the ability to walk miles are important.

The cattle were in two mobs. One was cows and

calves who are being milk ranged. They are separated from their calves at night and milked in the morning. On nothing but permanent grass Ole Sein is not disappointed with a gallon a head and that is a much needed cash crop. The second mob are coming on to calving.

How gentle those Masai pastoralists were in bringing in their cattle. They used their sticks only as guides and spoke gently to the beasts all the time. I think they would be too slow for Maud.

The plan was to corral a mob and then put four at a time into another pen for inspection. I made my choice and the foundation stock went one way and the rejects went the other. I was terrified that at the end of the day the rejects would look better than the foundation stock. There were times when I saw my friend's eyes widen as I rejected another of his favourites. And remember that this is not some simple pastoralist. This is one of the feared and respected Masai, whose traditional belief is that the cow – all cows – were God's gift to the Masai. Other people who had cows could only have title to them from the Masai or have

29

stolen them. And here was The Farmer telling them what to do about cows.

And if the Masai are no ordinary cowmen Ole Sein is no ordinary Masai. He is an educated man and a leader. He it was who spoke for the Masai at the independence negotiations with the British in 1963. And again he rolled his eyes as I rejected another beautiful big beast with that typical dropped tail head which helps make the Zebu cattle such wonderful walkers.

We got 70 cattle acceptable to the Society and then I had a wander through them and threw out about ten which, although they were Simmentals all right, I wouldn't have fancied in my herd, mostly because they were too small.

March 13, 1995

Death in the street

LIFE HERE isn't dull. Last Friday we were witnesses to our first shooting, not including the time the Red Rooster was winged by a pellet from a twelve bore. We were going to see our travel agent in downtown Nairobi. The Breadwinner having pulled a calf muscle while running for a bus a few days before so that even I can now keep up with her, we were two very slow-moving objects indeed.

Suddenly there was a very loud bang. We weren't at all startled until we saw that people round us were bending down behind cars and two serious-looking gentlemen were assisting a ragged-looking youth to the ground.

It was no more than 30 yards away so I suppose the spirit of scientific enquiry should have propelled us along the road to see exactly what had happened. Instead we turned smartly into the safety of the travel agent's door.

The last we saw was the two serious-looking gentlemen, who turned out to be plain clothes policemen, helping the youth to his feet and leading him off. Inside we were met by one of the most impressive sights Africa has to offer. A cascade of secretaries with eyes shining as only African eyes can shine, was tumbling down the stairs to see the action. They had all the intimidating eagerness of the fourth form at St

Trinians arriving to dance with the boys of the local grammar school.

Our urbane travel agent had the story. A thief had been shot by the police along with a bystander. There had, in fact, been three shots and it wasn't at all like it is on the telly.

Since I was a boy I have had a romantic vision of having sundowners on Lake Victoria among the beautiful people. For that we really needed to get to Uganda and then to get on the ferries that ply Africa's biggest lake. And lo and behold, the overnight train to Uganda has started to run again and so has the boat from Kampala to Mwanza in Tanzania.

Our travel agent was extremely doubtful about two ageing Scots making such a safari but when I reminded him about David Livingstone he booked us the tickets.

And so it was that at ten o'clock one morning we slipped out of Nairobi on our scheduled 18-hour trip to Kampala, once known as the Pearl of Africa. Idi Amin returned it to the jungle in his years of barbarism but it is at last re-emerging into the light.

Winston Churchill described a trip on the East African Railway as being like Jack climbing the beanstalk. Starting at the Port of Mombasa you climb up to the centre of the continent and find heaven in Kampala. You have climbed 5000 feet by the time you reach Nairobi. Then it is a stiff climb

for a couple of hours through the mass of tiny fertile farms where, from as little as an acre, a woman can grow food to send her husband and a stream of children to Nairobi in search of cash employment,

At the top of the escarpment and at over 8000 feet, you are chugging through the real White Highlands. Coffee and tea estates were put there by men with peeling noses who arrived in Africa, said "this land is mine" and made it so. No wonder the blacks have pinched it back, for anything will grow here.

Then the line plunges down 3000 feet or so to the floor of the Rift Valley. These are the traditional lands of the Masai herdsmen. As few as ten years ago the tribesmen roamed free here, little puffs of dust marking where each herd was. But now it is all entitled and most is fenced. They are beginning to grow maize and even wheat.

It takes half an hour to pass the slab of Masai land that Lord Delamere (one of the original peeling noses) marked out for himself and a bit less to pass the chunk taken by Kenya's first President, Jomo Kenyatta.

Then you start to climb up the other side of the valley. Here is sheep and cattle ranching as well as the small peasant farms growing their subsistence crops based on maize. As Africa claims its eleven hours of darkness we are in the forests at nine thousand feet at the top of the Western escarpment of the Rift Valley.

We have a bunk each in a cabin to ourselves. The electricity doesn't work so there are no fans, the water is off and it is filthy. But this is first class. We complain to the very nice guard who says he has been expecting to hear from us. He moves us to second class. That is clean. We now have four bunks to choose between, running water and light, though the fans don't work here either.

Dinner is taken in style reminiscent of the days of the Raj. It is silver service in the dining room with three courses and coffee. Wine is £15 a bottle so we made do with the excellent beer at less than £1 a pint.

The company was jolly too. There was a party going up to Kampala for the 60th anniversary of the Lake Victoria sailing club and the star among those was the broadcaster Charles Harrison, who has reported for the BBC from East Africa since he arrived here in 1954.

The beds must have been comfortable. When we got to the Ugandan border the customs people couldn't waken us so they just let us lie. They would not have been so accommodating in Idi Amin's time.

The stuff of dreams

THE SCOTTISH explorer who gave his name to Thomson's Falls here in Kenya was responsible for at least one stroke of genius. When passing through Masailand he was challenged by some of those wild tribesmen and in extreme peril for his life.

When nothing but prayer seemed left for him, Thomson saved himself by taking out his false teeth. So impressed were the Masai that they not only spared his life but invited him to stay on in Masailand, where he attained something of a cult status. However the Masai soon tired of this trick and when they asked him if he could not take out an eye for a change Thomson decided it was time to be moving on.

That was in the nineteenth century. Now another explorer – The Farmer – was close to fulfilling his boyhood dreams of taking sundowners on Lake Victoria.

When we awoke in Uganda it was easy to see why they used to call it the Pearl of Africa. What fertility – and I don't just mean the soil. Don't believe all you read in the papers about the ravages of Aids. There are fat babies everywhere here.

Throughout the six hours we chugged slowly towards Kampala the route was lined with cheering and waving totos while other little black heads could be seen tearing through the banana groves lest they miss the fun.

The staple food in Uganda is not rice like in China, or maize like in Kenya, or salt and vinegar chips like in the UK. Here it is bananas. And they grow everywhere. There are neat commercial plantations, of course, but this must be the only country where the staple food is also the commonest weed.

And whenever the train slows sufficiently the local produce is offered up. One of our carriage-mates got a plateful of fish curry and mashed banana which smelled delicious, and another bought 25 huge bananas for 40 pence. I used the negotiating skills honed at Maud Market to acquire half as many for roughly twice as much, but they were still cheap. A 12-year-old boy got no sale for a fruit which must have weighed 20lb, looked like a plucked green porcupine and we later discovered was called a jack fruit.

We took at least half an

33

hour to pass what must be one of the world's biggest sugar plantations. It is owned by the Mudavadi family, who were kicked out by Amin because they are Asians and made new fortunes in the UK before returning to produce enough sugar for the whole country and a lot more for export.

And suddenly there she was; Lake Victoria, the source of the Nile, with the Nile cascading out. It looked much bigger than any Scottish river – and that was just the source. When I thought of the source of our own river Ythan, where a hard drinker could keep up just watering his whisky, it made me wonder how all those early explorers could have missed it.

And soon the slow-moving objects were on the streets of Kampala, where only a couple of years ago it was hard to sleep at night for crackling gunfire.

The atmosphere on the street was good and we never felt threatened. We toured the tomb of the traditional King of the Buganda, and met some of his widows, who take it in turns to live in the circle of widows' huts there.

After the enterprise of the railway halts the shops were a disappointment. In the home of the banana and the Tilapia fish there was tinned tuna on offer and corn flakes at £5 a packet. That nonsense is because most of the money around is yours and mine being spent by United Nations and other aid workers. What good people like that are to Africa I cannot imagine.

And so to the steamer for Tanzania.

It wasn't quite as I had imagined sundowners on Lake Victoria. There was no use for the white dinner jacket and there were no pink gins. Still, as the sun went down we shared a bottle of excellent Tanzanian beer before going below for delicious chicken and chips costing only a big pound.

We travelled in comfort compared with the real explorers, but I cannot imagine Dr Livingstone had to brave anything more intimidating than the combined ladies' and gents' lavatories on our boat.

An old college friend once said to me, "When you have slept in the bosom of Mother Africa, my friend, you can never sleep soundly anywhere else." And indeed, having slept through the border controls to Uganda and the heart of the continent, we were soon fast asleep as our tub rolled gently southwards.

Africa always bites back. We had determined to finish our safari by flying across the Serengetti in a light aircraft on our way back to Nairobi. We fancied a bird's eye view of 300 miles of one of the world's last wildernesses.

But the plane turned out to be an airliner which whisked us eastwards in 50 minutes at 27,000 feet. All we saw were clouds.

Editorial note. Two years later the "tub" sank with the loss of an estimated 600 lives.

March 27, 1995

Potions feels the strain

WHEN WE left for our Kenya holiday we thought we were being so clever, leaving the snow for the equatorial sun. We'd come back to springtime ... surely Scotia's best season.

Rejuvenated, The Farmer would return with the lapwings from Africa and get on with the calving and the spring work.

But he has returned to find Little Ardo still in the grip of winter. The grass is brown and the oilseed rape, which was such a show when we left, is turning brown also as hoards of starving pigeons work their way round the place like locusts. On our first night home we had four inches of snow.

You could be excused for wondering how The Farmer, who claims to be so busy, can horse off to Africa for five weeks, even in mid-winter. Granted the crops don't do much beneath the snow, but who will look after the cattle?

The answer is Potions. The chemist who so loves to come and play at farmies in his spare time has got his chance. Having married the elder Investment he is currently favourite to succeed me when The Breadwinner and I retire.

And he's fairly been earning his pole position.

He, the Investment and their own two little Dividends moved into the farmhouse for a dummy run. Potions had the chance to pose as laird of the place, to wake up with 100 cattle bawling at him for their food and 10,000 pigeons needing scared off theirs.

Of course the farm is so well organised that that hardly constitutes a full-time job – and it's just as well.

You see, the small shops in Potions' village are feeling the competition from the super-duper shopping centres. The old butcher was determined to retire and there just wasn't anyone willing to sell sausages.

This was a serious threat to Potions the chemist. If people went to the city for their beef they might get their toothpaste and aspirins at the same time. So he's bought the butchers.

Not content with finishing his apprenticeship as a farmer, he has started from scratch as a butcher as well. That, with his duties at the chemist's shop, means Potions is a busy man.

During our holiday he rose at six and chased his tail all day, hardly leaving time for a couple of pints before bed-time.

And he hasn't been content to do the minimum at the farm. There are all sorts of little improvements he's managed to make. Like the new fence round the wood at the bottom of the steading. He's made a nice job of that. Posts every three yards instead of the five that has served me well enough, and seven wires where three would have done. Worse than that, it is all new posts, wire and even staples.

"What a hero," you say.

Well, not altogether. Potions knows the more he can get done when I am paying the better.

So we have three nice new garden gates and a fine piece of new concrete alongside his new fence. The enormous plain tree which for 150 years deprived the kitchen of the morning sunlight, is away. In its place is a surprisingly small pile of logs.

All in all Potions has acquitted himself well. Nothing has died, seized, blown down or blown up. Five new calves have been born. There has been no growth so we are not behind with sprays or fertilisation. The Farmer has not been missed.

So should we just retire to the death house and let the young man have his head while he is still young enough to enjoy it? Too many lives have been blighted by being kept waiting too long. Goodness knows how many in recent years have not had their turn at all because the generation before them didn't manage to stop before the money went done and the farm had to be given up.

And yet I am reluctant to go. You see, now young Potions has proved himself able, now his dander has been further raised by the realisation that he can do it, and that farming is truly what he wants to do, I have him just where I want him.

After all, there is nothing in writing. He can't be quite sure of his succession.

I should be able to have a few years yet on top of this hill. Meanwhile I will have plenty of cheap labour, the place will look well after my long holidays, and I will have very few and very short arguments.

37

Straw price goes bananas

IF SUCCESS is judged by how many times you get the better of your friends, then the job has gone a good deal better this week. It's all because of the price of straw.

No one quite knows why there is such a shortage. Is it because so much land is now set aside, or because the drought last summer meant the straw was shorter? Is it because the welfare people are bullying pig farmers into fattening their piggies on straw? Or is it all those people growing carrots? They need eleven acres of straw to cover each acre of carrots.

Some of the problem is that people like Mossie and me have done the sums that show silage is a thing of the past where grain is an alternative. How can you possibly grow an acre of grass to feed cattle if you can grow barley on it, sell that for up to £400, get another £100 plus from the government and feed the straw which costs you nothing to your cattle? The straw may not be as good as the silage but it isn't £500 an acre worse.

Well, well. We have a couple of hundred bales spare and selling them has been a delight. I entered 50 bales in the electronic auction at Thainstone with every hope that I'd beat Mossie's record-breaking average of £9 at harvest. I had even dreams of beating his top bid of £11.50.

The first indication that a good sale was imminent came when no fewer than three potential purchasers came to view the straw. Then, on the morning of the sale, down the field stalked a tall, shambling figure with a head of hair which is not quite so shocking now that there are so many silver threads among the red. It was the Red Rooster, looking a bit sheepish, I thought.

The Rooster has hill cows and finishes the calves on barley and silage. He just needed a 'wee suppy straw' for bedding. How I enjoyed telling the Grain Baron that, much as I'd like to help, this crofter was going for a world record and had committed his straw to the auction.

And I got a good score off another neighbour. You will remember my pride at harvest time with the Dutch barn full, the old cornyard full and a line of 400 bales down the strip of setaside which I am using as an auxiliary cornyard. Well, I was daft enough to tell Waterside of my pride and asked him to agree that my straw made an impressive show.

"I see naething impressive aboot it. It's just a lot o' strae." I was hurt, of course, but tried not to show it.

The tenant of Waterside is more impressed now. He was still trying to buy that straw when the bidding was over £13.

And I even got one over Mossie. My price of £14.60 a bale for four footers was far above his record. I was ashamed to take it though I need not have been. The phone has never stopped since, with others needing straw at the same price. I keep making another trip to the cornyard to see if I can spare a few more. Usually I can.

And to think that they've had to pass laws in England to stop them burning straw. Indeed they will have to rewrite the fairy story about Rumplestiltskin who knitted straw into gold. At today's prices it would hardly be worth it.

It's not often Mossie gets it wrong but he has this time. He has plenty surplus straw but it has all been treated with ammonia to increase digestibility and palatability. That cost about £6 a bale and it isn't worth as much as the untreated stuff.

"It's nae for me to say," he says sulkily, "but my strae is a far better buy."

Maybe so Mossie, but nobody's buying yours. These people want bedding.

So it has been a good week. On top of that we have 20 calves now, half bulls, and I still haven't seen one calving.

Our yearlings are much the best we've had, in the sense that there is hardly a tail-ender. The Jersey blood is all but gone. I will sell the heifers as soon as the grass is here. The graziers will go daft then.

I had intended to finish the bulls but I'm tempted to let them go. "Why be the workin feel?" says Mossie.

Mind you, we have had a warning.

The prices of houses in the village being so high we have more or less decided to build a death house for ourselves on the farm. We've a site looked out and if we can get planning permission we'll move there when Potions and the elder Investment take over in three years.

The Breadwinner went on Sunday to show the site to the Investment and her little Dividends.

Now, when we were in Africa, Potions cut down a huge plane tree in the garden and some scraggy firs and we have been enjoying a great supply of logs since we came home.

That clearly impressed the Investment's elder daughter. She said to her grandmother, "When you're living here, where will you get your logs?"

The Breadwinner said, "Oh, there'll never be any shortage of logs here. There are woods all over the farm."

"Oh no," said the little girl, "they'll be our woods then."

April 10, 1995

Potions' portions

THERE ARE increasing signs that Potions may be man enough to follow me on Little Ardo. He has the wit for it, even if he is serving his apprenticeship in the butcher's shop.

He's into freezer sales now, in another desperate attempt to keep the supermarkets at bay, and I'm impressed with some of his ducking and weaving.

Like when the lady who had given him an order for half a pig came bustling in. He could

see there was something wrong. "Pork all right, Mrs Wilson?" he asked.

"Aye, it wasna bad but there were four trotters and you only got two on half a pig when I was at school," said she, suspicious that she had got all the trotters and somebody else had had more than their fair share of the fillet.

But Potions had the answer quick as a flash. "It must have been the bottom half you got, Mrs Wilson. Now I've some nice spicy beef olives today." She was out the door before she had worked it out.

You don't get service like that in a supermarket.

The cattle continue to as-tound by refusing to lose loads of money. We have 30 new season calves and I have only seen two being born despite looking as often as possible and even rising in the night when I hear the alarm.

I am blaming the diet of treated straw for somehow making the calves smaller or the cows better at getting them out. At any rate it is definitely the way forward. I am getting too old for sweating on the end of a rope.

And this week we sold three odd beasts which some-how missed the sale last spring. They have been getting about 15lb of cake and treated straw so I suppose they owed me a

41

bit, but how handsomely they paid me back.

The best was a Blue-grey stot. That is to say it was bluey grey in colour, though it was by a Simmental bull and out of a Blue-grey cow. A real Blue-grey has to be by a Shorthorn bull. Anyway, he made 128 pence a kilo, which was third top of the sale. He was a dumpie little fellow and I wouldn't have believed he fetched £876 if I hadn't got the cheque. Even the runtie Black calf, whose mother was a heifer and hadn't enough milk to suckle a goat, came to £554. The three averaged £743 at 22 months old.

The crops are another matter. "It's nae for me to say, but I was fairly right stopping you growing that spring barley rubbish," Mossie told me on Wednesday. And apart from the fact that I had seen through spring barley before I met him, he is quite right. What a disaster it's going to be in the North-east. There is hardly anything sown and they do say that the yield falls by a bushel per acre for every day's delay after the first of April.

It has been nearly dry enough for far too long.

Of course that shouldn't stop them now the principles of "plough and plant" are understood. If they put a six furrow plough in front of the drill machine they should be able to sow in just about any weather.

But they can't do that. They've got it all ploughed already.

"I'm away to the mart (or the shooting or the fishing or the fitba or Smithfield). Put the loon awa tae the ploo and oot o' the road." That used to be not a bad idea because you were getting forward with the spring work. But in a wet spring all you have done is let the water in.

Why should I worry about the malting barley men being late? After all there is plenty in stock for my needs as a consumer. But I am worried.

You see as soon as the boys get scattering their barley seed o'er the land the pigeons leave my rape alone and go and take the one seed in four that is traditionally sown for the crows.

That time should have been four weeks ago and, as they have eaten four of my six fields quite bare, I really want them to stop now.

Everyone is the same and once more the Vale of Ythan is like the valley of Ypres in the First World War. Volley after volley of gas guns, which have grown e'er more fearsome, boom across the land, causing the pigeons to flutter over a bit.

As you know, I believe that these noisy polluters are so bad for the farmer's image that I won't use them. I used to think they didn't work anyway. Now I have to admit to being less sure. Certainly my crops seem to have been the tastiest in the district this year.

My preferred strategy is to get my machinery into the fields to make them think I'm working there. It has always seemed to work up till now, but it hasn't been a success this spring.

I used to put so much plant out in the rape fields that Mossie thought I had gone burst and was preparing for my roup. But now that I have six fields of rape the machinery is spread too thin to scare a hungry pigeon.

The Breadwinner has another theory. She sees the doos are not fooled by all this plant. They know it is unattended because all is quiet while the modern farm worker must have his radio blaring at all times.

We put the old Cavalier and the Ursus in the most eaten field and left the radios going full blast. There has not been a doo there for two days and a coy tinge of green is beginning to reappear.

April 17, 1995

The heifers make a run for it

I WOULDN'T tell you this were it not for the fact that the whole of Aberdeenshire knows already, but I have had my first serious breakout of the year. The 15 heifers that I was looking forward to offering to an expectant public managed to get out and were two miles away before anyone noticed. The day I wasted getting them back really brought it home to me how things have changed for the farmer with 250 acres and a bad memory.

Had this happened in my father's day his grieve would have taken his five other men, two of whom had reasonable working dogs, and any children that were available and brought them back, while my father worried about the affairs of state as reported in the Glasgow Herald. Along the way the folk who worked on the other farms would know immediately what was up and move seamlessly to block their road ends and see the cattle through nasty cross-roads. Cattle on the road were nothing when I was a boy. We used to walk our Canadian Holstein steers from the railway station five miles away, with only minor hiccoughs.

It was different last Thursday.

I went out at 7.15am to find the gate open. Now this has happened before with that gate. It is held by a bolt and there is a catch to keep the bolt shot. It should stay that way all winter, and so it does if you tie the catch with wire.

There was no handy bit of wire last November when I shut that gate and I well remember deciding string would do. When there was more time I would find a bit of wire.

So the 15 ladies, with very little to do all winter, had worked away at the string until it burst. Then with persistence they had eventually managed to unshoot the bolt and escape.

Usually vagrant cattle make straight for either their mothers or their brothers and The Farmer is wakened by the delighted roaring, kicking over of bags and trampling of feed that ensues.

But in this case they just vanished. There were none of the usual signs, not even a trail of dung. I would have thought that someone had come with a lorry and loaded them up had it

not been for the fact that there was one heifer left in the court. She must have been asleep when they had sped away.

With no staff to call on, I took Honda the four-wheeled dog in search of my heifers. I found three in our last field of rape. I was able to open a gate and let them onto our hill.

After searching in ever increasing circles, I found four more only two farms away looking bemused in a ploughed field. I do not know what I was thinking about, but I tried to get them to submit by chasing them round and round that field while my poor old bones were practically shaken to bits by the roughness of the terrain. When I did get them out of there I ran slap into one of the sad facts of modern Aberdeenshire.

Now that most fields are down to permanent cropping very few of them have gates and none is kept shut. My heifers just walked straight into a field of spring barley. In half an hour I had got them one field nearer home.

I went home for the Wasting Asset who was up despite it being no more than nine o'clock. The Breadwinner said that the remaining seven heifers had been located. They were at the Salmon Inn.

My hope was that the heifers would recognise me and a yellow feed bag and follow me

home with the Wasting Asset, in the car, encouraging them from the rear. This worked well for two fields until we came across another hazard of the modern countryside; a clueless canine. When my heifers saw their first yappie dog they fled.

There was no way they were going for the feed bag gag twice so we would try to drive them home. Now we were joined by two youths, so the team was up to four.

But driving cattle is virtually impossible along country roads nowadays. As well as the gates being non-existent the fences are also negligible. As soon as they tired of the hard road (which was soon) they scattered over the fence into whatever field was next.

To cut a horrendous story short we eventually got them home and onto our braes, having been on six different farms. They and we and Honda the dog had charged about on all their fine new crops, and created a spectacular mess. That included the final desperate pursuit involving seven herders on foot and me, as Colonel in chief on the dog, in a high speed, cross-country chase which gave me an idea what fox hunting must be like.

When I shut the gate on the last four heifers I had been chasing cattle without a break for almost five hours.

They were now among our hill cows and when those came in for their cake next morning the heifers came too. I was able

45

to return them to their court. When I sell them in a fortnight's time I'll be able to say truthfully, "Been outside."

When I was telling the boys at the discussion group, most of them made quite a good show of being sorry for me. Even Mossie refrained from calling me a damned fool. "It's nae for me to say," he said almost kindly, "but should you nae have shut the gate right in the first place?"

April 24, 1995

The first grandson

THE BREADWINNER and I are grandparents again. This is altogether a good thing. It has been the excuse for almost continuous celebration for a week. Nine pounds at birth (you wouldn't call me a liar for one ounce), it has the wide forehead with which our family have been blessed for generations.

"Big head and little wit, never gaed thegither yet," we say proudly, though the women who have to do the child-bearing are not quite so enthusiastic about big-headed babies.

I like to think of life as a series of doors to be negotiated. Birth, marriage and death are the great big doors. And then there are all sorts of smaller doors; going to school, getting your first thrashing, your first game in a real team, the first time you walk a girl home, being old enough to vote.

Then there are the stages after coupling; the first child was special. And the first boy child, even if it did have the hooked nose of the other side, was special. That might well have been extra important to me because I was an only child, and my father having been illegitimate and his uncles having emigrated, I was effectively the last of the Allans.

I was very pleased by the birth of my first son but I think it was really more biological than anything to do with the continuation of the name. There does seem to be something in us that makes us want to see our genes survive through the male line.

So is The Farmer, who already has four grand-daughters, extra pleased that there is another and that it is a boy?

Well, yes, but only because it is a change. It is another of life's doors that I have gone through. When it comes to the third generation, male chauvinism no longer seems important to The Farmer. And he is not interested in the name being carried on on the top of this hill.

It was only this last two generations of us here who were called Allan. My mother's father was here and his name was Mackie. And his wife's father and grandfather were here and their name was Yull. The older Investment, whose name is now Purdie, and her husband are to follow us here.

The name is of no interest. As usual with babies, the main thing was that all was well.

All is not well, however, on the ancestral acres. The Farmer has been caught napping, bringing the wrath of Mossie.

The barley is at the crucial stage where the three tonne crops are separated from the four tonne crops. With precise timing we must heap the manure onto the crop and a great splurge of chemicals so that growth goes into the production of seeds instead of straw. If you are late with the chemicals you get the classic 'All show and no dough' crop.

And that is what is threatening. I bullied the Man of Few Words to come and spread a hundred units of nitrogen on our six parkies of winter barley and he came on Saturday despite earning a huge hangover at a wedding on Friday.

I put the chemicals on a third of the crop and then

nipped off to watch Aberdeen play Celtic. Sunday would be time enough for the sprayer.

But it rained all day Sunday and intermittently on Monday. That was just what the crop thought it needed and it has started to shoot up. I am looking at a great crop that will fall flat on its face at the first shower of rain, when the heads start to get heavy.

It was no use telling Mossie that Aberdeen FC has never been relegated and must have as much support as possible. It was no use telling him that the whole of the North-east would be depressed if they went down. And it was quite pointless to tell him what a great win we had had against Celtic.

"And how much have you lost by nae sprayin your crops?"

I was greatly chastened by Mossie's attitude and realise that if I don't start behaving better he might resign or, worse and worse, he might start charging for his advice.

When I woke on Tuesday I could hear a great stillness in the air. No wind to worry me and certainly no rain. I would do it today. I might have a crop yet.

At six-thirty I drew back the curtains and could hardly believe my eyes. The whole countryside was under a four inch blanket of snow. It has mostly gone by mid afternoon but the ground is far too wet.

Poor Big Hamish still has 400 acres to sow at his baronial castle by the sea. What he can have thought this morning when, with May looming, he saw the dreaded white blanket, I shudder to think.

Mossie can't imagine either, but he'd like to find out.

He phoned about ten o'clock, "C'mon and we'll see how Hamish is doing. I've a couple of chains in case he's needing a tow with the one-pass."

I had to decline. "Mossie I'm sorry. But with the mess I've made of the spraying I can't bring myself to go for a jolly to see somebody else's disaster."

"Oh well," he said. "It's nae for me to say maybe, but I've aa my sprayin done."

North-east out of kilter

WE'VE HAD three more mornings of snow on the trot, and we're further behind with the spraying. The nitrogen's on but no straw shortener. I am well on the way to a great green crop that will collapse if we get rain.

Mossie phones every day asking if the barley has gone flat yet and if going to watch Aberdeen and Celtic was really more important than looking after the crops.

If I do get into trouble then I will not be alone, for the husbandry part of farming in the North-east is far behind and out of kilter. It is looking well at the moment, but it is growing too fast and so is the disease. We will need low cutting bars at harvest this year.

Of course, some of the malting barley men may yet be saved such embarrassment. Their crops cannot go flat if they stay in the bag. Big Hamish has half of his crop planted and we're trying to persuade him to put in rape in the rest. After all, it doesn't matter how late you are, you still get the big rape subsidy.

The livestock job isn't looking too bright either, with the grass so slow and straw up another £3 on Friday. To think I sold for a mere £14.60 a bale.

I'm still holding half my cows inside because even at one cow to the acre there is hardly anything for them outside.

I was tempted to try to hold onto my last year's calves until the grass really gets going, but on Friday I weakened and put 15 heifers to Thainstone.

You may recall that my heifer sale last year was a pantomime and a disaster. The float arrived far too early. After chasing them around the place and shaking tonnes of liveweight off them, we just made it in time, only for the sale to run so far behind that they had another four hours to stand. When they finally came into the ring it was after 6pm. They were dehydrated and there were only two bidders left.

I was anxious there would be no cock-ups this time. The float was due at 11am so I had plenty time to get them ready. We had to get them from their court down to the loading bank. That is where things have gone wrong from time to time, even in the days when there were staff about the place.

To make quite sure that all the weak links were reinforced so I wouldn't have to rely on the goodwill of the stock, I had seven extra gates, the digger, the old Cavalier and the tractor with the sprayer tied together to make a corridor to the loading bank. It worked.

The trouble only started when the float arrived. You would have thought the animal rights people had been at the heifers telling them about the cruelty involved in transporting of calves. They just blank refused to enter the float.

We twisted their tails, poked them, and beat them, but not enough. We took them back to their pen a dozen times to see if a fresh start would get them going, but to no avail. We put straw down on the loading bank and up the tail door and into the float so that it looked like one big pen but no. It was as though there was a door which only the heifers could see and it was shut. I've seen it like that when there have been pigs in the float, but that was not the case this time.

Eventually we haltered one calf and walked her in. The invisible door having been opened, they all marched in as if it were the most natural thing in the world.

All was well. We made the sale in time, the heifers looked

50

good in the ring and sold well. Indeed my average was up £76 per head at £466. That was because they were much heavier this year at 384 kilos compared with 300 in 1994.

That huge difference can't all be down to the bad handling of last year's sale. In fact at least three-quarters of it is good news for our feeding regime. This year they were wintered on straw and 7lb of cake, while in 1994 they got silage and about 4lb.

Of course they did look a bit polished. What graziers are really looking for is cattle that are desperate to get out to the grass. Because they haven't been well done by inside, they can offer compensatory growth. So my average price per kilo was down from 129 to 119 pence.

And I had a bonus. The first five were bought by Neil Barclay (Yes, Harry's son at HRM) and I waved acknowledgement from the box. He waved back with a little gesture which suggested a luckpenny. I knew he was at least half joking, for the tradition of giving the buyer a small part of his bid back in cash has all but died out in the North-east. But when he bought the next five I resolved to give him a tenner. After the sale I made my way to pay him but Neil was gone.

Another tenner saved and 23 of the heifers' big brothers to go next Friday. Brace yourself, banker.

May 8, 1995

Spring at last

NO SNOW for a week and spring is here. The first blackbirds' nest is hatched, the pheasants are hard at it, the elms are in flower and we are already heartily sick of rhubarb.

Dod is away on his holidays. Gowkie always borrows my bull for a three week warm-up before he goes in among our cows on the first of June. But Gowkie has only six cows at the moment and when we let Dod out of the float he looked a bit disappointed. He seemed to be thinking, "There must be more to life than this."

I hope it will make him all the more eager when he comes home.

The cows are all out and very happy about it. For all they have done well on the treated

51

straw it isn't the same as spring grass. They have 38 calves, only two of which I saw being born. There were two losses and two sets of twins so we look set for 100%. I will make my quota of 39.6 if 1.6 calves are born alive to the remaining two heifers and a cow.

Last year's bull calves did me proud at Thainstone on Friday. The oldest was just 13 months old and yet I got a top of £700 for a pure Simmental. Only two of them had made half a tonne but still I was pleased with my treated straw. As long as we can grow cereals and sell it, I can't see how we can ever make silage again.

Top price per kilo was 'only' 139 pence but they were carrying a good bit of liveweight, which is code for 'they had full bellies' and the butcher doesn't give much for gut-fill.

The 23 bulls all went to their new home in one float, for they were all bought by John Fowlie of Aberdour House.

My last week's buyer having left before I got to him with my luckpenny, I took my time over going to speak to John. There was no such luck this time so I slipped a note into his pocket and said "That's the price of your dinner."

"Oh, that's fine now. I'm going to Thainstone House, as it happens."

Now, I know a man who complains that he was charged 10 pence for an ice cube when he went to a wedding there recently, so I don't suppose you get in the door for a fiver.

I had to explain that I had had the mart cafe in mind when I selected the note. In fact I only had two notes with me and I needed lunch myself.

Anyway, Mr Fowlie and I then worked it out that we had spent £350 on commission to the mart for arranging this deal. Not only that but I had to take them to market in a float, and they would have passed Little Ardo on their way home to New Aberdour. Then again, with 3000 cattle there from all over Scotland, who knows what the cattle might have picked up at the mart?

Surely two neighbours could get together, fix a price, split the commission, and take one float journey between our farms.

We resolved to at least look at that for next year.

But I would be sad not to get to the mart to sell. It is fine to expose your stock to the ridicule of your neighbours, and it is a chance to get off the place, for it is often lonely on a farm nowadays.

This last two weeks I have enjoyed meeting the Irishman at the mart. He has a good sense of humour and, having given

Mossie a king's ransom for his outfarm, he needs it.

It turns out the Irishman is new to what we would call farming. He has made it thus far by spending his time looking at cattle in auction markets until he can tell the weight of dangleberries on housed cattle from 50 yards. He must have bought cheap and sold dear, to build enough credit to buy from Mossie, and he still hasn't sold his 40 acres in Ireland.

He was bowled over by the sheer scale of it when he came to see Mossie's farm.

When he'd arrived Mossie had ordered the Irishman's wife to look at the house and told yer man to jump in. Then he drove like a maniac right into the middle of a hundred and forty-five acre 'paddock'. The Irishman, used to the big field being the one that was one and a half acres, got a bad attack of agoraphobia.

"I was sinking down into my seat and putting up a wee prayer he wouldn't ask me how many acres I had in Ireland. If I'd had to tell him that he'd've put me out, right in the middle of that paddock. In 145 acre of rape about that high, I'd never have found my way out."

And he discovered another thing about Mossie. The truth varies depending on whether he's buying or selling.

"When I was looking at the place for to buy he had two main phrases – "It's a show," and "It's tops." But as soon as I had her bought he had a much

53

longer word – 'Disaaaster'."

And the Irishman has a lot more to learn before he makes a right job of his new farm. Mossie's doing his best to help with the growing of the winter barley and rape.

He's giving him all the good advice he has been giving me, but at least I was brought up to expect crops to cost something to grow.

He told the Irishman the other day, "You'll need to get on and spray your crops. You've got every disease except BSE."

"But, did I not spray them in the autumn," said the Irishman, aghast, "and did it not cost a fortune? Don't tell me I have to spray them again?"

"It's a disaaaster, but it's up to you. You dinna need to spray your crops unless you intend staying on for another year."

May 15, 1995

An expensive Ayr Show

Kilmacolm for hills and heather,
Brig o' Weir for rainy weather,
Johnstone for it's raggie weans...

IT IS amazing how little of a show you see when you are on a commercial stand. Really you are confined to one small part of one alleyway for most of the time. If any part of the show doesn't pass down your alley you don't see it.

Mind you, I did meet a wheen of folk who seemed to be enjoying the uncharacteristic fine weather. Certainly it was my third Ayr Show and the first time I had seen it in sunshine.

I met Allan Black, who told me that Hereford crosses are far worse than Limousins for destroying dry stane dykes. This sounded like good news for the breed that is generally believed – by people who don't breed them – to be very nervous. It wasn't, though. The Limousines, he explained, are far better. They don't knock down your dykes because they clear them.

I also met two Irishmen from Crosshill. Sammy and Willie Rownie are big men with hands for knocking in stobs.

They milk 300 cows and have a reputation for making a good job of things.

I was convinced of that when it turned out that the two were philosophers of the game of rugby.

We agreed that the game was now played in all the wrong spirit and they illustrated that belief with the story of the time that an opponent jumped on Sammy's back. "Hey that's my brother you're fightin," said Willie and swung a great fist which broke the offender's jaw in three places. "That stopped him."

And I met other Irishmen when I got away from my stand for a few minutes to see the judging of the native beef breeds of cattle.

The man looked like a cattle dealer and I think he was having me on.

"Would dat be de Aberdeen Angus?" he asked.

"No, that's the Galloways. The Aberdeen-Angus are over there."

"Dems Galloways, mother. And what would dem be?" he asked, pointing to the Highlanders. I thought everyone in the world knew that but I told him patiently.

"Dems de Hoilanders, mother," he said.

I thought I should complete my man's education. "And do you know what those are?" I said, pointing to the only remaining breed on show.

He looked at me as though I was soft in the head, "Sure, everybody knows dems de Herefords, surely."

Everyone was delighted about the fine weather except me and I have regretted it every day since.

You see, while I was away enjoying myself in Ayr the boys were all catching up with the crop spraying. I got a load done on Friday before disappearing again to Neilston Show on the Saturday and then I got another load on on Sunday before the heavens opened. As I write we are into the fourth day of rain. The barley is growing half an inch a day and the Twerp-all is still mixing away in the sprayer. I have now got the tractor parked under the diesel tank. If it hasn't stopped by tomorrow I think I'll just connect her up.

And at least twice a day Mossie is on the phone. "How much did they pay you to go to Ayr? And how much have you lost because you werena at home to spray your barley? And are you intending staying on for another year? It's nae for me to say, but mine's all sprayed." I dread the phone ringing.

But it is very difficult nowadays when the farm is a one-man band. And the weather is so uncertain. If I had declined the invitation it would have been the usual Ayr Show weather and no work would have been possible anyway.

And the penalties of my swanning off to the shows are greater still.

When I was away at Neilston a pure Simmental heifer produced a big bull calf in the wood. Had I been at home I might have been able to help. I still might not have seen her, but hurrying away to judge cattle isn't the best way to look after the calving.

It has cost me £200 to replace that calf with a Simmental cross Holstein and I reckon when I sell it it will be worth £200 less than the natural calf and to add insult to injury it will likely have eaten more per kilo of weight-gain.

Still, there is an entry on the credit side. Even though the sun shone again I did enjoy the Neilston Show.

The organisers are a canny lot. When the learned judge arrived the committee invited him most civilly to have a dram. It might help with the judging, after all.

But it was not to the usual committee tent that we repaired. My hosts piloted me straight into the magnificent mobile premises of the Clydesdale Bank. I thought it a very economical move and only fair considering how much the farmers have contributed to the welfare of the bankers over the years.

Missing ingredient

THE SPRAYING is all up to date at last. I had a weather window of five hours and got the job done.

I no longer dread Mossie's phone calls. He has really turned quite mellow since the pounding he gave his body at the Pig Event at Birmingham.

In fact despite himself he has to admit that my barley is looking well. I got four tonnes last year off one of the home fields and the best of this year's looks better still, though, being a yaval crop, there is little hope of a new record. You need a change from oil-seeds or setaside to get that.

"It's nae for me to say," says my honorary consultant, "but your crops are looking second to mine."

Now you might think that, as Mossie is advising me, my crops would be every bit as good as his. But the trouble is he deliberately leaves one important ingredient out of my mixes to keep me in my place.

I was reminded of that this week by what has happened to the rape. Everybody else's is coming out in flower but Mossie's isn't. This, he tells me, is because he has applied a special chemical that inhibits the flowering until, as the heat of summer builds up, the plants, like the bursting of a dam, cascade into blooms that produce bigger and better seeds.

When I reproached my consultant for not giving me the secret ingredient, he was fit for me as usual.

"You dinna need a chemical to hold back your flowers, you've got the pigeons."

He's right with half the fields. While three are bursting into bloom, the three that the cushies found are a fortnight off flowering. Mossie says the eaten crops will shock me. I hope so, for they do not look well today.

Penny Washers, the white settler who made that first impact on the village when he refused angrily to pay 15 pence for a penny washer, is into sheep now so he has discovered about the knackeries and how expensive they can be when they start coming regularly.

He's adopted the principle that the old College advisers developed in the fifties and sixties. 'If a few sheep produce a small surplus then more sheep will produce a bigger surplus.'

Now, when poor Penny Washers phones the knacker

the girl says, "Naa! Nae again?" It got so bad that Penny Washers started spreading his business around until one day he was embarrassed by a queue of smelly red lorries.

There is a natural number of sheep to the acre. A good farmer can buck that trend by careful stockmanship, but Penny Washers is finding out the hard way.

I feel for the poor young man because I tried the same system when I started farming. I soon had five times as many cattle here as my father ever had and lost money like it was going out of fashion. Now I have fewer cattle than he ever had and I may soon have to start paying income tax.

Despite the wealth of loss-making experience he can call on, Penny Washers is still buying the odd replacement.

He bought a ewe and Texel twins one Friday at Thainstone. A bargain, he told me with eyes shining, "Only £17 a head."

Wrong again.

Sandy Fowlie, who used to buy stots for me when I needed them for the grass, was at the ringside and afterwards Penny Washers thought to pull his leg. "What's a big farmer like you doing round the poor man's ring? I thought you would only be seen at the cattle rings."

"Oh well," said Sandy, "It was just an old ewe of the wife's. She has a blind spot; she canna see fences. She's been in every parish in Aberdeenshire and I'm so fed up I'm here to get rid of her."

Penny Washers thought for

a minute. "She didn't have twin Texel lambs at foot did she?"

Sure enough.

And that hasn't been his only problem. He bought a fine bargain pen of 13 ewes and 26 lambs and there wasn't a single set of twins. He had six sets of triplets and seven singles. (Or so he told me, but having counted that out several times I see he can't add either.)

But Penny Washers is learning. He had them back at the mart last Friday. He even made a small surplus on the deal – if you don't count anything for his week spent chasing the ewe with the Texel twins round Buchan.

May 29, 1995

The Farmer gets on his bike

I HAVE to tell you that The Farmer is the subject of a steward's inquiry. It is most embarrassing and I wasn't going to tell you. But who would read a diary in which only the successes were recorded?

It wouldn't have happened if I hadn't decided to take up cycling.

That would have been a smart move if it was taking the bike down to the pub rather than hazarding the licence. But that's not what I have embarked on. You see I have raked out an old racer that must have belonged to one of the Wasting Assets when they were younger, and joined the Ythan Wheelers. I have put my foot on the bottom rung of a ladder at the top of which is the maillot jeune in the Tour de France or the gold medal at the Olympic games.

You could be excused for thinking that I had left this endeavour a bit late, but the truth is that I have wasted at least half my total energy in sport since first I got into the school football team 48 years ago.

After too long at that sort of ball game, and after becoming good enough at tossing the caber to get my photo in the papers, I became so overcome with arthritis in my knees that I had to stop.

In my forties I discovered that with the aid of a skilfully controlled limp I could protect my worst knee sufficiently to allow me to train for and complete several marathons. Now, it is easy enough for these crackshots you see on the tele to do a marathon. They do the 26 miles in little more than two hours. But the middle-aged Farmer, on the starting grid at sixteen stone, is fully four hours from the home straight.

Before The Farmer was 50 even the slowest and shortest of trots became impossible. That seemed to be that. A sporting life seemed to be over. Terminal decline had apparently set in.

It was an advert in the local Squeek that gave me the idea of trying the bike. The Ythan Wheelers were advertising for new blood. There was no mention of just how new this new blood had to be so I decided to try it. A wee run on the bike the night before the first ten-mile race showed that the pedalling put no strain at all on the arthritic joints.

After the race my unfit body was sore all over – except on the knees. The muscles ached but the joints were untouched.

Hallelujah! The Farmer's infatuation with sport can continue.

I was last, of course. The winner took 24 minutes and I just inside 40 minutes.

By the next race I had improved quite a lot technically.

That means I didn't once have to stop to put my chain back on. It comes off nowadays if you back-pedal as we used to have to 40 years ago when first we got three-speed gears. I was down to 37 minutes and becoming subject to speed-thrill, though still last.

Which brings us to last Sunday morning, when I was due to be first off at seven o'clock.

That suits me fine because with 45 competitors leaving at one minute intervals the best cyclist (who starts last) would have to arrive before he had set off if he were to overtake a 37 minute man like me. I was bound to be home at least seven minutes before him.

All the same I did my best to foul up that advantage. You are supposed to appear with a clean bike and I was still cleaning mine when I should have been at the start. In a flurry of officials I finally made the off 50 seconds late ... and that delay was to prove important.

Soon the crack-shots were speeding past me as usual, but all was not well. I was uncomfortable. In 48 years of competitive sport I have never before started at 7am, unless you count the time I competed for the caber tossing championship in Australia. They said it was 5pm but I knew fine it was 5am in Scotland, where it counts. I

60

knew my geography even then.

What was worst was that I have a very excitable digestive system which needs attention at about 7.30am. And then, in the excitement, I had forgotten to start the stop watch on my on-board computer, so I had no idea where I was. Anyway, I finished and slunk off home to waken The Breadwinner with an encouraging cup of tea.

I had hoped to hear no more of the race, but that was not to be. The phone rang that evening. "You went off with-out your prize."

It took me only a few seconds of breathless excitement to modify my guess to there being a booby prize.

"Correct."

"What was it?"

"£7."

"Magic!"

Well not really. Bang goes my chance of an Olympic gold medal. Bang goes my amateur status. My pinnacle will have to be the Tour de France.

"And do you want the bad news? They're accusing you of cheating. If you hadn't started the race 50 seconds late you wouldn't have been last and somebody else would have won the £7."

I have always known the race was not always to the swift or the battle to the brave. Now it appears that the same applies at the other end. The spoils of de-feat may be denied even to the slow and the cowardly.

Cutting rape out of season

NEW GROUND has again been broken on the little farm on the hill.

We had the first water-closet in Aberdeenshire; we sold the first heifer with a CCD – the cattle control document which all males must have – and our forage harvester scrambled the eggs of the last corncraik east of Rothie-murchas. Now we are the first to cut oilseed rape in May.

Unfortunately, I have to admit this is another of my firsts which is less than a triumph.

As you know we have to set aside a large area of our farms if we want to qualify for the money the Common Agricultural Policy puts the way of we needy farmers.

Last year, 15% of what would have been combinable crops was left idle. This year only 13% must be left to the weeds and the wildlife but there they are, over 20 of my ancestral acres growing (mostly) volunteer crops of wheat.

Those acres are not all loss. They save the CAP a lot of money in disposing of un-wanted food. I get paid more than £100 an acre (about a third of the gross margin I dream of getting from my barley or rape). I spray the setaside to kill a host of persistent weeds which only growing potatoes used to control. On top of that, I can sow my setaside when we are waiting for harvest. What a boon that was last year. The rape that had to wait for harvest went into a very dry bed and fell well behind the earlier sown setaside.

But to qualify for setaside you have to follow the rules carefully, and that isn't my strong suit.

The plan was sound enough. I would leave an acre of one of the home fields for a cornyard. I instructed the contractor, the Man of Few Words, to leave such an area. "Uh-huh," he assented.

Quite sensibly he left the gushet, that awkward bit you get in all Aberdeenshire's fields because they are never square. In the gushet the drills get shorter and shorter and you do more and more turning and more and more damage to the crop. If they could, everyone would set their gushets aside.

Unfortunately one of the many rules of setaside is that it has to be at least 20 metres across.

If the department spies were to find that my setaside was too thin I could lose all my subsidies (what cattlemen sometimes call "an undisclosed five-figure sum").

I could have chanced it but my native honesty militated against that. And so did the fact that they check one in five forms, appearing on the farm with maps, compasses and measuring wheels.

And so it was that I was the first to cut rape this year. I had to make my setaside up to 20 metres wide by cutting down some of my beautiful crop.

I used my grass-topper and it made a first rate job. But I didn't enjoy it. It was sad to see the burgeoning, yellow froth laid so low and so green. And it was particularly frustrating to be going to all that trouble just to recreate a gushet.

Mossie's having his troubles too. He is going to have to redrill his sunflowers.

You will recall that he has confounded the critics for the last two years by growing crops of 25,000 Happy Faces per acre and selling them to the shops and as Pick-Your-Own at a pound a bloom.

This has been hard for we jealous neighbours to bear and we are glad to be able to report that the cold weather looks like beating him this year.

The crop has been very slow to come which has given the yellow hammers (who eat

the seeds) time to pick them clean whenever the little cotyledons appear. They sit on the hydro wires high above the field and whenever anything stirs in the field below, down they come to scoff it.

It happened last year too but then the plants all came up together and enough escaped. This year nothing. And you can't shoot yellow hammers as they are not a pest species ... though I wouldn't advise you to tell Mossie that.

And there's more.

He was over the other day in a state of some excitement. It wasn't "It's nae for me to say but blaw blaw blaw ..." It was "Disaaster! That frost has aborted all the winter barley."

"Come on, Moss," says I, "everyone can see the winter crops never looked better."

"Aye that's what they all think because all they ever see is a blur as they drive past. It's only when you go into the crops and if you know what you're looking for that you see disasters like this."

And he showed me a handful of barley heads. At first sight they seemed to be remarkably far advanced, beginning to turn, even. Look closer. The lighter colour comes from empty heads.

"You think you're doing well and then, Bang! Nature hits you on the chin. I've that all over and you've got it tae," said the honorary consultant.

He's right, of course, but only about 10% of the heads in one field are affected.

He says it's much worse at Moss-side where it is less exposed than on our braes, but I suspect he's just building up an excuse for harvest-time.

June 12, 1995

An unusual feein

IF YOU let the Herald print extracts from your diary you get some strange jobs. I was asked to perform the opening ceremony at the Stonehaven Feein Market. It was a jolly occasion in the town square, with a pipe band, highland dancing, cake and candy stalls, cheap Johns, barbecued kippers and pints of very cold lager. The ladies of The Rural turned out in pre-war costume and there was a knobbly knee competition and an ugliest grimace competition.

The chairman, in introducing me, welcomed me to the 21st Stonehaven Feein Market.

I couldn't let that go. I just had to tell the listening throng of two old ladies and a man with his dog that my host had miscounted. As feein markets were held twice a year from deep inside the 19th century until the 1930s, this could hardly be less than the 121st feein market in the county town of Kincardine.

Having started on a lecture, I determined to continue. Though I am far too young to remember a real feein market, I would tell them all about it.

The feein markets were where the farmers and the farm workers went to make short contracts of employment. The married men signed on for a year and the single men for six months. Towards the end of each contract was 'the speerin', when the best men would be asked to stay on for another contract, but most moved on. If the grieve moved, all the men had to move and the farmer had what was known, here in the North-east, as a 'clean toon'.

Most of the old people who went to them describe the feein markets as a humiliating experience for the men. "Bought and sold like cattle" is the phrase often used.

Horses might have been more like it. It is said that the grandfather of Jack Sleigh, the past President of the Royal Highland and Agricultural Society, was just about to hand over the half crown 'arles' which would seal their bargain for a half year, when he thought he noticed the man making an awkward shuffle with his feet. He withheld the money and asked the man to "Run yersel oot"; to trot up and down (as a dealer would do a horse) to show that he was sound.

My grandfather, Maitland Mackie, is the unintentional villain of another story about the humiliation of the farm servants at the feein markets. He fee-ed a man at Ellon and made the casual remark as they were parting, "Man, ye've awfu big feet." Two days later a letter arrived returning the shilling he had given in arles and saying, "Dear Mr Mackie, if the feet doesn't suit the man won't either."

One who was less sensitive was our old grieve, Jimmy Low. He told me quite a bit about the feein markets and seemed to have enjoyed them. It was the one chance every six months to tell the farmers exactly what he thought of them, and a good man like Low got the chance to send a number of big farmers away with their character well explained.

I really suspect Low missed the battles at the feein markets. Certainly his eyes shone when he told me about going to a great rally in the Ellon Town Hall at which the workers were addressed by Joe Duncan, who spent most of his working life on the impossible task of organising them so that they couldn't be picked off one by one by the farmers. He formed the Farm Servant's Union in 1912 and Jimmy Low was a member as soon as he was old enough. Indeed he made Little Ardo one of the few 'union shops' on Scotland's farms when he was grieve here.

Joe told them how much to ask and how much to stick out for, then, most of them veterans of the First World War, they lined up behind a pipe band and marched down to the square, where the farmers picked them off just as usual, but not before they had had some cheek from young Low.

After the deals were done, there was drink to be drunk, young women to be met and fighting to be done, some of it organised in the boxing booths. There a line-up of old pros worked their way through a queue of young farm loons, who were willing to be knocked out for the small hope of winning a week's wages for standing up for three minutes.

Jimmy Low won his pound several times because he cracked the system. All you had to do was to remain standing. So he ran away as skilfully as he could within the small ring, and covered his head as best he could to fend off the blows. He would never, on any account, hit his opponent. He knew that meant a very quick knock-out.

The modern feein market has nothing at all to do with those old days. They are gone without trace and I suppose we should be glad.

June 19, 1995

When will summer arrive?

ANOTHER few days and the nichts will fairly be drawin in again already. The year on the turn and where's the summer?

I have had the sprayer full for six days to spray the setaside and it has rained on each. Now it is far too windy to spray weedkiller, especially as one field is right next to a row of

66

houses. I once let some drift into a row of very fancy gardens and I don't want to do it again. It was no good telling them that round-up wasn't a persistent chemical, or that the roses looked quite attractive with little brown holes on the petals, or that the lettuces wouldn't be poisonous just because they were a bit burned.

In fact, my neighbours were very reasonable about it, though you couldn't say they were pleased. Another time and they might not be so understanding.

So there is a change of plan. I am going for the head-spray on the winter barley first.

Despite the cold and sunless weather the barley could be a most rewarding crop again this year. And not least of that success could be the straw, that by-product that some among us used to harvest with a match.

Last year's straw was worth up to £100 and more per acre and it looks good for this year again. All that rain having upset the timing of the straw-shortener will mean more straw. Mine is almost up to my chest already.

And demand for feeding straw is bound to be high again as the first cut of silage in the North-east has been a disaster.

But this long straw will only be a bonus if we get it safely at harvest time and the Red Rooster has already got 30 acres flat. He made the mistake of asking Mossie what the problem would be.

Without a moment's hesitation, Mossie replied: "Management." It really is a wonder he has any teeth left.

And Mossie's been diversifying again. The yellow hammers having made off with nearly all his sunflowers, our man has invested in a most extravagant toy.

It is a Starshot, which is an imaginative variation of clay pigeon shooting. It is favoured by those who have acquired all the gear for shooting clays and have then got fed up of shooting them (a very easy thing to do).

The Starshot is like an enormous dartboard in the sky, or to be more precise, half a dartboard. Clays come flying skyward out of the bull's-eye and the shooter has to hit them when they are opposite certain areas of the board.

The shooter shouts "pull" and a clay pigeon comes winging out of the bull and proceeds skywards. The shooter has to wait until it is in the area valued at one point and if he hits it he gets a point. Then he shouts "pull" again and this time he has to shoot when it is in the area worth two points. It gets progressively more difficult until, for 12 points, you've got to fire as you shout "pull".

The 50-foot monster is mounted on a trailer and Mossie's idea is that his poor son will pay his way through university by taking the Starshot to the shows. It looks as though it could maybe pay Mossie through the university too (though that would be a waste) for at the Game Fair at Straloch at the weekend, customers were queuing all the two days at £3 a time.

"Mind you, I need it aa," says Mossie.

For it is a big investment, including the little plywood hut behind which, in direct line of fire, sit the two lads loading new clays into the traps. "Are you sure that's safe?" asked the Red Rooster.

"I dinna ken, but let's find oot. Stand back." With that Mossie let the back of the shed have it with both barrels. It made a lovely pattern but it was thought wise to clad the plywood with a sheet of three millimetre steel.

It was in the further interests of safety that our man was so grudging about the young lad who appeared at the head of the queue. He looked nine but might have been small for his age. A wiser man might have said he was too young and left it at that but Mossie doesn't like to refuse anybody's money. "Can ye shoot. De ye ken what to dae? Haud the gun tight to your shoulder. Watch and nae hit onybody?"

"Aye, aye, aye," said the wee boy. "Pull," bang! "pull,"

bang! "pull," bang! "pull," bang! and the top row was demolished. When he got three of the more difficult second row Mossie was embarrassed. "That's the last time I'll ask onybody if they can shoot," he said.

£3 every four minutes looks good, but that is only a start. You see the Starshot is a most unstable affair, reaching as it does far into the sky. It has to be tied down.

And that's another financial opportunity for our man.

He sells the right to let him have a lorry to attach to the wire rope to support his dartboard. His first victims were Nicol from Keith and Butcher Bain who each lent him about £60,000 worth of artic. Last I saw they were still arguing the price.

"Fantaaastic value at a thoosand pound apiece," was Mossie's valuation. There was much room left for negotiation, for the boys thought he'd done well to get all that plant for nothing, but just to shut him up they were willing to go to £100 between them.

June 26, 1995

Summer at last

A WEEK is a long time in farming. There was I complaining that we were at the fourth week of June without getting a summer. Now we're enjoying a heat wave and The Farmer has nothing to do but enjoy listening to the grass growing and the corn filling.

And the grass is growing. The cattle are wading deep in the stuff and those who made later silage have full clamps.

The barley is filling at a rate which threatens to be embarrassing at harvest time. In five days last week it went from empty to a half-decent grain size, and still filling.

The rape doesn't look so good, though. It is definitely shorter than in recent years and I expect the yields to be down.

But Mossie hasn't given up on his rape. He says it all depends on the size of the pods and he's giving it every encouragement. He's sown three acres of garden peas in setaside next to his rape and every day he goes out and tells the rape: "Watch what the peas do and do likewise."

If you're wondering how it

is that he is growing peas on land the government has paid him over £100 an acre not to grow cash crops on, the answer is that these peas are not a cash crop. Mossie and I are going to eat the lot. He's sown them at fortnightly intervals and we hope to have fresh garden peas to our hearts' content, right up to Christmas.

This is the life for a king, surely!

And then again there have been little snags.

When I was spraying my setaside with round-up to get rid of the couch, the sprayer didn't seem to be delivering properly. I kept increasing the flow and yet the level in the tank never seemed to fall. Too late I twigged it. There is a great lot of sticker in round-up and that makes froth. When the stuff ran done I was left with the tank half-full of froth and half a field still to spray.

And then there was the trouble I had with the calves' ear-tags. We've given up on the single FASL jumbo tags because we can't get them to stay in. It was embarrassing how often we had to change the numbers on the cattle's passports. If Farm Assured Scottish Livestock was supposed to increase consumer confidence those tags weren't helping.

We've a new set of the UK metal tags and the plan is to give them a jumbo tag with the last numbers on it for easy identification. So a calf gets a metal tag with UK AB 8283 00006 and a jumbo tag which just says 6.

We thought it a great idea until I found a bull and a heifer both with the number 6.

A willing horse is an irresistible gift, especially when it is a gift and doesn't require payment. But I knew exactly whose fault it was. Potions had helped with the numbering of the calves.

We got them all in again and found the two number sixes. The heifer was indeed number six but the bull ... the one we had to get right for the passports, should have been nine. It was Potions who wrote out the numbers but he wasn't putting his hand up for the mistake.

"I definitely wrote the numbers out right. It must have been one of the tags that was upside down." He should have been a lawyer.

Then there was my little faux pas at the Highland Show.

Scottish Pride, which now does some of the work formerly done by the Scottish Milk Marketing Board, had the decency to invite us to take a light lunch, and hear something of their trials and triumphs.

Lord Sandison was in the chair and made a first rate job of

giving the press what they were entitled to and no more. When the drink was finished the press went off to their next conference and his lordship went off to provide a 'photo-opportunity'.

The Breadwinner and I, having arrived late, and The Farmer being not yet replete, were left with a nice lady who plied us unstintingly with more coffee, more wholesome sandwiches and pleasant chat .

I should have left it at that of course, but no. " Have you been with the board long?" says the farmer, like a neep.

"Oh, no," says the lady, kindly. "I'm Russell's wife."

So our hostess was Lady Sandison. I defend myself. Would I have looked a bigger fool if I'd asked a waitress if she was Lady Sandison?

Mossie had a quiet show. At least that's what his sweet, patient wife thinks. Her reasoning is that he didn't appear to be ill when he came home after his two days away with the boys.

In fact he came home inspired. Next year he and Butcher Bain plan to sell barbecued beef from the converted muckspreader.

They had a triumph in Aberdeen the other day. It was the 500th birthday of the University and they sold 12 whole sirloins as "steak in a bun" in four hours. Every time the queue got below ten yards long Mossie gave the old muckspreader a kick, spilling some of the fat from the trays into the fire. The explosion of reek and fire turned every head for half a mile and the queue was soon up to 20 yards or more.

"That's marketing," says the butcher, "give her anither kick, Mossie."

And of course Mossie's been insufferable since, "Oh, aye," he keeps saying. "I've been to the university, ye ken."

Cycling farmer climbs the ranking

I HAVE a friend on the flat plains of Strathmore who often patronises me about how plucky we Aberdonians are, struggling away on our marginal land. When we were glad to grow 35cwts to the acre he and his pals in the Angus Thousand Acre club were crying into their beer if they couldn't sell 50cwts for malting.

In recent years we seem to have been catching up. We are now looking for 70 cwts of winter barley while three tonnes for malting is still acceptable to the southern fat-cats.

Well now, my barley is such a show that I just had to phone my friend. Would he come to his lunch on Sunday, ostensibly to meet an old and mutual friend?

No he really couldn't. It was the start of the strawberry season and he would have to stay at home.

"But surely," says I. "You lads in Angus do your harvesting by proxy. You have staff for that sort of thing."

"Changed days now, Charles. I'm a hands-on farmer nowadays. I have to put on my wellingtons and keep my hands on the farming, and meanwhile the bank has its hands on my money."

Having had £1000 an acre of debt on this place in the seventies I know what that feels like. It is not good. I will have to enjoy watching my harvest ripening without the added benefit of impressing my friend.

And I am enjoying it hugely. Better than that, I have lots of time for enjoyment. The spraying is all done and, with the good Lord feeding the cows, the cows feeding the calves and Dod inseminating away, I have time for my new obsession with the push-bike.

I am pleased to report that there have been no more booby prizes – indeed The Farmer is climbing steadily up the ranking. The ten-mile time trial which first took 40 minutes can now be completed in 30, leaving time for an extra pint before he goes home.

And that could be a barrier to progress.

You see, competitive cycling is a very technical sport. Every £100 you spend on your kit saves you a second or two. You can get aerodynamic spokeless wheels. You can get an aerodynamic seat that splits the wind and feels like it is splitting you. And you simply must have those excruciatingly uncomfortable aerodynamic shorts. You can even spend £100 on a special hat, developed as a by-product of the space race, which positively sucks you along the road.

Then there are special handlebars upon which you lean your elbows and hold your hands out like a diver to part the wind. I passed the kirk just as they were coming out on Sunday and the minister was pleased. He remarked to the Red Rooster (who is an elder) that he would get The Farmer into church yet. "I see he's putting up a prayer while he's training. At least that's a start."

The weight of your bike is very important and people will spend a fortune to get a bike that is a pound lighter. I was able to get a huge gain there. For £250 I was able to upgrade from the Wasting Assets' old 30lb banger to an Italian job weighing 22lb. I was even tempted to spend another £1000 to get another 2lb off the machine.

The Breadwinner kept me right. She is worried about our retirement fundie.

"How heavy are you," she demanded?

"16 and a half stone, only," I confessed.

"Well what's the point of spending a fortune getting two pounds off the bike when, with a bit of self-restraint, you could get two stone off yourself, and save a fortune on the booze?"

Such self-restraint is beyond me but the exercise is making the weight fall off anyway. In two months I have lost over a stone. At that rate, in little over a year I'll have reached a weight below which my body cannot sustain life.

In fact, it will be a close run thing whether that gets me first or if it is the heart.

Training makes your heart beat faster when you are on the bike, but slower when you are off it.

Certainly my heartbeat is down from 72 to 52. I haven't dared to consult my quack about it but there must be a limit. If it slows 20 beats every two months for another six months I might be the fittest man in Methlick but I will be clinically dead.

In that case the retirement fundie will certainly suffice.

As you can tell, I'm enjoying the bike but not quite so much as at first. When first I took to the narrow breeks and crash helmet no one ever recognised me. But now that my secret is out every second car toots at me, often making me jump near out of my skin.

The Farmer is now the butt of endless jokes, only one of them funny.

When you accelerate or climb a steep hill it is common for fit young cyclists to stand up. In the jargon of the sport they are "dancing" as they bob up and down on the peddles.

"The Farmer is fairly improving. He was dancing up the Big Brae this week."

"Aye," came the reply, "but it was just the "Auld Fashioned Waltz."

July 10, 1995

Off to the Highland

THE BOYS have found a hotel which hasn't heard of them and are set for the Highland. Unfortunately, I have a prior engagement further north and can only go for a day. This is a source of great sadness to me. As a student of animal psychology I don't like to miss the opportunity to witness the boys at play.

Mind you, we do have rather different interests. None

74

of them is very interested in livestock. Even Big Hamish, who has a dairy to keep the smile on his face, has no interest in the show rings. Debate could range around him about whether it was possible for a British Friesian to get a prize these days. Old men who believe there should be enough beef on a dairy cow to make a plate of stovies can be close to blows with Holstein men, but Hamish's eyes will have wandered to some new or bigger machine.

And they're all the same. The Red Rooster has hill cows but that's only because he has some cliffs where even he wouldn't dare to drive a combine. He will only see the cattle judging in the unlikely event that he can't find a better place for a drink than the Herdsman's.

Mossie shudders when he passes cattle, "C'mon. Let's get passed these brutes. We dinna need ony loss adjusters." He has pigs, but they're a bit of a write-off at the Highland because they are so hedged around by health legislation they can't get to the show, or more exactly, they can't get home in case they take any disease home.

I don't see the attraction of all those fancy aids-to-bankruptcy you see on the machinery stands. I am sure I am right that the optimum size of farm nowadays is about 600 acres and that that is far too small to make £100,000 combines and £30,000 ploughs economic. No, no. I leave that to Davie the contractor. He may be the Man of Few Words but he has the credit to buy the machines and the acres to spread them over.

Anyway, for me who has wasted half my life on sport, the essence of the working show is competition. I notice they are having pole-climbing competitions this year. Great. That will show off the skills of the tree surgeons, the linemen and the woodmen.

So why not expand that? What about combine races? Or changing-machinery-on-the-back-of-a-tractor races. Who can hitch and unhitch the most machines in five minutes ... special section for screw hitches?

And if, like me, you prefer the aesthetic competitions like in the cattle, why not classes for tractors? and even tractors decorated like their predecessors, the Clydesdales?

That might be worth a try but for me the main attraction will always be the livestock and the Blue Riband, the cattle. It is a quite wonderful feeling to take a beast to the Highland and get a red ticket – better still a championship. Many men have spent fortunes on trying. You

can breed a champion or you take the easy way and buy them. To buy a champion should cost you at least three times what it is worth and there is no guarantee that you will have the skill and the luck to gain a championship no matter how much you pay.

But what I really admire is the man who can buy below the middle of the market and then win at the Highland. George Anderson of Keir has done it and I am full of admiration.

He bought a heifer calf from me for £1200 and took the supreme championship at the show with her when she was a cow.

I would like to do that.

Now you will recall that I bought a bull at Perth this year. He has some of the criteria for fulfilling my dream. He was certainly cheap enough. I'd call myself a stockman if I could get a ticket with him.

"What do you think of that," I said to the Red Rooster when he came home. "Oh dinna worry about it, Charlie," he said, "The worst-looking bull can be the best breeder."

All that I knew, but what was wrong with my bull? He still looked good to me. Still, with all the weight of opinion against him, I decided to try him locally first, so Dod is entered for New Deer Show. My idea was that I would show his detractors.

I'm no longer confident.

You see I can't afford to have Dod sitting around eating cake until the third week of July. He has to see to 47 ladies before then.

That doesn't mean that a prize at New Deer is impossible. Some bulls conserve their energy very well. They don't join the foreplay which can go on for days. Wise bulls just wait until they are spot-on, do the business and then rest up.

Unfortunately Dod is not that wise.

He got a start among Gowkie's small herd. Only four were available and that didn't set him back at all.

But when I got him together with the 43 at home it was like a comic blue movie. There were at least six in heat or near it and the poor young bull didn't know where to start. He tore back and forward among them and had no sooner started to case one than another would come past and distract him. Even after he had served one he chased on and in seconds was mounting another, but without result.

He has been in for two weeks and I haven't seen my bull sitting down yet. If this goes on much longer he'll be able to hide behind a fence post.

Dod's pedigree name is Doodo, a horrible name which is Swahili for "insect". If he doesn't slow down we may give him his old name back.

Three cwts lighter (and falling), I see what everyone else doesn't like about my bull now, and dreams, even of New Deer show, are waning.

July 17, 1995

Irishman's revenge

"WE COUNTED them out and we counted them back in again," said Mossie as the Irishman left with his little truckie to try four of his heifers at the sale of bullers at Thainstone.

A lot of people wonder why the Irishman was so willing to help Mossie with his marketing after Mossie sold him his farm for a Buchan record price. Well, I think the Irishman is after his revenge. By getting Mossie back into cattle (which our man hates and refers to as the 'loss adjusters'), he hopes to inflict some sort of emerald retribution.

At any rate 100 loss adjusters arrived at Moss-side last

back-end. Black heifers, they were bought near the bottom end of the market. They were maintained on two pounds of the Irishman's patent meal and Mossie's ammonia-treated straw.

They did well and some even went fat. Others sold quite handily onto the grass. Mossie is pleased and his banker is delighted. "Yes, Mossie's heifers are ahead of budget," he told me when I was in to see him the other day. "We budgeted for a loss of £50 a head and he's only lost £45 ... some going, eh?"

Yes indeed, but, as anyone who has kept cattle knows, it is easy to do well on the first half of the cattle. The problem comes with the tail-enders. They are proving "stiffer to cash". And I don't know what the Irishman is up to but he seems to be making it a point of honour, as the original buyer of these cattle, to see Mossie's losses minimised. So he has been running around with little batches of heifers trying them in this market and that.

And that is why Mossie was quoting from the Falklands war when he waived goodbye to the Irishman and his four heifers on Friday. He counted them out all right.

But Brian Hanrahan on the deck of his aircraft carrier never achieved with the fighter bombers what Mossie did with the heifers at Thainstone. When the Irishman brought the heifers back and he counted them back in there were five heifers where he had only counted four out.

"Well, it's like this Mossie, It was a cheap sale so I couldn't sell your heifers. In fact they were that cheap I thought it was grand opportunity for to buy. She's a nice heifer, isn't she?"

Sadly, he was asking the wrong man.

Maybe the Irishman is trying to bankrupt Mossie after all?

I'm afraid I've been in the heifer trade myself. You will recall that on the spring day I sold 15 of my last season's heifer calves. They were well grown and all went for breeding which I was very happy about. It meant my buyers thought they looked well and would breed well.

They were right, too. In fact they were too right. One has calved already.

That was not a credit to my stockmanship.

The heifer is only 14 months old, which means she fell to one of her half brothers when she was five months old.

It is difficult to know what to do about this. We have stopped castrating the bull calves. They grow faster with testicles and the market no longer pays a premium for steer

beef, so why pay the vet to come and castrate them? It is not a job I fancy myself, not on either side of the fence.

We could separate the cows with bull calves from those with heifers, but when you've only got 40 cows that becomes a bit impractical.

Anyway this 14-month-old heifer had been seen calving by a neighbour and they had managed to get a calf out of her which was not yet dead. Would I take her back?

The rules are that if a beast turns out in calf the seller must take her back and pay full compensation for her transport, feed and medication, offer a rebate of a third of the price or make other acceptable arrange-ments. But the seller must be informed before she calves.

My buyer was too late to have any legal claim, but that was not the point. The heifer was not going to fit in with his breeding pattern now that she had calved out of season and she'd never be the sort of big cow this man was looking for. I had sold something which did not meet her trade description. It is bad enough doing that without getting a reputation for being hard to deal with.

So I borrowed the Irish-man's cairtie and off I went to see what fate had landed me with.

I didn't ask if it was a bull because you don't get told about such bull calves. They carry £100 worth of subsidy into the world.

The mother was all right though sore about the backend. The calf was huge in relation to her teenage mum but not yet on her feet, though this was her fourth day. I returned the buying bill of £440 and £60 for her keep and a fiver apiece to the cattlemen. We loaded them up and off she went to Little Ardo.

At £515 the Irishman was not impressed with my purchase. "Would that calfie have had its colostrum?"

"Definitely. The cow is very handy and they were able to milk her and the stockman was most particular that she had had plenty of colostrum."

The Irishman was doubtful. "It's just that it might have been the same 'particular' man who didn't notice that the heifer was in calf until a neighbour told him she was calving."

Anyway, all is well. The first day I held her up to suck. The second day she stood on her knees and now my £515 looks like money well spent. She will be running about by the time you read this.

July 24, 1995

Shifting goalposts

IN THE late fifties, when we who are no longer young were playing rugby, the field and behaving generally as though tomorrow would look after itself, The Farmer and his pal Jonnie Moffett, two athletes for sure, played in a remarkable match in Edinburgh. At least, the warm-up that the two athletes put themselves through was something else.

Friday was the night of the Arts ball at Aberdeen's beach ballroom. It didn't stop till 4am and that gave the two heroes two hours to kill before catching the train for the capital. Sleep was out of the question, so a party was arranged at a team-mate's flat.

At about six in the morning we boarded the train and were looking for somewhere to get a night's sleep in the three hours journey when we came upon the thing we needed least. There was a fully stocked bar with a barman behind it.

I can honestly say that I don't remember having any other drink that night, but it was so unusual, in those days when bars shut at 9.30, to find one

open out of hours, that we did have a night cap, or was it two?

At any rate five minutes into the game, which started at eleven, we got a penalty wide out on the left. That was the position from which Moffett later scored six of his points for Ireland against England at Landsdown Road, so we had every chance of success.

And yet, as he tee-ed the ball up, I felt there was something wrong. I ran up to him to see if I could help and sure enough I could. Our man had set the ball perfectly to kick a goal on the next pitch.

I got him squared up and in fact he kicked the goal which gave us a three each draw against the young veterinarians in the Royal Dick College.

I tell you all that because, 35 years older, he came to visit us last week. Jonnie now farms in New Zealand, where the government abolished all farm subsidies eight years ago. I was interested to hear from someone who had been through that what it was like.

Nearly every farmer I meet nowadays says: "It canna last." These are good times we are having, they all agree, but they are dependent on a heap of money being thrown at us by the common agricultural policy. There is bound to be a taxpayers' revolt and it is likely to be sooner rather than later.

So they all say and they may be right, though for many of them it will be the first time.

First of all, these good times we are enjoying aren't that good.

Farm incomes in Scotland, according to the Department of Agriculture, are the highest since 1977. But surely that isn't very good. All right, 1977 may have been a good year too, but most people expect to get a bit richer year by year.

To put that statistic another way, even though farm incomes are up this year they have not yet reached the levels they were at 18 years ago. Is there another sector of industry or sector of the population who have done as badly as the farmers? I doubt it, and remember that something like half the businesses which enjoyed that good year in 1977 have left the industry since then. And, if you know farmers, you will know how many of those left by choice.

The New Zealanders used to have a highly subsidised industry and then, eight years ago, all at once with no messing about with transitional periods, they gave them all up at once. Farmers were thrown onto the world market.

It was horrendous. Prices crashed and so did one third of the farming businesses. Support groups were set up to help farmers to come to terms, not with just being broke, but with having lost the family acres.

And yet, my old pal tells me, "It would be hard to find a farmer in New Zealand who would like to go back to subsidies."

I'll need to watch not to put words into Jonnie's mouth so this is my interpretation of how it benefited the successful New Zealand farmers to give up their government support.

While one third of the farmers went out of farming, they didn't take their land with them. The flood of farms onto the market meant the strong and the ambitious could get on and expand and there was plenty of cheap land available. I am happy with Little Ardo but, if the same happened here, the whizz kids, like the Red Rooster and Mossie, would be able to get into some real acreages.

When government support was withdrawn Jonnie was able to buy some first rate land and get going with building up his fruit and veg growing business, which sees him gallivanting round the world selling carrot juice to Japan, and onions and apples to the UK.

When pressed Moffett, who is vice-president of the New Zealand Apple and Pear Board as well as a farmer, says that the main disadvantage of subsidies is that they can be cut from under you at any time, so you can't plan ahead.

That's true, of course, but the same would be true of cutting off your legs. Once it is done it can't happen again so you can safely sell the shoes.

I was able to tell him that subsidies were equal to 73% of farm profits in 1994 and the two just about balanced in 1993. That money may make us inefficient, it may stop Mossie getting another farm, but it's keeping Little Ardo in business and that will be important to me, even when it's Potions' bank account that it affects.

July 31, 1995

Hairst is upon us

THERE IS a breathless air of expectation in the North-east. Those still in the dark ages or who have dairy cattle which don't need to be fed economically, have made their silage and a surprising number of people have made good hay. There is nothing more we can do about the crops short of prayer.

And we are praying. We are praying that Turriff Show which starts today will not bring the usual thunder plumps. They look like the only thing that stand between us and another fulsome expression of the Lord's bounty. The winter barley looks uncommonly well. There is quite a bit more straw and, though it may be an illusion, it seems to me that there are more berries as well.

Brace yourself, banker!

In the meantime all we can do is wait.

Mossie has been doing quite a lot of his waiting in the pub. Indeed he has been drinking left-handed because of a very painful arthritic condition he's developed in his right arm.

I thought that might have been something to do with washing his roofs and outside walls with a 4000 pounds-per-square-inch pressure-hose. Two days perched on top of a Hi-mac left the house shining but the whole area covered in broken slates, seedling trees, moss, dead leaves and other detritus. The strawberries were inedible, the patio was filthy and the wife's car was a disgrace – so was her humour.

"Well a body has to dae something to pass the time till hairst," he says, "and it's nae that that's wrong with my arm. I've had it afore. It's Tennant's elbow."

A lot of us have been filling in time with a thing called

83

Quin-ag. That horrifying piece of advertising jargon denotes the farming graduates' effort in support of the University of Aberdeen's 500th anniversary fundraiser. They're trying to raise £25 million for a number of new projects including a medical research building and a heritage centre, which would at one time have been financed by the government.

The farmer graduates have set ourselves to raise £250,000 for strengthening the University's work in the countryside. There are to be scholarships for country kids who find that the last £1000 makes it too difficult to take up college courses. There's to be assistance for research in Rural Stud-ies, a biannual conference and a donation to make sure agriculture is given proper weight in the new heritage centre.

It was to that end that we were all at the mart on Saturday morning; for the Quin-ag roup.

Graduates had donated a pair of statues liberated from an English Country House (£700), a racer bike (as new but that was some time ago and it wasn't very good even then, £40), a Newsome gilt and enough to feed her for a year (£290). A split new eight tonne Marshall trailer (£3200), and a dying MF combined harvester (£950).

The Breadwinner and I were operating at the other end of the market. She bought ten kilos of black pepper (£2). That

84

made me a bit sad. I cannot see us ever needing to buy pepper again. That heap will trail around after us till death do us part. I see my life stretching before me pursued by a huge bag of pepper.

And we got into a furious row over the pair of Guy Rogers chairs. For a start, we are no more than three years away from moving from this big draughty farmhouse to a compact Death House, so what do we need with two more chairs? There is more need for us to set up an antique shop and cash some of what we have.

But it wasn't that that annoyed me. She missed such an opportunity. The chairs were knocked down at £80. In a fashion which will shock you if you are an antique dealer but which is commonplace in agricultural auctions, she was asked how many she wanted.

"Both, of course," she said, a little haughtily.

What a blunder! If she'd taken only one she would have got the other for nothing. After all the value of half a matched pair is far lower than half of both of them together.

If you don't understand that explanation you'll sympathise with The Breadwinner. I couldn't get her to understand and she didn't see why she should. After all, had I not landed with four sets of yellow oilskins? In 20 years of farming I had worn out two sets. Did this mean I was planning to farm on for another 40 years? And what about the six pairs of dungarees? They were only £2 a pair but they were 48 inches round the waist. Now that I've taken to the bike I'd be liable to fall out of them and the Safety man would throw a fit if he saw all that cloth flapping around our power-drive shafts.

Anyway it was a fundraiser and grossed £14,000. Like everyone else I believe I got the snatch of the day. Aberdeen University must have moles in the fish-smoking industry, for there were three handsome consignments of smoked salmon and sea-trout. All the lads were buying, at up to £24 a pound so I look forward to some up-market barbecues. I got a five pound side for the price of fillet steak. But I'll maybe have to keep that for the younger Investment's wedding.

Judgment days

THE TENDER loving care with which we have pampered our winter barley is paying off. And the invoice has arrived for all the things we forgot to do or did too late.

Sadly, we seem to have made more mistakes than usual. The first few fields have been a bit of a disappointment. Bushel weights are down and many of the grains are not much more than a swelling at the bottom of the awns.

It's so disappointing because it looked so well. When the grain started to fill our hearts perked up and then soared. But it must all have been water. The plump berries shrivelled in a few days and harvest was suddenly upon us.

The first confirmation that all was not well came when the Red Rooster's 15-tonne cart only held 13 tonnes. And Crookie, who was looking to save some seed, calculated that he'd need his entire crop to dress out a suitable seeding.

Mossie ordered his men to shut the door of his big shed between loads in case the crop blew away.

Mind you, I think he may have been being a bit too cautious for his first field did work out at three tonnes eight cwts.

Against that background, and remembering that I am not allowed to be better than Mossie, the Little Ardo crops are not doing too badly. But it did come on quickly. I tried a sample on Saturday and to my astonishment it read 14.6% moisture on two different meters.

Now that is perfection itself. The merchants hit you for drying charges, shrinkage and take a little bit for themselves if you go over 15% so you want it just below fifteen. If you go further below you just lose weight. And worse than that, if you lose 2% of water it reduces your overall weight by nearer 3%.

So up I went to see if Mains had the combine greased and ready to go.

He had, but he was going to start his own on Monday and would come to Little Ardo about Wednesday. By that time my barley should be at 10% in this heatwave. That would mean we would need to throw a tonne and a half of water into each artic load to make up the weight. Tricky times were here.

Or so it seemed.

But as Davie, the Man of

Few Words who does most of our contracting says: "Naething ripens crop like the sound of the contractor's phone." I begged Mains to come to me on Saturday and Sunday and return to his own on Monday. Mains started two days early and came to me last Monday.

He had pulled out all the stops. He had even postponed his second cut silage, which made the meter reading on our barley something of an embarrassment. We couldn't get it below 19%. Where the samples we had taken three days earlier came from, I just do not know.

Anyway, with young Ochyoch there with his combine as well, we did 32 acres in perfect conditions. The Farmer was tired by the end of the day, for he had to cart all day to two combines.

I can't say what it yielded. It's not the 75cwt I was looking for but I'm confident it is 60. And the good news is that the first load is away to the merchants where their meter said 16.5% and gave me a respectable bushel-weight for Pleasante of 61.7.

The bad news is that I'll have to keep quiet about it. Mossie has me well warned that if I want him to stay on as honorary crops consultant I'd better not beat him.

So I'll have to join in the general moan.

On the positive side we have never seen so much straw. Mains got 176 bales off a 13 acre field. A few short years ago that would have just meant so much more smoke giving farmers a bad name in the countryside. But a few short weeks ago it was making £17 a bale in the electronic auction at Thainstone. And that comes to almost £230 an acre.

You will say that this year there may not be such a scarcity of straw. You may be right, too, but if you believe reports from the rest of the country, where silage yields have been from reasonable to disastrous, and where wheat and spring barley are dying on their feet before they are ripe, then 1995-6 could be an even better year for straw.

Mind you, the farmer of Waterside seems to me to be taking his optimism about the market for winter fodder too far.

Watery is impressed by reports from England that maize silage crops have failed, that there are few second cuts, no third cuts of grass silage and that straw is short. He is seriously considering cutting and baling his wheat, treating it with ammonia and selling it to the English dairymen as a whole crop diet.

Anyway I am trying to get the lads to take the view that if the yields and bushel weights are down, so are the moistures. And if half of what they say is true the straw will make up for any expectations which are not met by the grain.

And if Watery's mad scheme to sell his wheat for fodder works we can get him to bring home a few cheap calves.

By the way, Watery has developed a new system for avoiding the blue flashing lights when he goes home from the pub which is neither early enough nor often enough. He leaves a gate to his newly ploughed field lying open. When the blue lights start flashing he doesn't stop, nor does he try to race off. He simply waits till he reaches the gate, nips down into four wheel drive and in he goes.

The squad car can't follow.

It has worked twice but I fear I won't be able to tell you about the next time which is sure to be subjudice.

August 14, 1995

Tricky times ahead

EARLY DISAPPOINTMENT with low bushel weights has been blown away. Moistures are so low and the cutting has been so easy that 1995 will be remembered as one of the good harvests for winter barley.

It has even been too hot for some. The Red Rooster's fans in the combine have been giving him trouble. In those eighty degree days his cab has been like a sauna. So it wasn't just his hair that was bright red.

That was until he could stand it no longer and tried to drive with the door open. Any other year, with the grain coming in at 20% that would have worked well, but with the grain in the low teens the dust and awns stuck to the sweat and produced a curious stubbly yellow Rooster in extreme discomfort.

And it all came on so quickly we were taken quite unawares. The worst case was Mains, who doesn't need to dry barley in a normal year because he has one of those blue grain storage towers. All his barley goes in there to feed his bulls through the winter. The bulls prefer the grain to be moist and it doesn't go off because the airtight container keeps the bugs quiet.

But Mains was too late this year. He found himself putting

barley at 13% into his moist grain tower. When Mossie heard about that he took on a grave look. "You're taking a bit of a risk, aren't you Mains? Should you nae have propcorned it jist tae be sure?" That would be as bad as having paper plates, a dishwasher and an au pair girl.

I fear I am in dire trouble with my honorary consultant. I am not allowed to have bigger yields than the master and yet I have one field which has yielded 81 cwts at 13%. Or four tonnes three cwts at 15%.

That is the greatest cereal yield we have ever had and it was with barley after wheat. The field which has a very good southerly exposure was for many years in grass and had a great crop of wheat last year.

The yield was spoiled at the last minute when it got droughted and burned. We never expected a yavel crop to yield, but it has done.

You may not remember but last year I managed my first ever four-tonne crop. Well, both were grown with Pleasante, a six-rowed barley which is generally thought to be past its time. Indeed I had the greatest difficulty getting any last year.

And such is the fame of my Pleasante that I am inundated with requests for seed. However I just cannot understand all that stuff about royalties so I'm not interested. I might keep a wee bit back for myself, mind.

I don't have an overall figure yet but yields range down to three tonnes five so I can't complain. Mossie's average is three tonnes nine so, if I can sneak my average in below that, he may yet be persuaded to stay on as adviser.

So it is going well but in the rush there have been some tense moments – like Mossie and the Red Rooster and their partnership in the swather.

The wonder is that the partnership has worked for so long. The Rooster does all the work. At least he provides the excellent driver. When he gets tired, at about midnight, the Rooster takes over and, depending on how much there is to do, he might drive all night. The Rooster's father then sends out the invoices or calls round with them and gets the money in. The Rooster's mother has to cope with all the aggravation from those waiting in the swather queue.

Mossie, on the other hand, is the "thinking, drinking partner." While the hash is on he is in the pub blowing that he is finished. "Oh dear me! You're nae finished? Canna get a swather? Leave it tae me." Then he gets on his mobile and tells the Rooster's mum to tell the Rooster to get his tail over to the Barnyards and cut another 50 acres. "Aye that's all fixed – I'll have another pint."

You can see the potential for strain, I'm sure.

And I had one of those moments of extreme embarrassment unknown to my father's generation. They had staff.

Mains was combining and the Wasting Asset, despite his hangover, was just about managing to cope with driving off the grain. I was loading an artic. Now the only way we can handle these monsters is to load them on the road. With my old digger it takes me forty-five minutes and in that time no one gets in or out.

I like to get them loaded in the early morning but last Wednesday the hash was on. The Wasting Asset arrived with a load from the field. I was asking the lorry driver nicely if he would draw forward to let him in to tip when I espied our Postie who had pressures of his own and was showing them. He wanted to get past. I was going to ask him nicely if he would back-up and let the lorry forward to let the Asset past when the biggest rigg I've ever seen on a road arrived behind the postie blocking him completely.

This was a swather which had taken the wrong turning. A huge Ford was pulling a low loader and behind that he had a trailer. If you have ever backed a caravan just imagine doing the same again on a narrow farm road with a trailer behind the caravan.

The warm air was blue.

Braced for a boon

FIFTEEN DAYS after the combine arrived 170 acres are cut and away to the grain merchants. It has been a wonderful harvest.

The winter rape has averaged 31 cwts to the acre. It looked poor all year and yet has yielded as well as ever. It is an enigmatic crop.

Because we are saving some barley for seed we don't have an exact figure for the yield. On bad days I look at the heap and say that the average is 70 cwts. And then I go back and have another look at the heap and get the yield up to 72. At all events it is good considering that much of it was following wheat. Next year it will all be after rape. That gives a complete break from the cereal diseases and it will be a case of "Brace yourself banker – here comes my barley cheque."

It has not all been plain sailing. You know I am not one to hide my light under a bushel-weight, but I have to admit to being one of the world's less gifted when it comes to unloading combines. That involves driving the cart alongside the moving combine and catching the grain as it pours from a great spout. Despite the fact that I used to field in the covers I am not a very good catcher.

The trouble is that, with my arthritic joints, I cannot look far enough round to see properly where the jet of seeds is landing. I can just about manage out of the corner of one eye when the ground is level and the wind is low. But when I am jiggling along at the edge of the field with one wheel halfway up the dyke I am in trouble.

And rape seeds in wind are very difficult. The trouble is they are so light that as soon as they leave the spout they fan out and by the time they land they are covering five feet across the six foot cart. So there is only one foot of margin for variations in the wind and for errors.

A few precious seeds blow out of the left side of the cart so you veer to the left. Just as you make it the wind drops and the black cloud starts depositing the oil seeds over the right hand edge of the cart. Worse than that, you have been so worried about the left/right problem that you haven't noticed that the combine has been gaining and it starts to pour off the front of the cart as well.

Then you catch a glimpse of the most terrifying sight the

Little Ardo harvest field has to offer; Mains is glowering down ferociously from the combine. His eyes are flashing and his lips are moving. Luckily you can only guess what he is saying. It amounts to "Here I am doing my best to cut the stuff and you can't even catch it. I have enough on my plate without having to shut the auger on and off to do your job for you." There may well have been other words I haven't heard since I was at school.

And there was another tense moment. Mains was anxious to get on because his father had just been down with the message that the rape at the Mains was down to 9.6 % moisture and there was a rumour that the merchants wouldn't take it if it got down to 6%.

Now, for trouble-free lifting of rape, it is important that the swathe be laid evenly out before the combine and this was not the case in this particular field. It was two steps forward and one back for the Mains. Every ten yards or so a great clump of rape straw would spew over the header amid an agonised rasp from the clutch and the air would turn blue once again. "That swather's jist a disgrace. It's jist like a row of feathery stooks. Every time I have to stop I'm losing time and you're losing rape."

Put that way I wasn't very impressed either.

Mossie's in good fettle. He isn't being very forthcoming

92

about his yields though which makes it difficult for me to make sure mine are smaller.

But he is fairly enjoying the good weather. And he is scandalised at how easy the English farmers have it. "They get weather like this every year and still we beat them," he says.

He's even bought himself a new combine with a starting price of £160,000. That's twice what I paid for my whole farm and to justify it he's going to have to do some contracting. But he certainly can't come here. The Mega cuts 22 feet at a time so it would be sore put to it to turn in some of our fields and, if there were any gates it couldn't go over it certainly couldn't go through them.

It has a computer which gives an hourly print-out of the yield per acre, moisture content and specific weight of the crop. It can do the invoicing as well, so I'm glad to be stuck with Mains. I prefer his gentler system of appearing in a couple of months' time with the handwritten invoice from the pad with the blue paper.

We could have a fair dram this year, for it has been a memorable hairst.

August 28, 1995

Farmer dreams of efficiency

So I took it to the smiddy
But there I found a queue
For Hillie and Mossie and
Mains were there
And their's was broken too.

I COMPOSED that rather sad little chorus last Monday.

It was going to be such a good day. The hash was on. The Man of Few Words was here to plough the barley stubble and sow the crops which will surely make me a rich man in 1996.

All day long a great five-furrow slab of Little Ardo would be folded over and hard behind would come the one-pass to sow the seeds. I would follow with the rollers to seal in what little moisture had been left by the summer's drought.

In the meantime Potions would clear a way in front of us by removing bales of straw from the fields and even the Wasting Asset would appear at before ten. His job would be to start sorting out the mess in the cornyard.

It would be almost like old times again on the farm, with people on it. And I suppose it was, really, for things broke down even in the old days.

The ploughing and planting had hardly started when the ram that shoves the plough over at the end of the drills so that the five socks that plough north can be engaged and the five that plough south rested, broke.

Though with all that weight of tackle it was by no means straightforward, we got the ram off. The Man of Few Words got on the phone. There was not a ram like this one to be had in the whole of Aberdeenshire. One would have to come from Leicester.

It was a lovely day and I knew that the Man of Few Words would be quite happy to leave as soon as the dew was off to bale some of the malting barley that is being cut round about, so my trick was to get the ram sorted quick.

So I took it to the smiddy
And there I found a queue
For Hillie and Mossie and
Mains were there
And their's was broken too.

The Red Rooster was there and all. He'd burst something about the side-knife of his combine and was adamant that his job would need to be done first as he had rape which was down

to 7% and falling. His rape cheque was shrinking before his very eyes. And Penny Washers, the white settler, had an even bigger crisis. His daughter's holidays would be ruined if she didn't get a bit brassed onto her pony's bridle.

By the time I eventually got to the top of the queue I had been joined by Potions with a burst oil pipe from the digger. The smith would make up a new unit for me but I'd need to go 15 miles to a hydraulics firm for a new ram as he didn't have one the right thickness.

Off I went and was returning on the hour when I overtook the Wasting Asset limping up to the smiddy. He always drives like time was short and a cup medal was at stake so it was no wonder that he'd broken one lift arm on the old International. That had sent the bale grab smashing through cab window.
So he took it to the smiddy
But there he found a queue
For Hillie and Mossie and
Mains were there
And their's was broken too.

There were countless delays that afternoon but I got all my equipment back to the field at five o'clock, by which time the Man of Few Words had gone off baling and my day was ruined.

It had all been Mossie's fault really. He it was who suggested I stop growing wheat and spring rape and concentrate on winter barley and rape. He's done the same himself. What it means is that instead of having four small harvests between August and September, and a sowing season that lasted till well into November, we now have two big harvests in August and must have all of what used to be called the spring work done by the end of September.

Maitland Mackie, like Mossie, has bought a Mega this summer, even though it will only be in use for four weeks in the year. Now the former Vice President of the National Farmers Union is lucky enough to have on his farm the man who (before VJ day) brought the first combine to Westertown. His many admirers will be pleased to hear that Sir Maitland Mackie wheels around the place in a battery-driven golf buggy and still takes a keen interest.

But even the great man had difficulty grasping the finances of the Mega. As he drove round the hulk which cost considerably more than his father had paid for the title deeds, the old man asked to be reminded, "How much did my first combine cost?"

"£880, Dad."

"And how much did this cost?"

"£108,000 plus the old one."

"And how much did my first one cost?"

"£880."

"And *how* much did this one cost?"

"£108,000."

Life's a hard row

I HAVE done my best, but I cannot get the winter barley yield down below three and a half tonnes. With yields like that, we could just about compete, as the Americans would have us do, at world prices without subsidies.

I put that to the lads on Sunday at the discussion group.

The very suggestion was greeted with a howl of protest. My view was not popular even where it was shared. Mossie and the Red Rooster were adamant that, while I could be right, it was the duty of every farmer to deny it.

"Farmers are going through tricky times and it is only the support of the taxpayer that is allowing some of us a decent living, though there is no meaningful return on our capital," sums up their view.

But I was more impressed by Young Ochyoch. "You maybe can survive, farming on the balmy southern fringes but what about us in the wilds of Central Buchan with nothing but our thrawnness to protect us from the north wind?"

And this is where he really made me sit up. "It's all very well for you to say we could do without the subsidies but you've been at it for 30 years. What about younger lads just starting? When you've got all these damned kids to feed and clothe, when you've borrowed over your neck to get some land and some gear together, you need all the help you can get."

That profound thought has led me to develop a theory of the life cycle of the farmer. It shows what a hard row we have to hoe and it shows that, while there is always somebody creaming it with the subsidies, there are always others, at other stages in their metamorphosis, who need every penny the exchequer can spare.

I see the farmer going through seven stages, if he survives that long.

Stage one is when the young farmer prepares for the great day when he takes up the reins. He learns all the skills of the trade. He may even go to college for some book learning as well as developing the skills which young ladies and barmen can impart.

All those things are done in stage one, but primarily, in my theory, the prospective farmer saves.

Stage two starts when the old man finally moves over or,

even better, moves out. If he has saved well and avoided marriage or married well, the young farmer will enter stage two with a tidy little sum.

It will disappear very quickly, as he discovers that all those things his father had on the farm were not, after all, there by magic. They had to be paid for.

Stage three is the expansion phase in the farmer's life. All the things his father did wrong are put right, or at least that is the intention. New machinery is bought, new sheds put up and the intensive unit is added.

But the thing that most expands in phase three is the overdraft. It seems to be controlled by a ratchet. When there is a good year a new shed is put up or the tractors are upgraded. When there is a bad year the overdraft rises.

Stage four starts when the farmer's credit limit is reached.

Now, you must not imagine that what we are talking about here is the farmer's overdraft limit. He will get one of those early on in his career and through time will develop great skill in renegotiating it onto higher and higher levels. On top of that he will discover that equipment may be leased and he can buy cattle at the mart and not pay for them until he sells.

Stage four is only reached when the farmer can borrow no more and when his creditors can not be relied on to allow further stalling on payment.

Many go under in stage

four. But for the rest, the sooner it is reached the better. For it is here that discipline enters the farmer's life. Sums have to be done, budgets stuck to. Wonderful ideas which are losing money have to be abandoned.

Stage five has been reached when the farmer has a credit window. That is when there is a time, be it ever so short, when, just after the harvest cheque has arrived, the farmer's overdraft is below its limit. As stage five proceeds the farmer finds himself in a virtuous circle. For longer and longer each year he can shop around for the cheapest instead of shopping where the salesman is the most patient. And gradually the interest payments fall as the credit window gets longer and longer.

Stage six is when, after the harvest cheque has gone in, there is a day when there is no overdraft at all. That is when the farmer usually dies. If not, stage six persists until the great day when the harvest cheque arrives before there is an overdraft.

Then the farm business is mature. In stage seven, with no interest to pay and cash for quick deals, any fool can farm.

This year we entered stage seven. The Breadwinner and I took the cheque down to the bank together and were happy.

It is true that we can manage without the subsidies but Young Ochyoch is quite right. We wouldn't like to go back to stage one without the support of the exchequer.

September 11, 1995

Beware of bankers who offer lunch

I THOUGHT everyone knew to beware the banker who invites you for lunch, but apparently not. Big Hamish was down the other day and told me how he was looking forward to Friday. He was being taken out to lunch by his banker, "Aye, and you get a right good feed."

Hamish was contracted to stack the big round bales in our Dutch barn. I have a digger of my own, of course, but it can only reach high enough to put three up. Even finishing with a triangle of three only gives me nine bales per stow, whereas with Hamish's supercharged all singin', all dancin' digger we could look for five high or 15 to the stow.

Even with the price of straw these days I would have been unhappy about employing any other contractor to do such a job, but Hamish is just the best digger driver there is. We persuaded him to come and make an attempt at the world record for stacking 600 bales.

The big man accepted the challenge and while Potions and I hauled the bales in about he threw them up. I have never seen anything like it. He has full torque on his digger and an extra spool valve which means he can turn the bales sideways. When he went from reverse to forward his front wheels came anything up to 18 inches off the ground.

He did it in four hours – costing me six pence a bale. And Hamish declined my invitation to cheat slightly and call it three hours, which would surely be an unbeatable record.

Anyway, he will need a long spoon on Friday.

I tried to tell him that as soon as the bankers get past the Christmas card stage, they are bad news. If you are summoned to the office 'for a chat about renewing your facility' you are fairly safe. All they want is the £50 they charge for it.

But if they invite you to lunch you are on a different ballpark. It isn't so bad if you are invited to lunch at Ellon, no one with the power to put you out of business works there. Things can be stickier if you're invited to lunch in Aberdeen. But if your banker invites you to lunch at the North British in Edinburgh, look out! You can be sure it's you that's paying.

And why do they use lunch as a stick with which to beat us? Our only crime is giving them too much business.

The answer is that the bankers are nice feckless people like the rest of us. They don't like confrontations. They hate being the bearers of bad news. They can't stand to see grown men cry. If they have to tell a client he has another six months to pull his business round, a banker feels the least he should get out of it is a good meal. And the banker can't very well eat while the unfortunate client looks on.

Mind you, how can you enjoy a meal when your heart is in your mouth?

I must admit I never got the call to Edinburgh, but I do know about the bank lunches in Aberdeen. I tried to emerge as a chap the bank couldn't afford to be without, no matter how unsound his business might be.

I used to go armed with two good jokes. I would get them in early and thereby establish myself as a man of humour. Then I

would proceed to flatter my hosts by laughing at all their witticisms, funny or not. That was quite an ordeal especially with my hiatus hernia. That meant I sometimes had difficulty swallowing. The food would go over my neck but wouldn't enter my stomach.

This condition, which was largely nervous, is made a hundred times worse when food is taken with anxiety ... and there is nothing more anxious than lunch with the banker.

It wasn't long before my neck was full.

The only thing to do was to drink more and hope the liquid would clear the drain. It was not pleasant and all the time you had to laugh heartily at the least pleasantry from the hosts.

"I'm afraid The Farmer drinks more than he eats these days," I could hear them say.

The bankers never did close me down. And I will always remember the wonderful relief when an even higher overdraft limit had been negotiated. "Yes!" I would be able to farm for at least another year.

Those were the days when I had credit at the mart for 200 grazing cattle, a £1000 an acre overdraft and a queue of bills.

I was telling the lads about it on Sunday at the discussion group when Penny Washers, the white settler, said in his public schoolboy way, "Gosh, it would be nice to get down to that." He's bought three farms in Aberdeenshire recently.

I wouldn't be surprised if he was invited to the lunch in Edinburgh soon.

Sale of the century for white settlers

AS I write Aberdeenshire is enjoying its ninth consecutive day of almost continuous rain. In that long week we have had a fifth of our annual rainfall. What had been our driest summer and looked two weeks ago like being our best ever harvest has turned into a disaster. We are right back to 1887 when Aberdeenshire was the county for sale. A new race of white settlers can get its chequebook ready, for there will be plenty of farms on the market when this year's harvest is all in.

You must not think I'm crying wolf. With 40% of the spring barley to cut the maltsters have closed their doors. With 95% of wheat still out, most is already a write-off.

We have had difficult wheat crops before. Two years ago we didn't get ours until the first week of November. Then we had a reasonable harvest and the grain was in decent order. So how can we have a disaster on our hands in the second week of September?

The answer is that the grain is sprouting. That means the energy is out of the grain and into little roots and stems. In 1993 the crops got wet and stayed wet but as long as they remained standing, the grains didn't germinate. For some reason this year, even when it is all standing perfectly, the grains are germinating like mad.

I've just been to see Mossie's two fields of wheat which he still has to cut and I have never seen such a mess. The crop is all standing and yet every head is sprouting. The worst crop is of Beaver. Each head has a tangle of roots hanging down like a shaggy white beard.

Where the crop is thick the little roots are matted together to make a solid canopy of porridge. On the top of this canopy is a delicate green tinge as the plants send up their first shoots to where the sun would be if there was any justice. And remember, all this growth is happening two feet above the ground.

It is quite extraordinary.

And why has it happened? We don't know, but one theory is that it is something to do with the very warm summer we had.

When the weather broke and flooded the fields, the shock of the water broke the dormancy of the grain and caused it all to sprout.

Everyone is affected differently, of course. The Irishman and I will look back on 1995 as one of our best harvests ever, for we have no wheat or spring crops. The Red Rooster is down from 200 acres to only 100 of wheat this year so he's suffering and Mossie's down from 250 acres of wheat to 30 and he's only going to have to write off 20.

But what about Big Hamish? He has hardly cut any of his 700 acres. And Young Ochyoch, Hillie and Mains all have disasters on their hands.

So is there nothing that can be done?

Well, Mossie and the Rooster are planning. They are going to spray their wheat with roundup to kill the airborne crop. Mossie's then going to mow it, bale it, treat it with ammonia and feed it to cattle. "That way I'll be able to lose even more money because I'll need to buy some loss-adjusters to eat it," he says.

The Red Rooster thinks he'll be able to cut his with the combine and get some value as salvage, but I doubt that. All those little roots will have his concave choked in minutes.

This weather has been a bugbear to Mossie in more than one way. His super duper combine is dripping in the field instead of tearing up and down earning £25 an acre. The salesman might have saved himself a sleepless night or two if he had thought about that before he phoned up to remind our man gently that he would like a cheque.

" Oh aye, certainly," said Mossie. "I'll just send you a cheque right away. And if you get it through, give me phone. If they cash yours I'll maybe try some others."

The poor salesman thought he was going to have to cancel the holiday in the Bahamas and book for Balmaha as usual.

And finally the Irishman made what everyone else seemed to think was a very witty remark at the discussion group on Sunday. I wonder if you agree.

I had been trying the lads with a point of principle. Did they think we should be boycotting French goods in response to them testing atom bombs in the South Pacific?

Of course Big Hamish didn't know they were testing bombs in the Pacific and most of the lads agreed that they were boycotting pretty comprehensively already as they didn't like anything French.

It was clearly an uphill struggle to get them interested

in anything that wasn't going to put a pound in their pockets. But I persevered.

I told them about my friend who farms peaches, pears and apples in New Zealand. He reckons the French know fine well exploding atom bombs is dangerous and that's why they don't explode them in Paris.

Worse than that, he sees the French tests as a conspiracy. They are trying to make the food-safety conscious fruit-eaters of the world turn away from produce from Down Under for fear of radiation. He was very pleased when some of his fellow farmers drove up to French Bastille day celebrations and emptied their muckspreaders at them.

The Irishman stirred. "That's it Charlie," he said. "You could put all these articles you've written for the last five years in a barrow and dump them outside the French consul's office in Aberdeen. That should larn them."

September 25, 1995

Mossie's field of dreams

I CAN think of no better way of illustrating for you the transformation of our year from glory to gloom than to tell you about Mossie's field of wheat.

On the last day of our tropical summer he cut half that field with his wonderful new combine. The gadget Mossie calls a 'clapometer' tells you to the pound per acre how much you are losing over the back of the combine as you go along. It will tell you how many wet tonnes you are harvesting to the acre at any instant.

On that last glorious day, when Aberdeenshire was going to pay off its overdraft at last, the clapometer showed Mossie was harvesting just over four tonnes to the acre. As it was at about 15% moisture the thing could hardly have been better.

But when Mossie got back to finish the field a fortnight later the yield had gone through the roof. The clapometer registered eight tonnes three cwts, yet there cannot have been any more wheat. All the extra must have been water, sprouts and roots. It is a fairly complicated sum to work out, and the losses over the tail of the combine will have been much greater after the flood, but the moisture content must have been over 60%.

At commercial rates the man who dries that stuff gets a huge bill instead of a cheque for his crop.

Yet so many people in the North-east still haven't realised how bad things are. I met a man with several hundred acres still to cut and he told me, and I quote, "Na, na. There's not too much wrong yet as long as we get a good week this week."

Either he thought his banker was listening or he's been assessing his crops from the road at 50 miles an hour. If you go in amongst you see that they are 90% sprouted. Unless it happens in a malting shed, "sprouted" means knackered.

Because the thing has got so serious, none of the discussion group are willing to be quoted. At times like this I wish they weren't real people.

Mind you, Big Hamish has told the local evening paper none of his 700 acres can be harvested.

One thing that is upsetting us is the misunderstanding about the effects of the floods. The flood plains of the North-east have carried much more water than usual. And many fields that normally get away with it have been washed out in the biggest floods in living memory. There is said to be a big bale of straw left by the receding waters half way up a tree on Turriff golf course.

But John Ross, the Scottish National Farmer's Union of Scotland's President, as reported in the Press, is making too much of the effects of the floods, we think. It is not that such floods don't devastate any harvest that is left in its way. What we think people are forgetting is that this year the crops were knackered anyway.

Those who have not been flooded can still salvage their straw and this year that will be important. But the man who grinds away with his combine and his drier choking to salvage sprouted wheat at 50% moisture is throwing good money after bad. At least if you have been flooded you can get on with addressing the problem of how and when to start ploughing.

Of course I haven't found a farmer who will refuse EC compensation if it can be won, but most feel that our case is weak. On the other hand, we will be very aggrieved if compensation goes to crops knackered by floods alone. The floods, photogenic and spectacular though they were, have been only a small percentage of the problem.

Bad as this harvest has been for many it has not been as bad as that of 1281. I have that on the authority of an Australian film actor-director, for The Breadwinner and I have been to see Braveheart.

A farmer's interest in the soil fairly spoils the film. The harvest field was a disaster. There was a tiny patch, maybe a quarter of an acre of tiny stacks, and heaps of straw had been left everywhere on the ground. There was obviously a problem with staff on the farms even then or they'd surely had somebody out with the smiler raking that up.

Mind you it would have been a complete waste of time giving that (or any other job) to the guy who tried to shovel earth into the Wallace grave.

The Simmental Cattle were looking well, though, and there was I thinking that they arrived in Britain in 1970. On the other hand there were two magnificent Longhorns pulling a cart with William Wallace's dead father and brother in it. They were a treat.

It was the first time The Farmer had been to the pictures for many years and he was on the whole unimpressed. Indeed he was infuriated. Not because there were times when you couldn't hear the action for the noise of his fellow Aberdonians grazing, but by the fact that the huge troughs they had their snouts in were of American Popcorn.

It would have been more bearable if they had been munching tattie crisps.

Sunny smiles as depression lifts

THE EXTENT of the disaster in the North-east is becoming clearer. Even so, wry smiles are reappearing on the faces. Whereas a fortnight ago all those caught in mid-harvest were in deepest depression, the mood now is more like, "Well, we have seen it all before."

We haven't, of course – not people my age anyway. But the boys with what might have been malting barley and those with a lot of wheat which they had written off, have all been able to salvage something. They have managed to get perhaps half the crop, which is a disaster for sure, but even that feels good if you had written it off completely.

The trouble is that half the crop doesn't mean half the profit. The expenses are way up and the wheat which might have made £115 a tonne and the barley which would have made £150 are being scrambled away for pig-feed at £60 to £70 a tonne after drying charges.

It's a disaster all right, but farmers are so resilient.

Take Young Ochyoch. He's in the early stages of a limited partnership agreement where he does all the work and takes all the risks on his 350 acres, while the landlord would take half the profit if there were any. He needed a good year. He was well on his way to getting it when he got 30% of his annual rainfall in twelve days.

He was depressed.

And yet, with everything tidied up at last, he reappeared on Sunday evening at the discussion group. The smile was back on his face. "I did try to come last week, boys," he said, "but I couldna get my bottom lip into the car."

Those of us who were lucky enough to have our harvest in before the flood are having to keep our heads down. Most of us don't protest when we are described as 'lucky' at having got our harvests in in good order.

Only one man dares.

Mossie had all but a few acres of wheat harvested with big yields and low moistures and that could earn you a scud in the lug about here. But when one of our agri-businessmen asked him the other day why it was that Mossie managed to get better yields, our man was as quick as a flash, "Management," he replied.

"Oh no, I don't think that's fair," said the agri-business-man, understandably hurt. "We had terrible weather this year."

"Right enough," says Mossie. "And there was me thinkin' you had the same weather as the rest o' us."

How he survives is a mystery.

He's been a bit hard on me, too. I had 11 of my 12 fields resown again before the flood. The ground had been far too dry but that didn't last long.

Now we have some problems with the new crop. The slugs have got at one of my fields which was in setaside and is now in rape. I got the pellets on quite quickly so it is nothing like the disaster in 1993 when we had to redrill a park of rape. You would have thought I would have learned that after setaside you need slugacide.

And it turns out the rape roots had blocked a drain in a field which was going into winter barley. That has meant an unsightly mess of black patches among the green shoots.

During the drought there was nothing in the drain anyway so I feel I was unlucky. How was I to know it was blocked? But Mossie still says I am hopeless. He still doesn't believe in luck.

I am not sure whether he is pulling my leg or not, but he has made me promise to get a graip and a bag of seeds and dig up and scatter the good seed on the

107

sodden land just to tidy the job up. It is purely cosmetic for all the patches put together can't be a quarter of an acre, but even that is a fair dig nowadays.

I'll have to do it, though I suspect he just wants to appear with the Red Rooster, Crookie and Big Hamish for a laugh. Or perhaps, he'll bring a camera to show what an antiquated place Little Ardo is. "There's Charlie with his latest cultivator. It's what we used to call a graip – only older."

I had Mains in the other night with his bill for the year's combining. He has a nice old-fashioned way of doing business. He presents his bill in decent time and saves a stamp by delivering it himself.

Those of us who can remember a gentler time would never see a colleague come to the door on business and leave without a business dram. There is no way you could grab the bill and shut the door. I suspect if I tried to shut the door I would find there was a foot in it.

It soon became clear Mains was not going to leave without his cheque and that he had a whole evening free. He was in no hurry.

There being no business dram without business, The Breadwinner went for the chequebook and I for the bottle.

Mains had a good harvest too so we had no embarrassment in toasting another good year.

I enjoy Mains. He is one of the few young men I know who likes the old wisdom. And on the third business dram he came out with a piece of wisdom of his own. We were agreeing that those who finished early on the night the flood broke must be kicking themselves for not combining away all night.

"Aye," said Mains, "hindsight may be more accurate but foresight is a bloody sight more use."

October 9, 1995

A quick escape

ALL HELL has broken out on the land of my fathers. From the farm on the little hill, the good people of Methlick, can hear the gentle calling of 40 mothers who have their 42 calves' suppers ready and want them home – at once. It is weaning time again.

We have taken them all in

except the four in-calf heifers and the one whose calf spent itself. We've wormed the calves and built the walls of their jails high. The cows have not been wormed because they are going out again onto pastures which after all those rains must be infested.

They aren't going out yet, though. We don't have a fence on the place that would keep them back from their calves. We tried it four years ago and they just made a straight line for the steading through two of my fences and The Breadwinner's vegetable garden and lawns.

There will be no such mistakes this year. The cows are penned and the door is shut. It

will stay that way until the old dears realise how nice it is not to be bothered with their offspring and stop roaring. It will take about five days.

And for those five days the good people of Methlick can expect little sleep.

The Breadwinner and I will be all right, though. We're going to take three days off for a run up to Gairloch.

It'll be nice to get away from the aftermath of the floods. No one's talking about anything else.

Mossie says it proves his new theory: "More acres less profit."

It is an attempt to justify the fact that he sold a farm to the

109

Irishman. Say what you will, farmers don't like selling land. Even if the banker is breathing down his neck, his wife has run away with the postie and is claiming half his wealth and there is a tax rollover available, the last thing a farmer will usually do is sell land.

And yet Mossie has sold a farm and lost a bit of ground he was renting. He says he gets his fertilisers and sprays from the local garden centre now. With only 700 acres left he feels it's hardly worth bothering the big agricultural suppliers.

So he has adopted his new slogan. But it really isn't so daft.

When things are really bad like they have been for the late crops this year, the more acres the bigger the loss.

But there is more to it than that. If you have a small acreage there is more chance that you'll get your harvest in decent order in a bad year. If you've only got a six-day harvest and there are six good days you'll get away with it. If you have a 20-day harvest you will struggle in a year like this. Furthermore, your crops are less likely to have been properly tended.

And what about the potato barons? I dare say I could have handled 30 acres if I'd won the lottery and could afford the equipment. But look at the state Crookie's in. He's got hun-dreds of acres and the land is so wet he can't get on it. There is no doubt it will be dry one day and it is wonderful how potatoes will keep in the ground, but Crookie can't even get on the land to spray them for blight or to kill them off for their protection. So he has hired every helicopter in the North-east to hold the line for him.

There are consolations in being a crofter of 250 acres.

Indeed the farmer's mind has turned to how he might profit from the misfortunes of those who have been caught with too many acres or the wrong crops.

When we had the calves weaned I looked proudly at Argus' last crop of bull calves. There are just 22 of them and they're fairly rattling in what was once my father's dairy byre. It held 40 cows and a bull then. The stalls are away now and so is the bulls box. Surely I could manage another ten or even 20 calves for the winter?

And surely a few extra calves will be easy to buy if half the country lost half their fodder in the drought and the other half lost half their crop in the monsoon?

There is no sign of it yet. Cattle prices are the highest I've ever seen them at this time of year.

Mossie says it's because so many big farmers have salvaged their wheat as whole-crop that they now have to find something to eat it. Farmers who long ago realised that cattle were for show and that grain was for dough have forgotten themselves. Desperate for something to eat all that remains of their harvest they are buying cattle "to lose a heap more money".

He could be right.

And it may just be that it will be into the new year before the farmers of the North-east fully realise what this harvest has done to their balance sheets. All right, they're feeling a bit better now that the salvage is complete. But by February they'll know just how small their cheques were for that huge heap of mouldy wheat in the close. And they'll have all the accounts in as well.

There just might be a blip in the cattle price then.

I'll be ready and to be sure about that I've bought some more wheat straw off Big Hamish.

"But Hamish, it'll be wet," says I, during the negotiations.

"Oh aye," says Hamish, never the best of salesmen, "But it's nae 'muck weet'."

October 16, 1995

My heart is in the Highlands

THE TRIP over to the west coast was great. We were able to admire all the crops of wheat and spring barley that were still dripping dry on the way up to Inverness. We were also able to observe how little black ground there is. The ripples caused by the monsoon will be felt for a long time.

But what really interested me was the Highlands of Wester Ross.

As a Lowlander whose forefathers pushed the Highlanders upwards and westwards out of Aberdeenshire in the first half of this millennium I have been brought up to despise the Highlands as barren and useless, save as somewhere to keep the Highlanders and for photographs to decorate tins of shortbread.

And yet I was impressed with what we saw of Wester Ross. The whole place seemed tidier. We didn't see a single dead sheep and the crofts were well fenced and shining with whitewash rather than over-run with hens, rusting tooth movers and binders.

There's a lot of new building, too. None of it is attractive, it is nearly all kit houses, and yet it is nice to see some action. And there seems to have been a new attempt to surround the houses with trees and even gardens.

Can it be that all the public money that has been poured into the Highlands is bearing fruit at last? I am told that the unemployment rate in Skye is now below the national average. That could mean something, though what it means I don't really know. The unemployment figures no longer measure those out of work, only those claiming benefit.

My idea of a West Highland shop is modelled on the one at Iona thirty years ago. Apparently the proprietor was asked for 20 Batchelor's. "No no," said the shopkeeper, "I don't keep them at all. They're not a good keeping cigarette. No sooner have you stocked them than you're sold out. Capstan full strength now, there's a good keeping cigarette."

But the shops all seemed well stocked, well run and relatively busy. Many are run by white settlers.

Now the pattern with many of the small rural shops in the North-east Lowlands has been of a hopeless struggle against the big superstores mitigated

112

near the end by a sale to a bright-eyed idealist from the south. He can't believe that he can buy a house with a shop attached for half the price of his house where he is.

After a year or so he has found out. He may find another soft touch from the south but then the shoppie closes.

For whatever reason, the settler shopkeepers of Wester Ross seem to be thriving.

I was impressed with the fish farms. Now, instead of letting the salmon roam half way round the world using tonnes of energy, being eaten by predators or cannibalised, and then having them battle and batter their ways up through spates and waterfalls to lay their eggs, they are produced in their thousands in nice safe little factories which give the locals steady work.

Of course, it may not be all gain. One version of the truth is that the wild salmon hang about the cages pinching food and getting sea lice infestations instead of getting on up the rivers and providing clean trophies for the tourists.

The Breadwinner and I get the best of beef when we are at home. We hang it for a month which gives it a flavour unattainable in hotels. So we ate nothing but seafood on our holiday.

We had good Achiltibuie kippers or very good Aultbay smokies for breakfast. For lunch we had average prawns Marie Rose or a fine seafood mixed platter of mussels (the biggest I've seen) smoked salmon, soused herring and more prawns, and some mankey fried haddock. For dinner there were more seafood starters and Lobster or Dublin Bay Prawns.

Boy! Were we glad to get home for a steak.

October 23, 1995

Anger greets "aid"

THE SALMON Inn was the place to be on Sunday – if you were looking for a fight. Like the rest of the farmers in the North-east the discussion group are absolutely furious. It isn't that the government has declined to give us a penny piece of help with the damage caused by the monsoon in September. None of the lads expected any so they were quite prepared to get nothing. But what they were quite unprepared for was the headlines that greeted them last Saturday. When they looked at Saturday's Press & Journal they were hit by a front page which led with "Flood hit farmers to get £35m aid package."

The lads were beside themselves with rage. The truth is that they are not going to get a penny that was not on its way already. All the Scottish Office are doing is letting us have our next bite at the European cherry either one or two months earlier than expected.

"Thousands of North-east farmers were celebrating last night after Scottish Agriculture Minister, Lord Lindsay, unveiled a £35m package for the victims of the floods."

Well, wherever those thousands of farmers were celebrating they certainly were not having a pint at the Salmon Inn.

"It is a disaaaster!" cried Mossie in exasperation.

Mains gave the paper an earful. And the Red Rooster was all set to resign from the Union when he remembered he already had. He didn't care much for the headline the week before which said, over a picture of John Ross (the National Farmer's Union President) looking disconsolately at a flooded field, "North-east farmers beg for flood aid."

"Dinna mak me a beggar for gettin what's due to me a month earlier than expected."

I tried to tell the boys that the early arrival of our area payments was worth a bit. If everybody had an overdraft it would save the farmers getting on for half a million. I had also worked it out that that was something less than £200 per farmer.

It was Crookie, usually the mildest of men, who would have none of that. "Rubbish! It's jist Harbro and the North-eastern (co-op) that'll get anything. They're sitting there waiting for the IACS money to come in. If it comes a month early that jist means the suppliers get paid earlier. It's worthless to us."

Yet plenty of people were saying: "Aye boys, I see you're gettin another £35 million."

It did not please us.

But we'll get over it, for a week is a long time in farming.

Look at Crookie. There was I saying last week that I wouldn't like to be him with 200 acres of tatties marooned in the sodden fields. It was a tossup whether he would have to sell the new MEGA back to the makers or try to get the builders to take the wife's new kitchen back.

Now, with a great crop of tatties coming in in good order with no signs of blight or cracking and the price of the tubers not sure whether it is going to go above £400 a tonne or dip below £300, he is looking for new ways to spend some more.

And Penny Washers, the white settler who, despite the difficulty he's had in getting to know how to work one farm, has now bought another two in Aberdeenshire, has more or less recovered from the floods. But he's had some difficult times.

None more so than when he saw what looked like a tiny weather-window in late September. He thought there would be just enough time to bale the hill field. The weather was not very reassuring so he decided to work on the principle that if a baler operated at five miles an hour would finish the field in three hours a baler operated at 15 miles an hour would do the job in an hour.

It was one of those theories which worked better on the computer than it did in the field.

To cut a long story short the speed was too much for one of the wheel-bearings on the baler. Penny Washers thought it would last out till the field was finished but he was wrong. The bearing heated and set fire to the baler.

That would have been a small problem for one of those farmers who carry a fire extinguisher in their tractor but Penny Washers isn't one of them. He decided to make a dash for the steading with his blazing inferno. This involved going even faster and heating the bearing even more.

As Penny Washers made it gratefully to the farm he looked back and saw to his horror that he had set the straw alight right across the field. The wind was in the east and his neighbour's wood was in the west but he had no time to worry about that. Just as he turned into the close the superheated baler broke its axle and the wheel fell off.

Tricky times had arrived at Penny Washers' door.

However his luck was to change. The straw wasn't nearly dry enough for baling and was only just dry enough for burning so the fire was unable to resist the rain that had started by the time Penny Washers had found the fire extinguisher.

Amazingly, the baler wasn't even damaged by the fire, though it no longer looked shiny and new.

October 30, 1995

Farmer's wings are clipped

HERE'S A question; "If it takes one man an hour to plough a five-acre field, how long will it take 60 men to plough it?"

Answer: "One minute."

I don't suppose children get that sort of puzzle at school these days. It's all new maths now and just as well. Whatever new maths is, it is bound to be better than teaching them lies.

Merciful heavens! Anybody can see it would take at least half an hour to get 60 men and their tractors into the field in the first place. And how would they turn at the end of each drill? You would end up hours later with the field half

ploughed, a tangle of expensively crashed metal and the 60 ploughmen at one another's throats.

And yet we used to sit there in the solemn days of school working those problems out. "If it takes a man and a half a day and a half to build a chain and a half of wall how much wall will two and a half men build in a week and a half."

Did you ever hear such nonsense? Where are you going to get half a man anyway? And doesn't it matter whether the extra man you take on is as good as the original man? And won't the two men fall out over

116

who bullies the halflin? And will the halflin still be with you after a week and a half of treatment like that?

You saw what happened when Penny Washers applied the principle to baling the last field of wheat straw. It was two weeks before he could finish the field.

Amazingly, despite all my years of seeing through the principle, I have been caught in the same trap. It was on the advice of Mossie, who persuaded me to alter my cropsprayer so it would spray 60 feet at a time instead of 40.

Question: "If a 40ft sprayer takes two hours to spray 30 acres, how long will it take a 60ft sprayer?"

Answer: "Disaaaster."

I know you get very good sprayers designed to cover 60 feet at a time or even more. They work well, I have no doubt. But what I have done is to take a thing designed to spray 40 and added 50% to each wing. Instead of each arm having one joint for folding up for transporting, we have a new section ten feet long and an extra joint.

The first problem is its weight. Unlike the automatic ram-operated affairs Mossie and the Red Rooster work, my sprayer, a snatch at £1500, has to be made ready for transportation manually. It was hard work with 40-foot booms but at 60 it is really heavy.

But it is when you are all set to go that the extra weight really makes itself felt.

Have you ever seen a partan half way between the sea and a crab salad? Without the sea to support it, the poor animal's body is far too heavy for its legs. The spindly shanks just collapse.

So it was with my sprayer this week.

Mind you, I was proud of its sheer scale after I had got the great wings spread. At 60 feet per pass I would soon be away down to the Salmon Inn to tell them that I too had a big sprayer.

But the great bird did not fly. I was maybe a bit rough with the clutch but when I set off my right wing was left behind and crumpled. I banged on the brakes.

The left wing kept going and crumpled forward. I was left there sitting in the wreckage of a partan out of water.

There was nothing broken. It was just that there wasn't enough strength in the sprayer to keep it in shape. I got the back wing forward and the forward wing back and set ever so gingerly off again.

This time I got about 200 yards before disaaaster struck again.

My fields are so hilly that, at 60 feet, there is always one wing or the other almost touching some part of the ground if you try to operate it at two feet above the crop. At the merest brush of the ground she crumpled again. That was fairly easily sorted. My new sprayer has to be set five feet above the crop which will be alright in a windless day.

The next hazard was a steep knapp. When I went uphill the giant partan collapsed backward. I got her going again only for her to collapse forward when we went down the other side.

If it takes a man with 40-foot booms two hours to spray thirty acres it takes a man with 60-foot booms a whole day. At the end of that he is feeling very glad that he only has three years to go to retirement.

Several days and three trips to the smiddy later I have the thing stabilised a bit.

I now have lugs on the elbows and wrists of the great wings, and bolts through them to stop them breaking. Then I have stays that run from the booms to the chassis to stop it collapsing on the braes.

It is not ideal.

All that extra metal weighs. And the wings of the sprayer are supposed to bend when you hit anything to save damaging the machine.

The next time I hit a telephone pole it is going to be either the sprayer or the pole.

Famine relief Farmer buys a Cadillac

THE BOYS are still fuming that what is now called the 'famine relief' is being presented by the newspapers as another handout at the taxpayers' expense.

Mossie's so annoyed he's refusing to bank the cheque. "I still haven't been paid," he says. "Sending a cheque doesn't constitute payment. They're owe me the money as long as it's not in my account."

For some reason his gesture reminds me of my pal Charlie Kirton who, when 13, took the greatest pride in getting the bus conductor to accept a full fare whereas those of his pals who were already 14 went to equal lengths to deceive the clippie into letting them go as a half.

I, on the other hand, have had no problems about whether to cash my famine relief. It has not arrived.

This was no surprise to me, I'm afraid. It would be because of my perfectly innocent little mistake in my IACS form. I had awarded myself an extra acre of setaside. In all those subsidies,

what is an extra £130, I ask you?

It is a field the size of which was unknown. It had been made from four fields by removing the dykes. Also, one of the four fields had given up five building plots since it was measured and another was at the junction of four ordinance survey maps, one missing.

The consultant who helped me with my first IACS form-filling had recommended claiming 21 acres and I had always done that.

But this year I noticed the contractor had been charging me for 24 acres every time he went into that park. Everyone says the most accurate measure of a field is the seed drill, so I asked the contractor.

"Has your drill been measuring 24 acres in the Sunnybrae Park, Davie?

After a pause for careful thought, the Man of Few Words said, "Aye". That meant an average of over £400 a year going down the sink.

I was scared to go the whole

hog. After all, they can take away all your grants if they catch you making inaccurate claims. Indeed, it is said the local Department lads have no discretion in the matter nowadays. But I felt quite confident in going for 23 acres – until I had sent off the forms.

The Red Rooster assured me the computer would throw out my application as soon as it saw the envelope.

"You canna increase the size of a park and hope they won't notice, Charlie. You're for the high jump."

Mossie was a great comfort: "I doubt it's 'Farm for Sale' right enough. I wonder if the Irishman still has that sign."

The Farmer's life became a

nightmare. He couldn't sleep and the phone made him jump, he had to screw up his courage to open the mail and strange cars coming up the road induced a panic attack.

Eventually the Irishman's advice was taken.

"Wouldn't it be an idea to find out what the size of that field is, Charlie, before ye crack up altogether? There's a wee man comes out from the College and stands in the middle of the field shooting lasers at each corner. He gives you an exact measurement. I've had the whole farm done. Sure, with my overdraft, I couldn't be worrying about my forms as well."

That was it. I would find the

truth and that would set my mind at rest. Next year I'd put in for the full 24 acres. Who knows? It could be more.

So the man from the College came with his laser and measured the park. Unfortunately he made it 22.8 acres. With the margins he should have left for dykesides, The Farmer was clearly in trouble.

Now my tale hath another side to it. I have a long-standing friend who has had an expensive fallout with his American wife. Stupidly, he had the fallout in the American courts. The fight started over £28 million and he is left, in the words of the bothy ballad, "wi' his sark and drawers".

Well, not quite. He was also left with the family Cadillac.

So, when he phoned up the other day, it was for a loan, or would I take the Cadillac?

Reasoning that a gas-guzzling car was the last thing a broke friend needed, and thinking that, if I took the car, at least I would be sure of that, I went for it.

It wasn't dear, but can't you just see the headlines? "Famine Relief Farmer Buys Cadillac." Little do they know that The Farmer's famine relief is in jeopardy.

November 13, 1995

Fortune favours chicken-hearted

THERE IS still no sign of the famine relief, but I have been assured they are not sending me to jail. As I had told them myself, they were just amending my form and paying me as normal – only later than everybody else. Once again, fortune has favoured the chicken.

I do believe them, but there will be a hellova party when the cheque arrives.

Perhaps I should say "another hellova party". For this week we had the Fisherman's Dinner, which marks the end of another season drowning worms in the Ythan water.

If in tallying up a man's three score years and ten the good Lord doesn't count time spent fishing, He must multiply by at least ten the time spent at the Fisherman's Dinner.

It was Mossie who got me involved. "Oh no," he said, "I

121

dinna fish, but I go to the dinner. It's traditional."

I'll say this for Mossie – if he supports a thing he supports it all the way. He had a table for eight to which I was invited. But our table wasn't "half-past seven for eight" like the rest of them. We had to appear at Moss-side for cork-popping and clay pigeon shooting at four. Then, when it was dark, we had to go down to the Salmon Inn for a couple of hours, which made us late.

It is easy to see Mossie's famine relief has arrived. Whenever anybody pulls his leg about the subsidies he says, "Oh I ken. I just told them to put the cheque straight to the Salmon. I wouldna risk the wife seeing it."

Anyway, by the time Mossie's 'table' staggered into the dinner there was no table for us. So we were interspersed among the anglers of Aberdeenshire, or so we thought.

There are those who could think of no torture so bad as a whole evening listening to fishers discussing their flies, their minnows and the ones that got away. But I'm not like that.

Little Ardo has about 300 yards of the Ythan, including at least two good salmon lies, and I fished there often as a boy. But my real passion was to go off for the day up the wee burns and worm for brown trout.

When I was seven I was given a beautiful greenheart rod by Jack Martin, who had a small chain of upmarket sporting tackle shops across Scotland.

Jack taught me to use it in a tiny burn about a mile up Glendevon from the Yetts o' Muckhart. Many years later I couldn't believe how small it was. A decent stallion could produce a bigger flow.

And yet when old Mr Martin took me fishing there 50 years ago it was a fair burn and teaming with trout which were large in comparison with the fisherman.

We caught one each. I remember mine very well indeed. I could take you to the very spot, about 20 yards above the trickle which we knew as 'the waterfall'. I felt it wriggling on the line and as though to that manor born threw it out over my head into the heather.

Mr Martin explained that it had to be seven inches long before we could keep it. That meant the length of a man's hand. I remember being so glad when he said that, as I was the catcher, my hand would have to be used for the measuring rather than his.

That was the start of many happy years of worming in the burnies scorned by people with double snooter hats and waders. I never caught so many trout that we couldn't eat them at a sitting, but I nearly always got something. I think that is why I preferred the wee burns. I couldn't go away for days like salmon fishers and come back with nothing but cold feet.

Some years on the Ythan there is hardly a fish taken but this year has been quite good. Just the week before last Willie Adie, who was once our second tractorman and later our postie, had an 18 pounder. And yet that was only his second fish of the season.

So The Farmer decided to talk fish.

To the man on the right, "Did you get a fish this year?"

"No, I dinna fish."

To the man on my left, "Did you get a fish this year?"

"No, I dinna fish."

Two down on the left I found my first fisher but he hadn't been out this year and I had to go to three down on the right to get a real fisher.

But he had a fisherman's story to beat them all. Never mind two fish in a season, he'd had nine in one short evening.

Big Massey is a game-keeper whose job it is to worry about pheasants. As such, he regards salmon as low life fit only for the pot. He was out trying to cut down the fox population one night when he saw a light on the water. He recognised the sounds of poachers.

Waiting until the bag was secure, he blew his whistle and flashed his torch. The poachers ran off and left him with a hundredweight of salmon.

123

November 20, 1995

In practice for retirement

THE FAMINE relief has arrived at last. The sprayer is at the blacksmith's being further strengthened so I can't get on with spraying the rape, and Potions is plastering the setaside with slurry. All is well, and The Farmer is hiding inside.

But how can he do that? I hear you ask. What about The Breadwinner? Will she not kick him outside to sweep the close or wash her car? After all, she's retired, is she not, and The Farmer is no longer the master of his own house – even during the day?

Well, there is good news on that front. The Breadwinner has gone back to what she does best – winning bread in Aberdeen. The cash flow is benefiting and so is The Farmer's lot.

Breakfast has been extended by half an hour, the coffee break is back up from its traditional seven and a half minutes to half an hour and the after-lunch nap is back.

Of course the place is becoming a tip again and the books are getting confused, but you can't be perfect all the time.

When I look at the piles of leaves in the close, the broken guttering in the Dutch barn and the obvious need for strengthening and slating all the roofs of the old steading, it seems like my two and a bit years to retirement are a long time.

And yet retirement scares me. I won't be able, like Frank Sinatra or The Breadwinner, to come back whenever I like. When I retire the elder Investment and her husband come in here and The Breadwinner and I get our one way ticket to the death house.

For the moment at least, we have given up the search for our death house. The houses on the market are all too dear and after living in this 18th century farmhouse we don't fancy a modern kit house. I don't think I will ever be at home where I can't hear the plaster rattling down the interiors of the walls.

Quite the nicest houses we've looked at have been converted steadings. It is amazing how the buildings our forefathers put up for their cattle and horses have so much pleasanter lines and are made of so much more douce materials

124

than those they built for themselves. But those steadings are usually right beside the farmhouse.

What we would really like is a 19th century steading where the house had been burned down or bombed. The Breadwinner and The Farmer were contemplating that one day when The Farmer had a stroke of genius or madness. Perhaps it was both.

We could build a steading on the farm and then convert it to a death house. It would be built as my great great grandfather built the Little Ardo steading: of stone-gatherings and roofed with real slates. It would have beautiful arched cartshed doors, little loft doors to convert to windows and it would be exactly the right size for conversion. It would not, like so many new houses in the countryside, stick out like a sore thumb.

And that is exactly what we propose to do.

Of course we won't build it and convert it. We'll do the conversion on the drawing board and build our death house already converted. The planning application is in, the soakaway hole is dug and we await with bated breath the decision of the planners.

The double garage is planned, and there will be plenty room for my bicycle.

It is a while since I gave you an update on The Farmer's quest for an Olympic medal.

My natural modesty allows

me to report a great improvement. From being faraway last in the ten-mile time trials, I am now in the competition.

Most of the improvement is in know-how and equipment.

It is no coincidence that cycling champions don't turn up in old trousers and tackety boots. You need shoes that tie onto the pedals so you can pull the pedals up as well as pushing them down. And those execrable shorts help streamline even The Farmer's figure. The old fisherman's sweater has been replaced by a skin-tight rubbery film in the club colours.

I was branded a cheat for winning the booby prize of £7 after starting 50 seconds late in my first competition, so I was determined to be on time for my second race. I was minutes early at the start, but with six seconds of the countdown left I remembered I still had my hooded track-suit top on. I struggled to get it off but it stuck fast on my helmet. Eventually I got the hat off, the jersey off and the hat back on, and set off 30 seconds late.

The terror of being branded a cheat for a second time put a tremendous spurt of speed down to the ageing leggies. I came home in 27 minutes and got a second prize. And to think that, if I hadn't lost that 30 seconds at the start, I would probably have been last.

November 27, 1995

Beef on mad cows

THERE IS no doubt about what is upsetting us this week – that television programme.

I refer to the documentary about mad cows. The message was that measures designed to keep animals which had contracted BSE out of the human food chain aren't working. The programme makers found that some cowboys had sneaked diseased animals away before they were diagnosed so as to preserve the status of their herds as BSE-free.

This is not pleasing those of us with beef cattle.

We're anxious about the effects of this publicity on the money we'll get for those calves on the Spring day. And what about poor Potions? How will his butcher's shop fare if all this publicity puts people off beef? Mostly we feel angry and frustrated. It is all so unfair.

BSE is a problem in dairy cattle. Only Big Hamish has milkers and none of the rest of us has even seen a mad cow. If people do want to avoid what chance there is of eating meat from infected cows, all they have to do is buy good beef.

Dairy cows go into pies and into that special offer mince. One of our antiheroes is the woman who says that after what she has seen on the tele she isn't going to chance having her usual steak. She'll just have sausages.

Our second anti-hero is the man who says (with a fag hanging out of his mouth) that he isn't going to take the chance on eating beef. As a heavy smoker, he has a one in three chance of killing himself. Set that against the fear that one day someone might die of BSE and you will see why the beef cattlemen among us are feeling got at.

100,000 people a year die of smoking and no one is getting very excited about it. And how many are dying of BSE? None so far.

Of course it could happen. I have always thought it likely that the human condition would be transformed at some stage by a monster new plague. At one time it looked like it would be Aids but that threat has receded.

The plague could even come from beef, but The Farmer and his pals feel distinctly put upon that our livelihoods are suffering now when there just isn't any evidence.

Never mind, it is the shooting season and we had a hellova shoot the other day.

As usual it wasn't what was shot that made the day. Indeed the bag was just over two per gun. It was a bit like Gazza. The shoot made headlines for all the wrong reasons.

The first thing that upset us was Tosh's dog. He was a grand working dog and Tosh so admired him that he took him to some of the up-market shoots just to see the dog picking-up.

Anyway Nicol from Keith, who sells lorries when he isn't shooting (which isn't often), got a high pheasant and Tosh's dog was onto it in a flash. But as he sped off he suddenly fell down – stone dead.

It was a sad moment, for everyone knew how much the dog meant to Tosh. A respectful silence was maintained as the poor lad went out and brought his beloved retriever back in his arms. Hollywood couldn't have done it better. Except that John Wayne wouldn't have finished the scene with Nicol from Keith saying, "I'm sorry aboot yer dog, Tosh, but did ye get my pheasant?"

Worse was to follow.

127

When we were having a quiet swallow to wash down the exquisite lamb Mossie had done on his mobile barbecue, Long John Silver, the vet, suddenly keeled over – just like the dog.

This was taken even more seriously. Within ten minutes Long John was being lifted into the ambulance. We were really worried. First the dog and now the vet. Who would be next? Even Norman Black was showing anxiety and he's an undertaker.

"Is he all right, doctor?" asked Norman with a curious gesture which looked to some like he was pulling out and putting back his tape measure.

"Stand back, you're nae needed yet" said the doctor and closed the door.

The lads were so concerned about the events of the day that they carried on with the shoot regardless. Life must go on.

But when we got to the Salmon Inn, Nicol from Keith got mixed up. "What like a shoot did you have?"

"Oh a grand shoot. The vet's dead and the dog fainted. But we had a grand shoot."

I am pleased to confirm it was the other way round, but it shows how rumours can start.

And they did. Long John has been a popular vet for a long time and the collection in his memory was over £50 before he reappeared in the village, as right as rain.

Lady vet wins me over

IT IS remarkable. You don't usually get pneumonia among your calves if you breed your own and keep them at home. And yet that has been the big excitement this week.

I had been busy and had been throwing the feed at them and skimping on the five minutes just looking.

It's an easy job. The heifers get one bag of nuts and the bulls get two. They are bedded twice a week and need a new bale of treated straw about every five days. So you can feed the 100 beasts in half an hour, nae bother.

But finally on Saturday I noticed. One of the bulls didn't get up for his nuts. Usually they stampede at you but there was only a half-hearted wander over to the trough. To my horror I realised that a fine black Simmental calf was going like a bellows. Worse than that, he wasn't just heaving the air in and out. He had that jerk in his breathing that shakes the whole body and so often means you need the knacker.

In the days when I had up to 400 barley beef bulls we had chronic pneumonia. There was never a time we didn't have a few being treated and at least one whose lungs were damaged and who was taking his revenge on my bank balance. That kind would save so much money if they would just die.

But of course those barley beefers were collected up from all the dairy farms round about and dealers would roll up with small lots of third-raters which they couldn't sell. I'd always give them a bid of some kind. Unfortunately, I often got yet more to add to the Little Ardo pneumonia bank.

The vets weren't much help. I suspect it was just that we called them in too late. But on one occasion when our usual remedies weren't working I announced my intention to try the vet again.

"Well," said Gordon the cattleman, "If you're phoning the vet you may as well phone the knackery at the same time."

That remark came back to me on Saturday as I surveyed the cream of the crop of 1995. There was another and another and another ... maybe. We

129

haven't seen any respiratory problems since we came back from Kenya. Six cough-free years. And there they were again.

So I called the vet despite my fears about sending good money after bad.

My natural honesty forces me to admit that when I saw yet another young lady vet I wasn't pleased. To me, a vet should be about 55, rather overweight and male.

Those older vets went into the profession when it had no glamour and academic standards were not the priority. They were practical chaps who would have preferred to be farmers but hadn't the capital. They came to the profession without much intellectual baggage and they made good vets.

Don't get me wrong. The calves died just the same, but with the old school you get a certain reassurance in their presence.

James Heriot changed all that. He glamorised the life of a vet and choked the vet schools. They had no alternative but to ration places to the very brightest. When a vet under 30 comes onto the place you can be sure you are being visited by an intellectual giant whose natural environment is the lecture theatre rather than the byre.

Anyway, this slip of a girl came up to the byre to see the worst case which I had tied up, not that it was going anywhere. My fears that she wouldn't know what she was looking at were reinforced when she didn't seem very impressed with the nearness of death. It was agreed that she would give the calf an intravenous injection and a course of some other stuff into the muscle.

After a brief look in the court she said I could pull out the coughers and give them a jab of the intramuscular stuff and that would be about it.

I got a pen for five out in our open-fronted shed and made them comfortable.

With fearful heart I looked in the court the next day and, Yes! there were two more sets of bellows in action. And then down to the sick bay expecting to find one dead and the others below average.

To my astonishment there were no bellows going and even the 'dead' one came to eat.

The vet may have been too young, too intelligent, too thin and too female, but she seems to have saved my calf and goodness knows how much money in piners' thriftlessness.

I'm not as keen as the boys on killing things, though I do like the social side of shooting. I'm happiest with the gun when I can call it pest control rather than sport. Sport should be enjoyed by both sides.

However we got an invitation to help a friend at Forfar who is overrun with hares. He told us we could take a pheasant, too, but cocks only.

We were a bit taken aback when the first bird to rise was a hen pheasant and our host shot it. Nothing was said but the second pheasant to get up was a cock. It was Potions' but he let it go.

"It's OK," said our host kindly, "you can shoot cocks."

"Oh," said Potions. "I thought that must be a hen 'cos it was different from the one you shot."

December 11, 1995

Pneumonia has me baffled

THE MIRACLE of the pneumonia and the calves goes on. The vet agreed with me that it is most unusual to get this sort of attack in a closed herd.

I was telling the boys about it at the discussion group the other day. "Aye, right enough," said Big Hamish "if you get a problem you usually find it

131

came fae somewey." A born philosopher is Big Hamish.

I told them about those who went in for embryo transplanting just to get twins to give them extra calves to put onto the cows that lost theirs. That would stop them having to get a calf from the dairies and make sure they kept their herds disease-free.

And then I remembered the pure Simmental that lost its calf this spring. Its milk had been late in coming in and its calf had become weak and died. We'd got a awful Holstein calf for it.

That had been a treble mistake. It could never have been a good calf, not having the bones to hang a good shape on. But worse than that, it weaned itself quietly when on the grass and the cow was ruined with mastitis anyway.

Could it also have been the source of my pneumonia? Surely not. After all, there had been a whole summer to blow away its bugs.

It was last Friday, four days into the epidemic. I had decided to pull out another two bulls for treatment when I saw a cheeky little black face peering nervously round the back of a red Simmental stot. I don't know how I could have forgotten.

Back in August, when the money from the bumper harvest was on its way and it was obvious that I would have plenty of winter keep, did I not go mad at Thainstone and buy two cows?

One was a Shorthorn that an honest man might call an Ayrshire cross. She was a decent old cow, though I do feel that at £530 she owes me a good calf in the spring.

The other was a dun Simmental out of a Friesian, with a good-looking Limousin bull calf at foot. She looked better value at £930 considering the calf would be worth close on £400 before I had to feed his mother.

And I dare say she would have been had her calf not introduced IBR to my 22 bull calves.

And there is worse. As I stood there damning the weather, the government and my luck, I noticed a bright white ring on the imported calf's eye. The little brute has ringworm, another disease we haven't seen here for ten years.

I hate ringworm. I've had it myself and it is itchy and sore, but it is not compassion for the cows that makes me hate it. When we had barley beef we had it all the time and we also had a huge investment in exotic cattle, the main market for which was overseas. One ring on the fancy cattle could cost you a sale at up to £10,000.

Those days are gone now and the odd ring doesn't have huge economic impact. I

wouldn't bother at all if we had found it in the spring because sunlight soon clears it up.

But one ring in a court on the first of December could be an itchy plague by the spring day. All 22 could be scratching ringworm spores into every available bit of wood in the old byre, laying booby traps for generations of calves.

So what should I do? My first inclination was to spray some blue antiseptic on the one ring and go to church next Sunday.

But instead I've decided to make it a second test for the new vet. It'll be a bit like the way the men of God in the middle-ages decided whether the unfortunate accused was a witch or not. I am told they used to throw the suspect into a deep pool. If she was drowned she was held to be innocent and got a decent burial with tears. If she floated she was held to be a witch and burned.

If my vet turns up trumps again, I'll have proved she is the exception to the rule. And if she doesn't manage the business it will justify my prejudice against young and female vets.

Despite these little problems I am enjoying the cattle. They are genuinely pleased to see you when you turn up.

So is a good woman or a grandchild, but they make emotional demands. The beasts are reassuring in their indifference so long as they are fed.

More bad news

WE'VE TOILED over a dozen pints of ale and figured it all out. There is a way out of the present predicament, but only one. And the news is not good.

BSE has to be eradicated. It doesn't matter how often the government tells people there is no proven link between BSE and human health. As long as there is one scientist willing to say there is a risk of this disease jumping to humans, we will be zapped by another blaze of publicity which will scare people off beef.

The problem is that scientists, clever as they are, cannot prove anything in the real world is impossible. It doesn't matter if they can't get monkeys to take BSE. It might make it seem unlikely that humans can get it, but you never know. If we were to inject brains from cows infected with BSE into the brains of humans, they might start to show symptoms.

We are hoping people will eat our beef, not inject it into their brains, but even if they can't infect us by one means, who can prove we cannot become infected by another?

So, while we should support all attempts to understand BSE and scrapie, the disease of sheep which seems to be related to Creutzfeldt-Jacob disease, such research can only damage the farmers.

The only way such research can settle the matter is if they prove a link between BSE and the human condition. They can never prove it is safe.

And that's what really bugs the boys in the discussion group.

The Salmon Inn on Sunday was in uproar as I tried to persuade the boys that I knew best. I had been to University for 17 years, after all. "Huh," said Big Hamish. "My wife's cousin was at the University and he came oot efter three years. You couldna have been that good if you took 17."

Anyway, I have more or less persuaded the boys we have to do all in our power to help solve the problem of BSE.

Every time some farmer is caught selling a beast with BSE that is more bad publicity. And why would anyone sell an old cow to the trade for the average of £500 when he could get £800 or £900 in compensation?

But as long as BSE exists we will be hit when some other scientist comes up with another theory about what might happen one day. There are only two long-term hopes.

The first is very fanciful. Food hysteria might subside. If people get to the stage when they can say, "Yes life is all about balancing risks and advantages. There is a risk from eating steak. If I have high cholesterol a big steak dinner could kill me. If the butcher is on the other side of the street I could be killed going over to get it. And there is another, far smaller risk – a risk so small you cannot put a figure on it – that I might get a disease people don't get off it. Those risks are no bigger than the risks attached to the alternative. After all, I could go on a diet of carrots but I don't know how they kill the carrot fly or if the insecticide might kill me one day.

And the other hope is the eradication of BSE. If there is no BSE then we can stop worrying about people getting it.

Of course we would still have Creutzfeldt-Jacob Disease ravaging one in a million of the meat-eating population. And smoking would continue to kill 300,000 of every million heavy smokers. And people would still be unable to see that there is any significant difference between those figures.

The value of those lovely calves with their ringworm has fallen this week by £50 a head and it looks like they could be

down £100 on the spring day, so the news is all bad on the cattle front.

The scientists can produce a big negative on my balance sheet without being able to prove a positive.

If I am right, the public are just not sophisticated enough to handle the information coming out. I cannot resist pointing out that if the scientists were locked up in their ivory towers until they had come to hard conclusions, there would be a considerable saving to the country.

December 28, 1995

Christmas repast

IF YOU have no stomach for the misfortunes of others, read no further. But if you have had enough of goodwill to all men, Christmas pudding, presents, wide-eyed children (whom some say Christmas is all about), and the good news that Jesus is said to have brought (which others still think Christmas is about), you'll enjoy this. This is the bad news.

We've been having weather. We have had 14 degrees of frost and a level fall of about a foot of snow. But on top of a hill in Aberdeenshire you don't get a level fall.

The roads are full because the dykes hold the snow. We have taken to the fields but even there we are struggling. Clearing a path sets up dykes of snow and at the next puff of wind the track is as full as the roads. The pipes are all frozen and have to be thawed daily for the cattle with no access to the snow. So far there has always been one machine which has started each morning so I can jump the rest, but I know the day is coming when nothing will go and I'll be back in the 1930s.

But it wasn't farming that was difficult this Christmas. Last year I stupidly told The Breadwinner the truth. Each year she overcooks the turkey. When I try to carve it, it falls to bits. All right, it wasn't tactful – but I've paid for it.

This year The Breadwinner had an old chef friend up from London. Fanny Craddock would cook the turkey to perfection.

No house is complete without one good woman. But two women, be they ever so good, are too many.

My reputation as a male

136

chauvinist pig is sound enough and I don't want it to get out of hand, but those two worried on about this damned feast as though without turkey there would be no tomorrow. Never have I seen a better illustration of my view that a trouble shared is a trouble doubled.

The shopping was doubled. For the stuffing I had to cart home four loaves of bread, two pounds of onions, six cooking apples, four pounds of carrots and half a pound of garlic. That is just what I remember. Where they were going to stuff all that, I don't know. I did well getting it into the back of the car let alone the back of the bird.

The Farmer managed to keep his head while all about him were losing theirs ... until Christmas Eve. By this time The Breadwinner was a nervous wreck and the chef was four feet off the ground and rising. Absolutely everything was bound to go wrong.

Then it did.

The lights flickered. They gave that fateful double flicker which is the signal that they are about to be cut off. The surfeit of women paled and then turned on The Farmer with a mixture of anger and satisfaction. They had told me so.

Strangely the lights didn't go out. But they didn't stop flickering either.

It was a wild night. The snow was drifting. Away over the Glens of Foudland I could see the lightning. But I thought the problem was nearer at hand. The middle of our three wires was loose, hanging down below the bottom one and waving in the gale. It must be whipping up and touching the live wire above.

I dared not tell them. How do you tell two women that they are unlikely to have any power with which to cook lunch for 12? What I should have done was switched the power off and hoped for a fine still morning, but I was too scared. I managed to get them off to bed early. "Big Day tomorrow."

The Farmer spent a miserable night until a call of nature sharpened by anxiety got him up around three. Sure enough, no power. Having done his best in the dark The Farmer was back in bed before it occurred to him to look out of the window. From the top of the hill it was apparent that at least a hundred square miles of North-east Scotland was without power.

"But surely you have a generator?" I hear you scoff.

Correct! But I hadn't looked at it since we left for Kenya nine years ago. How did it work again? What is it you have to do to make sure you don't knock some poor lineman off his perch when he thinks he has switched everything off

137

and you suddenly fire up a twenty kilowatt generator? The manual was certainly lost.

It was a relief to get up at six and start trying. It is a long and boring story and it will be no loss if I summarise.

First I separated all our wires by stapling them to the Yorkshire boarding of our stockade. I found the generator still plugged in, under a heap of heavy rubbish in the corner of the piggery. Once I had dealt with the frozen diesel I was able to plough out the road and use the digger to shift the rubbish. The old tractor had to be bled and the drive shaft straightened as best I could. At half past nine I had her going. I was generating electricity but it

seemed to be all going to knocking linemen out, for none was getting to the house.

The Breadwinner was good about it. Quite calmly she accepted that Christmas dinner would have to be smoked salmon, and soup and Christmas pudding warmed on the primus stove.

Fanny Craddock was distraught ... not that that was a big change.

And then I had a brainstorm. Maybe when it said "on" the generator was really "off". It was a long shot but that was all that was left. At 10am we had power and at 2.30pm we had a wonderfully overcooked turkey that fell to bits when I started to carve.

New Year drowns in fizzy water

THE EFFECTS of the weather weren't all bad. For the first time in years we felt able to go out first footing without fear of the drink-driving laws.

The police were run off their feet with accidents anyway, but with drifts up to ten feet deep who was to say whether we were on the roads or in the fields?

We have the snowplough on the Ursus so that was the obvious choice. Perched on a pillow on the hydraulic handles, The Breadwinner was good enough to say she was almost comfortable.

On Hogmanay we were invited to the Recovery Stock's. It is only four miles in summer and overland it is less so we were only a few minutes late.

He and the wife were hanging out of their cottage as we came roaring up with the ploughing lights flashing front and back. The idea was to have a quick meal and be home by nine o'clock in case the weather closed us down again.

The food turned out to be a sort of up-market camping idea they called 'fondue'. I suppose his wife brought the idea from Holland with her, but what it amounted to was a pile of uncooked meats and a fork each. You spear yourself a bit of steak or a spicy sausage and stick it in a pot of boiling oil, which hotters and spits on the table.

It looked a dangerous outfit to me but the result was exquisite. It was a joy to have my beef and lamb done to my taste – no more than heated up.

Nine o'clock came and went, there was 'A guid New Year tae ane and aa' and we trooped up to the big hoose to first foot the Young Laird. He was entertaining his boat people and I thought it would be interesting to meet some of that pathetic tide of humanity which fled from Vietnam.

Sadly these were far more deadly boat persons. The Young Laird has a boat on the Thames and his idea of boat people are the friends he makes while summering himself among the Yorkshire Broads.

I really fear for Old Scotia. There he was offering us champagne. What hope is there for 1996 if its health is drunk in

fizzy water? We couldn't get the boat people to sing 'A guid New Year'. They were determined to sing 'Old Laing Zion'.

How things have gone down hill. When I was boy Christmas Day wasn't even a holiday whereas the whole district closed down tight for a good three days at the New Year. This year Christmas was a holiday and there was even a Herald on New Year's day. I am glad to say that though the paper was produced, it didn't arrive in Methlick. Anyway, the shop still respects the pagan festival of the New Year. It opened on the third.

We first-footed the shopkeeper on our tractor and he told me a fine story which illustrates other changes in his industry. One of his predecessors had gained some local celebrity when he saw Lady Aberdeen picking her way through his tomatoes. To his clan chief and landlady he said pointedly, "They're all for sale M'lady."

Nowadays you expect to get your fruit thoroughly handled and to choose only the best. And you don't expect your shopkeeper to be stroppy about it.

We arrived home at four, just before the hangover. At least that was what The Breadwinner blamed, but I'm sure it was a bad pie or that town water they have in the village.

We're lucky having our own supply. Every pipe has

thawed and there isn't a single burst. Not so poor Big Hamish. His dairy is said to be like a display with waterfalls all over the place. He even has leaks underground and his water meter is spinning fit to take off.

I don't think the storm has cost me a penny, but it did cost me some anger. As usual, most of that was directed at people who should have stayed in their towns.

Penny Washers is one. He simply could not stand being deprived of his telephone. You would think that as most of his neighbours had no electricity and livestock to keep, he would consider the phone a small loss.

But not Penny Washers. The BT men came, had a look at the mile of blocked roads and went away again. Penny Washers wasn't having that and when I had at last managed to clear a slim path through the fields to let him out for supplies he told BT to get back immediately.

So when I went out on Boxing Day to pull another chocolate out of the snow, I couldn't get there for not one but two BT vans stuck in our little roadie.

The vans were not made for snow and the drivers were not trained for it.

Everything went wrong. I eventually got a rope on one, but the driver would try to keep up, letting the chain go slack. That let the hook come out right at the field gate. We could get neither back nor forward. Eventually I would push the van back into the field. I asked how strong his bumper was and when the laddie tested it the number plate fell off.

Engineers like that should be kept indoors till spring and I'm going to give Penny Washers a mobile.

January 15, 1996

Mossie left out?

ALL THE lads have been able to think about is whether or not Mossie was invited to the Butcher's shoot. You might think it a small matter compared with the future of the Common Agricultural Policy, whether the farmers' government can survive another year or whether Mossie's snow-rot spray had protected his barley, but you'd be wrong.

The Butcher's shoot is important. It isn't just that it is held at the most up-market of venues. It isn't that there is plenty to shoot and no need to walk. It isn't even the marvellous meal you get at midday. It is essential to be invited to the Butcher's shoot if you are to be seen as one of the Top Men.

The Farmer isn't invited. He isn't even a top boy. He never could be – 250 acres isn't enough to merit a Grand Prix shoot and The Breadwinner would never let him spend the £5000 that would be needed to buy a suitable day for a dozen of the Aberdeenshire Ivy League. That's what it takes to buy a place on the invitation lists.

But Mossie is different. He's a Top Man without a doubt.

At least, he was until the Butcher's shoot.

He began to get uneasy on the Thursday. The Red Rooster phoned up and mentioned in passing that they were all looking forward to a great day on Saturday. They'd had over 200 kills at the Butcher's shoot last year and there were lots of jokes about beating that.

But the call left Mossie uneasy. The Butcher had mentioned it as far back as September. And there had been several references since. But it was always like, "And then there's my shoot in January." There was nothing as definite as an invitation. One by one his pals phoned and said they'd see him at the shoot. Even Nicol from Keith, who isn't a farmer but makes a crust hustling lorries, said he would see Mossie there.

But would he? Our man was distraught. Surely the Butcher wanted Mossie at his shoot? Maybe he forgot? But then again, how could he?

There was only one thing for it. The Butcher would be lubricating himself at the Salmon on Friday night so down Mossie went.

"Aye, Butcher. You'll be lookin for a good day tomorrow?"

"Oh hallo, Moss. Happy New Year. What like a holiday had you?"

Not many minutes later Mossie tried again, "Have ye a big company tomorrow, Butcher?" he butted in.

"Aye about 15. You must be doing well just now with the price of porkers gan through the reef?"

Mossie was getting desperate. Rather before the next opportunity, he tried again, "Fa have we got for the shoot tomorrow, Butcher?"

"Oh well, There's the Rooster, Crookie of course, Nicol from Keith and ... " at that stage somebody came bursting in from the back with wishes for a great New Year. The list was unfinished.

A lesser man would have

shrunk away in despair, but not Mossie. This time he got the Butcher's undivided attention and asked him again.

"Oh aye, I was telling you," said the Butcher and started reeling off the names. Now, he's not a sensitive man, but even the Butcher could see that what Mossie wanted to hear was not the names of all the others who might be shooting, but his own. Some that were watching thought they caught the glint of what in weaker eyes might have been a tear.

The Butcher finished his list. "Mind you, Waterside says he's not sure. So if he cries off, I'll give ye a phone."

Poor Mossie went off home to suffer a night of suspense. He went to bed with all his shoot-ing gear on to be ready, how-ever late the call came. But it didn't come. The Butcher's shoot went ahead without him.

How they would manage he could hardly imagine but, no shrinking violet he, when the top men came into the Salmon after the Butcher's shoot, Mossie was there. "Well?" he challenged.

Nicol from Keith broke what might have been an awk-ward silence. "Hallo Mossie. You werena shootin today? Grand shoot, grand shoot, gra-a-and shoot! 230 birds. A record. Ye ken Moss. It's a funny thing. You introduced me to shootin and now I seem to do more shootin than you."

I hope this doesn't escalate into civil war.

The Irishman's been looking for our man, too. He now knows why land in Aberdeenshire costs less than that in Northern Ireland. The fact that he was cut off by 15 foot drifts would have been bad enough, but the Irishman has filled every inch of the old steadings with "Cyattle" and he has changed the system.

Where Mossie would have big bunches running together and all drinking out of one wee bowl close to the ground the Irishman has them carefully batched up in twos, threes and maybe tens. In order to get water to all these he has run a spider's web of half inch pipes all over the steadings – along the couples.

It's a show when the weather is fair. But for two weeks the spider's web went solid. Mossie's one drinking bowl might have thawed with a kettle of water or, with 200 queuing for a drink, it might not have frozen. But on the Irishman's system, it was a nightmare.

As he said to Mossie on Hogmanay, "I don't remember reading anything about this in the particulars."

January 22, 1996

Davie's tip was fit for a rascal

DAVIE STEVEN was a great piper from Caithness. Like so many pipers, greater and lesser, he was a sociable chap, which is not always easy to fit in with the keeping of livestock.

But Davie had an ingenious and humane solution. When he was setting off with his pipes he used to let all the cattle out. Should he be held up or land in a ditch, at least the cattle would have something to eat.

Now Davie had a son, to whom he gave this very sound advice, "Dinna be a piper. It just makes you a rascal." That is as near as I have ever heard a piper come to admitting to any flaws.

But John is not sure that his father's advice was sound. "Here I am a rascal and I can't even play the pipes."

Hearing that story was part of my reward for a trip to Caithness last week to address the annual meeting of the area's National Farmer's Union.

144

With my fences I couldn't risk putting my cows out to eat mud but then I didn't have to. I had no difficulty in getting Potions to agree to come down to feed the beasts on Wednesday morning. I would have a leisurely drive up to Wick on Tuesday, a relaxing evening with the farmers of Caithness, a night in Mackay's Hotel and a leisurely drive south on Wednesday.

I yoked the Jaggie at one o'clock and headed for the north coast of Buchan.

How green it all is. The grass has been growing under the protection of all that snow and it has been very mild since the thaw. The winter barley has been growing, too, and is radiant green. Even the wheat, though thinner, is growing. I even saw one field of rape sending up hard green shoots in search of summer.

From Banff to Forres seems to be spring barley country. The fields are black, for they are well forward with the ploughing.

If what they say is true (that the Chinese are going to be bidding the malting barley through the roof in the next few years) they will be quite right to keep their barley in the bag till the Spring day. But surely they are wrong to be ploughing?

If they would only 'plough and plant' they would be able to say, "The best time to sow is the last week of February. We'll start at seven thirty in the morning of the first Monday". Barring deep snow and avoiding swamp land, the new ploughed earth will show a fine tilth, whatever the weather.

After Forres it was back to the green though it didn't seem to have quite the brightness of Buchan. And as Inverness drew nearer the light from the fields grew dimmer. It may have been that dusk was gathering, but it seemed to me that, particularly after Inverness, my progress northward was also a progress through the greens to the light brown of grass that had seen too many sheep to darker browns of the bracken in Caithness.

The Farmer has been to Wick before, though previous trips have not been successful.

Some 30 years ago, when he was a budding caber tosser, he went to the Wick Gala. It was as wet a day as you get, the river was almost up to the level of the playing field and the event was cancelled. The Committee bravely gave the competitors £3 each and abandoned the whole idea. That worked fine for the lads who came pouring out of the pubs to claim the generous handout. But after a drive of about 250 miles, it was a poor return for The Farmer.

Then there was the judging of the coloured cattle at the Caithness County Show. That went well enough, though it took four hours to line them all up because that category included all the continental crosses and they kept bringing the same cattle back in time after time in various combinations to compete for the "stot, no hard teeth, confined to crofters from the parishes of Lathernwheel and Watten".

I had beasts placed differently in different classes but that wasn't the worst of it. I put a stot from Willie Sinclair (yes, that's the one who became crofter's convener) third in his class. That beast went on to the Scottish Winter Fair, where it not only beat my champion, but won the supreme title.

So what was the disaster this time?

Well, my carefully prepared talk was about the success of the cereals regime, what a good thing setaside is, what a breakthrough treated straw is instead of silage and the virtues of 'plough and plant'. When I saw the hills of Caithness again I realised I was living in a different world.

Still, the farmers were very nice about it and after the meeting I was whisked into the accordion and fiddle club to give them a couple of teuchter songs. There they were even nicer to me.

Danger lights were flashing. I could feel another hangover coming on. In an instant I was in over the Jaggie and by 2am I was back at Little Ardo. And with Potions fee-ed, there was no hurry in the morning.

Plans for Death House come to life

THE CIRCLE which started with running errands for my old man half a century ago is within sight of completion. Admittedly there are another two years before I have to give up farming here, but, suddenly it seems a lot nearer.

This week we got planning permission to build the Death House.

It has been quite a struggle. It has taken us ten months but it seems we have made it.

There are three good sites on Little Ardo – sites from which I could imagine myself watching the light slowly fading on Aberdeenshire. They have a view of Bennachie, our only mountain, and of the Prop of Ythsie, the monument to Prime Minister Lord Aberdeen, which stands on my grandfather's farm. That was my point of entry to the farming community in 1943.

The house must not look like a transplant from Marbella or indeed from anywhere else. The Breadwinner and I must have a house which looks like a native.

All three sites were rejected. They are all on land which the planners are reserving for anything other than building. Indeed, despite the fact that half the village has already been built on Little Ardo, the whole farm was now beyond the pale for building.

And that was lucky.

You see, there is a law that the planners have to find a suitable site on his land for any farmer who wants to build himself a retirement house. Had there been a little nook or cranny that was in their development plans we'd have had to take that, but as there was not, the whole farm was clearly open for consideration.

That didn't mean it would be easy.

The planners often seem more like obstructors. They don't want higgledy-piggledy development, with a house here and another there. They want them grouped in villages. If they are on their own they don't want them sticking up like sore thumbs. That means it is difficult to get a new house with a view. If you can see a view, the view can see you. They don't like that. It also means the planners don't much like what most people propose to build in the country – modern kit houses.

I have seen my friends and neighbours near to apoplexy at planners. "What business is it of theirs what I do on my own ground?" they ask – and they swear a lot.

But my sympathies are mostly with the planners. The worst of new building in the countryside are the kit houses. I consider them a blight, however good they are to live in. And the reluctance of the planners to allow these kits to proliferate has led to quite the best new housing in the North-east.

A large number of unwanted farm steadings have been converted into houses. They look as though they belong in the countryside and are a joy to behold.

So our Death House is to be one storey high, built of stone, with slated roofs and the dimensions of a traditional H-plan steading. It is only a matter of chance that there was not a similar steading built there in the nineteenth century. If all goes to plan it will look as though one had.

By good luck my father planted shelter belts to the north and east of our site while we will have the fullest views to the west and south. True, the Death House will not get much of the morning sun, but seeing less of the mornings is one of the things to which The Farmer looks forward in retirement.

By further good luck the half-acre site is in permanent setaside. Do you think I'll be able to claim the payments permanently?

There have been bad moments, one of which had its roots some 18 years ago.

It was in the dark days when I had debts on the farm of £1000 an acre. There was just myself and the cattleman working to pay interest of up to and over 20 per cent, though The Breadwinner was doing her best as a teacher. Into the close drove this guy in a smart suit. "I'm from British Gas," he said.

I jumped off the tractor and shook him warmly by the hand. The British Gas man was not used to such welcomes. Many farmers blamed the pipelines for breaking their drains and destroying their soil structure. But I knew that they were willing to give full compensation. I also knew I'd have a far better idea of the damage that was really being done and would get the best of any negotiations.

They treated us very well. There was a lump sum for start, some £10,000, and then generous compensation every year. I thought it a gift from the gods.

But at that time I had no thought of the Death House. At that stage the previous generation was not even dead.

After every hurdle had been cleared, the planners were satisfied and it seemed that we would achieve our dream house, the Health and Safety Executive intervened. No building could be safe unless 184 metres from the pipeline and ours was only 182. Luckily there was just enough room on the site to move us two metres east. Now all is well.

Soon my farming circle will be complete. Soon I will be the old man available for running errands for his son-in-law.

Counting the cost of the co-op

TRICKY TIMES are here. Buchan Meat, once the jewel in the crown of the co-operative movement, has called in the receiver, and our Burns Supper was a shambles beyond belief.

We had seen the end of Buchan Meat coming. Last year's loss of £698,000 was a clear sign that all was not well, if one were needed after the loss of £391,000 the previous year. And everybody knew there were too many slaughterhouses in the North-east.

Still, it seems a pity that Buchan is the one to go, for it was a pioneering outfit.

Sadly, those who spend on technical development can often be the most vulnerable. When times get hard, it is the firm with the strongest balance sheet that most often survives.

That was not Buchan Meat. Last year the company made a loss of 1% on their turnover of £70 million. The balance sheet showed a surplus sufficient to trade at that rate for three years. Yet seven months after its last report the receiver was called in to try to salvage as much as possible from the wreckage of

debts reputed to be £5 million.

The boys are devastated. At the discussion group on Sunday we were counting the cost and, concerned as we were for the 285 workers who are redundant, the loss of our shares was sorest. A quick count round the bar revealed that the boys had lost over £10,000.

Even Mossie was caught. An abattoir would have been the last thing he would ever have invested in but, as you'll remember, two years ago he bought 90 steers to get his beef special premium. He killed them at Buchan and at that time they were retaining one half of one per cent and putting that into shares.

Now he's furious. He was pleased with his 90 cattle. If only one hadn't died he'd have broken even and not many people manage that if they count it properly. But now, with his 300 shares going down the plug, he'd have made a loss even without that death.

The Farmer has lost £1420.

That money was invested in the great days when Buchan Meat was at the cutting edge of co-operative development in Britain.

They had a vision. A series of specialist co-ops would organise production of traditional cattle, bull beef, lamb and deer with the membership committed to selling its livestock to Buchan in exchange for secure outlets in the major supermarkets.

For a while, The Farmer was the chairman of the bull beef lot. We sold to Waitrose supermarkets at prices that promoted Friesian bulls up from the bottom to the top end of the market. It was a secure outlet for the farmers, a secure source for the supermarket, and Buchan had 200 bulls a week to

kill. There were ambitious plans to monitor every calf from conception to consumption. We all saw it as putting an end to the chaos of traditional markets.

Marketing was never so well thought out. If that philosophy had been maintained Buchan would have had a feeder co-op for ostriches before long.

But suddenly Buchan's gone.

The boys have many theories on what went wrong. With the libel laws in mind, I can't really say much about them, except that there was very little emphasis on the brilliance, skill, integrity and diligence of

the current management or directors. What was unanimous was that it had nothing to do with BSE as claimed by the liquidators. All North-east plants faced that.

My own theory, illuminated by hindsight, is that we should all have been alarmed when two key personnel left. They had a very good accountant called Wilkie and a top meat man called Green. You can't afford to lose men like that. That was particularly true when the company gave up its idea of the feeder co-ops and became just another slaughterhouse.

But the boys can't afford to be too hard on those who piloted Buchan onto the rocks. Not after our Burns Supper.

I had heard that there was to be haggis at the discussion group but I had also heard Potions saying there was no need to make it a ladies' night, so I presumed it was just a snack.

About half an hour late and having had my tea as usual, I swanned into the Salmon Inn, wearing my moleskins and trainers, my sweat shirt and a shirt that wasn't clean but would easily do.

I was shocked!

Here was Mains in the dress kilt, pipes at the ready. Every table in the pub was laid, down to the paper hats and crackers. A company of 50 was clearly expected. With a couple of lads we pressed to join us, a disreputable company of 11 finally sat down to what must have been the worst organised Burns Supper in history.

Mains piped in the haggis but then it was down hill all the way. The Farmer did the address well enough but missed the second verse. There was no one to do the immortal memory, Tam o'Shanter or give us a song. And there were all those empty seats.

February 19, 1996

A load of old bull

WHEN I came back with my first cheque from the Perth bull sales some 23 years ago I was greeted by Auld Jimmy, the grieve who didn't think much of my attempts to take over.

"Well?" he said in the manner of one who had caught a naughty boy in a compromising situation and was going to know the reason why.

"I got six hunder pound," I

said as defiantly as possible for a man whose neighbours at Uppermill had been used to getting ten times that even before the war. And that for Shorthorns just.

James Low was one of the Aberdeenshire grieves of whom someone said: "They are a race of potential prime ministers with far more important things to do." He could wither me with a glance but this was worth more than that. "Huh!"

I wasn't to be scorned. I was out of short breeks by now, a man with four children and a huge overdraft. "It's a start," I said.

"Aye," said Auld Jimmy, turning away in perfect disdain, "a bad een."

Oh yes, I've fairly come up in the world. This year I was down at Perth to propose the health of the Simmental cattle breed in celebration of the 25 years since it was introduced to Britain. The damnable thing was that Auld Jimmy wasn't still around to see it.

It was a very good party so I would not normally be able to remember what I told them but, unusually, I not only had notes but still had them when I got home. I'll tell you all that's fit to print.

First I told the diners that they were there on false information. Their dinner was to celebrate the 25 years since the breed was introduced to Britain from Germany and Switzerland. But I had certain knowledge that Simmentals were in

Scotland in the thirteenth century. Indeed William Wallace's father had some, for I saw a fine pure bred Simmental calf on his croft in Mel Gibson's execrable film, Braveheart.

My interest in foreign breeds started with jealousy of my cousins James and Maitland Mackie, whose fathers had imported Charolais. Those ate half as much again as ordinary cattle but the calves sold for £3000 apiece when £200 was a good commercial price.

As my father hadn't provided me with Charolais I would have to provide for myself. I was explaining that to Archie White of the Spott in Glenprosen when he said "There's some more in the paper – Simmentimen something."

Sure enough, clearance had been given for an importation. I rang the Department but I was far too late. "People have had their names down on the list for years. It's all arranged. In fact they're having a meeting at Paisley this afternoon."

Paisley could only mean the Scottish Milk Marketing Board. Yes they were having a meeting at two o'clock. I got there in time and sat as low as I could in my chair until the chairman, that Collosus of Scottish farming Sir William Young (as he later became), asked if there was anyone

present not on the list. Expecting to land in the street I owned up, only to have my name added. I was in. I would get six heifers. Soon I would be rich.

But first I had to see the banker.

You will know that I do not hold bankers in very high regard. That is partly because so many of them were unable to see what a bad risk I was when they were plunging me deeper into debt in the Seventies. But it is also because of one banker's reaction to my proposal to buy Simmental heifers.

"Fower hunder apiece!" he exclaimed incredulously. "Oh, no no, Charlie. I couldn't advise you to go into a thing like that. Dear no, buy some stots."

I had to go to a banker who didn't know the difference between a heifer and a stot. He could see the difference between the £400 for the heifers and the £2500 apiece I was offered for exporting the calves. The buyer even stood good a bull with a soo-mou – a short jaw which meant he had to be killed.

The foreign excitement only lasted for three years and then we had to make the brutes pay in the hard world of commercial cattle breeding.

At Edinburgh, the main centre for Simmentals before the action moved to Perth, we bought the champion bull from

Tom Barr of Hobsland in 1972. I was proud but Auld Jimmy was still around to cut me down to size. "Ony feal can buy a champion – as lang as he's money. It's jist as well you bocht it this year."

And Tommy Laughland, the main man at the meat co-op FMC and Kilmarnock FC, also helped my humility along. As the proud new owner admired the bull he said, "Aye Charlie. Take a good look, son. He'll never look as good again."

True, true. But two years later I was back with a good son who had been junior male champion at the Highland Show. I took Tom Barr to look at his bull's handiwork. The young Farmer was nervous as the great man looked the bull over and under. I had to walk him out a bit. He looked grave. "Charlie, yer bull just has one fault that I can see. The cheque's going into your pocket, no mine."

He was supreme champion, though he didn't make the top price. And the funny thing is, I can't remember what Auld Jimmy said about it.

February 26, 1996

Bangers replace pedigree cattle

IT CAUSED great excitement in the village when we had the first Simmental calf to be born in Aberdeenshire. Auld Jimmy the grieve didn't think much of me as a farmer, but he made the most of this bull calf.

On the morning of its birth Jimmy was holding forth to the old men who gather at the shop to collect their papers each morning, when Waterside, the biggest farmer in the parish, approached. "Aye Low, I'll give you £100 for your calf."

Moving the old Mersham to the corner of his mouth, Auld Jimmy dismissed the bid with the disdain only he could convey, "If ye HADa hunder pound I'd maybe gie ye a look."

And that would be about right. A ten gallon hat offered me £20,000 for four Simmental heifers to smuggle into Canada. One heifer did go to New Zealand for £10,000 and the buyer even paid the seller's commission of 5%.

The Farmer should have

become rich but he didn't. Practically every penny was reinvested in other exotic cattle and they weren't all as good as the Simmentals. We got Blondes d'Aquitaine, Marchigiana and South Devons, to mention some of the less successful ventures. Little Ardo was once referred to as Charlie's Safari Park.

The export bubble burst in 1973 and we had to make our way in the much more competitive home market.

The first problem was recognition. In 1970 farmers were just beginning to get used to recognising Charolais. So our Simmentals were referred to as 'Charlais' if they were good and 'Seminals' if they were not. In Aberdeenshire they got a reputation of being good 'sideways' cattle. They looked well from the side but from the back they were too narrow.

And people had difficulty grasping the idea that these cattle were dual purpose, because here cattle are traditionally either beef or milk. I heard two old farmers discussing another European import at the AI station at Perth. It was a rather slack backed Maine Anjou bull.

"Mind, Andra, it's a dual purpose beast."

There's nae such thing," said Andra. "They're either ae thing or the ither."

"Oh, but this is dual pur-

156

pose. Ye can saddle it and ride it after foxes and if it draps dead ye can sell it for pet food."

Anyway, we won through. The Simmental breed is recognised everywhere now and set fair for the next 25 years. My best pedigree cattle were sold before I went to Kenya. I decided the pedigrees are for rich men to lose money and very few very clever stockmen to become rich.

I've moved to the other end of the beef trade altogether. I am buying old bangers out of the jingoring. My ideal is no longer the Highland Show Champion. Now I am looking for a cow which has been so badly looked after that she is too thin for the butchers, and which has landed in the farrow ring despite being in calf.

The idea is to calve her down, give her a pleasant summer at the grass and then sell her with as much flesh on her as possible. The hope is that there will be profit and the calf will be in the deal as a bonus.

The key is finding those which are safe in calf. And that is where the Irishman comes in. He uses witchcraft in diagnosing pregnancy. He can be seen before the sale bending down among the farrow cows singing a weird incantation before the sale. This generates a list of those which are in calf.

I don't really believe it, but we are off to a flying start. We got a fine Charolais calf last Wednesday and banger and son are doing well.

And finally I have to report that only one of the boys in the discussion group has been caught unpaid by the collapse of Buchan Meat and now Thistle Meats.

I have two neighbours who are looking anxiously towards the receiver for £20,000 and more for cattle consigned in the weeks before the companies were overwhelmed.

But we've all been lucky except for Penny Washers, and his loss was self-inflicted.

He had sent three score of sheep to Thainstone. One had damaged a leg and was sent straight to Buchan Meat for slaughter, being unfit to go through the ring. One kilo of the hogget was condemned. All the same Penny Washers was outraged and offended by his reward. His cheque came to just over a fiver.

There was no way he was going to accept that. He would need at least £25 and that was letting them off with murder. He would show them a battle.

Unfortunately brave noises in the pub was as far as Penny Washers got. He kept forgetting to do anything about it. And then one day Buchan Meat was gone and he hadn't even cashed their cheque for a fiver.

You can bank on your pals

WHAT A success the Spring Show was. Five thousand payers had plenty of room at the Thainstone Agricultural Centre. There was a fine show of livestock judged (among others) by John Jeffries of Scotland, Kersknowe and the BBC. There was the usual show of enormous machines, none of which could get into any shed at Little Ardo. The sun shone. Yes, Tuesday was a great day.

I can't think of anything good to say about Wednesday.

The trouble was that we had to attend the farewell party for Eddie the Eagle. The last of the gentleman bankers is taking early retirement after 40 years' service. He's to be replaced by a computer screen which will refuse your application for an overdraft instantaneously, saving time and the expense of giving you coffee and biscuits – and it can measure you for a new suit at the same time.

I had been cruising, in a relatively restrained way, the various hospitality venues with the Red Rooster and Mossie, until Eddie's do. At five o'clock the bank's blinds were drawn, so were the corks from too many bottles and the ball was well and truly on the slates.

It was a fitting sacrifice to honour that rarest of birds – a popular banker.

And Eddie might well have been an eagle that never flew at all. His career might have ended when he was a teller of 17 years.

It was not a busy branch and the boy played little games to keep himself amused. One of those was to sit with his back to the door and guess by the sound of their step which of his regular customers had come in.

That was what he was up to this horrible winter's day. It was half day in Kemnay and he knew that both the general merchant and the shoemaker would be in as usual, but he would not have been surprised had no one else come in on such a day.

He did think it was odd, though, when it came three o'clock and not one soul had come in. Still, it was a bad day. That was it. There was no one coming so he went to lock up, to find he'd forgotten to unlock the door in the first place.

The poor lad suffered a sleepless night. What would the shopkeepers say when they came in with their money the next morning? And what about all the other customers who might have been turned away?

In the event not a word was said by anyone. From which Eddie concluded that everyone had been put off by the weather and that the good Lord was back in his heaven.

When Eddie started in the bank there was only one mechanical aid – a manual adding machine which couldn't even subtract. Everything had to be done with the fountain pen – not biro.

So the job Eddie the Eagle, the low-flying banker, finished up doing bore no resemblance at all to the job he signed up for 40 years ago. Even the installation of the alarm system was a revolution.

It is said that the bank's Inspector came to one of Eddie's charges and found the branch open but apparently unmanned. Idly he looked around, spied the alarm button and stood on it, thinking "That'll make them sit up."

It certainly brought action. Within a minute a waitress from the hotel appeared with a smile, a nip and a half pint.

Then there is that other dehumanising innovation. Who would have thought 40 years ago that most of the cash would go out of the bank through a 24-hour hole-in-the-wall?

It hadn't occurred to me until Eddie told me at his leaving do, but the banker has to fill up the hole in the wall every now and again.

Well now, Eddie and one of the lassies had been doing just that one night and he, always looking for a new angle, had a teet out through the hole-in-the-wall.

Behold, here comes his cousin Jimmy to make a withdrawal. Eddie waited until his cousin had pushed in his card, then shouted out through the hole, "Get to hell oot o there. You're gettin no money today."

Poor Jimmy took fright and ran away, and the manager and girl had to run after him, return his card and explain. It can't have been easy.

Those were just some of the stories that were told at Eddie's farewell. But it was interesting to meet the modern bank managers. It is said that none of them really is a manager now. The man who used to advise on which bulls to put on your cows to get the best yielding heifers now thinks milk comes from a supermarket. All he can do is refer you to someone else who'll turn down your loan application.

And it is no wonder, for they are all so young. We met

all the important computer screens at the do. And the astonishing thing was the higher up the bank you went the younger they got. The top boss doesn't look a day over 17.

Of course Eddie made a speech and a thoughtful one. He said he got on well with people because he was a hopeless delegator and so had to see everyone himself. He also said that his customers had always been his friends and his friends had always been his customers.

I bet it won't be long before the computer comes up with that as a good idea.

Never let the truth spoil a good blaw

IT IS one of the most endearing traits common among farmers that so many of us like to blaw about our farms. If a farmer makes a technological breakthrough the first thing he does is invite all the neighbours to see how clever he's been. And when the press get to hear of it they are welcomed with open arms.

You wouldn't catch any normal businessman doing that, would you? He would play cards like that close to his chest. He would pull a long face and pretend he was just surviving. The only time he would admit to doing well and be willing to blaw about it would be when he was just about to go under.

It's not that businessmen don't blaw. They blaw about their golf, their women, and their cars. That's why they think farmers are so backward. All our blawing is about our farm and farming.

In case you are unfamiliar with this genre, let me reiterate a couple of classics.

The grieve at Balquhindachy, the biggest farm in the strategically vital parish of Methlick, is once said to have put a visitor in his place by explaining that, when they went to Arnage station to collect their turnip seed in the springtime, whereas most of their neighbours could bring seed home in a shopping bag, they had to send two carts, so great a consignment did they need for their rolling acres.

Then there was the loon

160

who went from Methlick in the North-east Lowlands to work in the Highlands about Strathdon. When he eventually made it home at the November term, the loon blawed to his friends that the fields he had to plough in the Highlands were so steep they didn't need a digger to lift the potatoes. At harvest time they just opened the bottom of the drills and the potatoes rolled down into the bag.

I had a further lesson on agricultural blawing on Saturday night. The Breadwinner had decided to have a dinner party. We haven't had one for ten years so nearly everyone had dropped us from their invitation lists.

But The Farmer agreed to the party, despite the risk of our being invited back.

It went uncommonly well and that was partly because we invited two veterans of the Lapwing troop of cub scouts from the neighbouring parish of New Deer.

One was Stanley Rothney, the legendary Bobby of Methlick parish who made sure that throughout the 1940s I never once appeared in the village with faulty brakes or lights, and never once failed to stop at the halt sign.

The other was James Fowlie, who for 60 years made what looked, from the road at least, like a comfortable living by the impossible means of buying forward stores and feeding them until they were fat.

You will know that what used to be called fat cattle are

now called "Prime" to fit in with the fad of today, which dictates that beef be consumed tough and unmarbled, and in minute portions.

Well, even in these days James' cattle are still called "fat".

When he announced recently that he was going to retire, I asked the old cub scout what he was going to do.

He thought for a minute, "Well, I could hardly do less, could I?"

So when I tried to introduce the old cop to the gentleman farmer who was no longer young, they soon put me right. They had known each other for some considerable time when I was born.

And Stanley was able to give us a blaw about James Fowlie's farm.

It was a huge place and according to Stanley, the cattlemen, when they were feeding turnips, had a white stone which they used as a marker. This was put down in the griep to let them know how far down the byre they had got.

After pushing the barrowful of turnips up between the two beasts and emptying it in their trough, the baillie would shift the white stone to the next pair.

There was no querying this unlikely story. "Na, na. They couldn't just look and see which cattle were still eating. The byres were so big at Auchrynie that the cows could be finished by the time you got back from the neepshed with a barrowful for the next pair."

Of course there is a chance that the story might not be true because James Fowlie hadn't heard of such a thing. But he did come up with a pretty good blaw of his own. "Aye, and this one's true!"

I can't remember if it was because this byre was so narrow or because the Auchrynie stots were so huge, but special measures had to be taken. It was a double byre which meant the cattle were stalled along each wall with the work of feeding, cleansing and bedding done from a centre pass.

We had the same at Little Ardo when we had milking cows here, so I know all about the dangers of reacting too sharply to danger from one or other side.

If you gave a kicker at one side too wide a berth you were liable to get a clout round the ears with a sharney tail from the other.

At any rate, the safety margin was so small in this byre at Auchrynie that, before walking down between the lines of cattle rear ends, the staff used to ensure that the flaps of their pockets were safely turned down.

Dawn chorus turns to dawn chaos

MOSSIE AND I have been active in the farrow cow ring. Between us we have bought more than 100 old bangers in the last month.

Oh how the mighty have fallen! The Ardo herd that once sent champions to Perth and to Edinburgh is reduced to buying in the jingoring.

And if Mossie hates stots and heifers, he loathes cows. So what has happened?

Well, it's all down to the Irishman. We all felt sorry for him when he came over and paid Mossie all that money for his outfarm. We felt even sorrier when it emerged that he was going to try and pay his interest off "cyattle". And yet, here we are, not two years later, dancing to his tune.

Mossie has a court full of old dears who were sent for slaughter, though they were too thin. The theory is that they were cheap because there was no meat for sale, only skin and bone. They are beginning to put on weight. They came home for as little as £200 and the plan is to double their value.

But I have a far better deal. I have all those sent for slaughter because they were thought to be past breeding. All of mine have been picked up heavy in calf. So far we have three calves, all bulls, and the system seems good. But I hope no one asks me at the calf sales next year what bull I am using, for the first was a Charolais, the second was a Simmental, and the third was a Shorthorn.

Anyway, the first cow cost £275 a month ago and her Charolais calf must be worth that today.

We really don't know why the thin farrow cows have turned so cheap, but every theory has something to do with failure of the meat companies Buchan Meat, Thistle Meats and Prime Meats having an effect on confidence.

Penny Washers, the white settler, has jumped into the old banger market, too. He's too mean to pay the Irishman his wee bit of commission and he's been doing his own buying, so there's no way he'll get bull calves.

But he was telling us at the discussion group at the Salmon

on Sunday how nice it was to go out in the morning and hear his own special dawn chorus. The old dears would be mooing for the calves from which they'd been weaned or for the breakfast which cattle expect. The sheep would be baaing. The baconers would grunt away in an industrious bass while a soprano squawk would proclaim the arrival of another egg.

To most of us, that sort of Old Macdonald farm chorus is a nightmare. I had a letter from one last week. Ian Murray of Rhynie had three complaints about the "Anglicisation of our beloved country".

First, he is outraged by old names like Cuttlesburn becoming Cuttlesburn House, as though "our old names were not majestic enough".

Second, he is fed up of peo-ple calling our farm roads "lanes", as though they were in "the soft-bellied parts of England".

Third, he hates seeing the crofts "our forefathers grafted to maintain, becoming like Noah's Arks and reduced to a laughing stock".

I'm not sure that I agree. That sort of white settler is keeping up the population in the country and they buy a lot more stock and crop than they sell.

But I think Penny Washers is undergoing a conversion away from the Macdonald school of farming.

He lacks the sixth sense for trouble, but even he could recognise on Wednesday that his dawn chorus was a bit different. They were all up an octave.

He rushed out and what he

saw took all his powers of description.

It had been a U-plan steading but the midden had been roofed over to give a decent court with byres on two sides and a barn on the third.

Penny Washers had all his species separated. The big court was full of his cows. The byre was for the pigs and the sheep were penned at one end of the little byre, with the horses in loose pens at the other. In the barn he kept his two dogs and the 40 free-range hens which provided delicious brown eggs.

At least, that was the plan.

But Penny Washers has no idea how strong pens have to be. The pigs chewed through the two bits of string and got in among the cows. The old ladies were none reassured when they saw where the stink had been coming from. They panicked through the propped-up pallets that did for sheep pens and when the horses saw the cows charging in they lashed out with their back feet, levelling the bales that formed their loose pens and broke down the door to the barn.

Amazingly, the outside doors and walls held, so nothing escaped altogether, but inside, total chaos reigned. The horses bit the cows. The pigs bit the sheep and the dogs bit everything, while the hens squawked and fluttered.

This farming really isn't a job for amateurs.

March 25, 1996

Mossie's tatties are too rich a brew

IF IT had happened to my cows I'd have known exactly what was amiss. After all, I learned to make bathtub gin 40 years ago from an old lady in whose mouth butter would have survived with ease. She also made passable medium sweet sherry from potato peelings.

But Mossie had no idea he was doing anything wrong or even anything risky when he gave ad lib potatoes to the farrow cows he's fattening.

As you will have noticed, unless you've been looking in the shops, the price of spuds has collapsed. They are down from £300 a tonne to £20. The Red Rooster and Crookie, who have enough seed potatoes to plant the whole South-east of England and still export some to Russia, have seen a fortune slip through their fingers.

But Mossie's your man in a crisis. Willing as ever to profit from the misfortune of his fellow man, he has taken a huge line in these tatties from the boys in a deal reputed to be around the £16 a tonne mark (but dinna tell anybody). Fine cheap feed for his cows.

Anybody else would have given them a few bags the first day and a few more each day, gradually to accustom the old rumens to this rich diet. But not Mossie. He has these huge hoppers into which he tips their rations, mostly treated straw, and the first day he simply filled them up with ten tonnes of tatties. "That should keep them going," he thought.

And so it did. But the sight which greeted Mossie when he entered the court at the crack of 9.30 the next morning would have feared lesser men. It certainly feared Mossie.

The first thing he noticed was that, whereas the cattle are usually all standing up waiting to see what goodies you have brought them first thing in the morning, most were still sitting. And some were more sprawling than sitting.

Then he noticed the eyes. Cows don't actually focus their eyes like humans do. They have one at each side of their head and they are hard put to get you with both eyes at once. But Mossie's cows' eyes seemed quite independent of one another.

There wasn't much movement from the cows that were on their feet but they were definitely unsteady. He knew it wasn't BSE because the cows did not seem to be in any distress, but they seemed to be burping and hiccoughing more than usual.

Long John Silver, still not dead despite the false alarm at last November's shoot, was called. "Oh vet. What's ado wi' my cattle? Could ye mak it BSE do you think, for the compen?"

Long John was not impressed. One look was sufficient. He strode over to the hopper and perused what was left of the potato gin. "Your cattle are drunk, ye feel goat," he said.

The odd thing is that the vet didn't prescribe anything. No lemon drinks, no three pints of water, not even an aspirin. And yet the next day the cows were as right as rain and seemed to have developed a head for the stuff. They still look happy but the old dears are back in complete control and the potatoes are going at the rate of about a hundredweight each per day.

Meanwhile, I've now got five calves off my purchases in

the farrow cow ring; four beautiful bulls and one slimline heifer which may have been sired by a whippet. It is amazing to me that people would put their old cows away so near to the calving.

And at last I have a calf off the bull I bought at Perth last February. It is a strong bull calf and appeared unnoticed when The Farmer was fast asleep. So despite the disgrace of only costing 1300gns Dod has produced a good calf that gave his mother no calving difficulty.

But he did, as I told you last June, fall down on the first part of his job – he hadn't much idea why he had been put in the field with all those excitable cows.

Dod could sense that his mission was pretty important. There were scents in the air that upset him. They came in varying strengths from four or five cows at a time and he tore round the field, trying to mount this one, mounting the wrong end of that one and always rushing off to another before the more experienced old ladies could help.

I really thought Dod was going to have a heart attack, for he ran himself to a standstill. Well, he was still except for his sides which heaved as he tried to regain his breath.

I was quite worried that we were going to have no calves and certainly there will be some that are quite late.

But now that a calf has been born we can calculate that it took Dod nine days to work out what was for what. His first calf is nine days later than Old Argus' first calf was last year.

Beef crisis shows farming is crucial

DESPITE my boast last Friday that I was off to the mart with my chequebook, the only change in the stocking rate is from births. There are 13 now and I haven't seen one calving.

I did almost see my nearly pure Charolais cow. She had two good feet and a tongue sticking out. I got ropes on the calf's feet and pulled. In my considered judgement she was stuck and, if she was anything like the Charolais I calved in the 1970s, by the time the calf got to the heart it would be dangerously gripped, then stick at the hurdies for sure.

I went for the halter, American calf puller, hammer to release it if I needed a fresh grip, pinch bar in case I needed to turn the calf, soap for lubrication, a small bale to sit on and a half bottle.

All were where they should be so I was back, ready for the long haul, in five minutes.

Too late. She was licking a fine bull calf. It shows how much I've forgotten about stiff calvings. I'm glad.

I've now 13 calves including nine bulls. That is surely a comfort. Even if the calves are worthless, we'll always get the beef special premia.

The mart on Friday was an odd place. I am speaking nine days ago, remember, and at the time the full market reaction hadn't happened. The cows were back a maximum of £200 and there was the Irishman mopping them up.

The stores were maybe down £60 for the average sorts, but the toppers were hardly back at all. I saw one pair of stots making £155 above their kilo price.

Peter the digger dealer opined that half the farmers there probably hadn't heard the news. That wouldn't be right, but I do think the resilience of the trade was too great in the circumstances. The boys just didn't realise the enormity of what we were perhaps facing – an unstoppable flow of prime cattle with no market.

I am a natural optimist and, though I kept the chequebook in my pocket last Friday, I still think a slaughter policy will be implemented, that confidence will return some day, and that there will be winners as well as losers out of this beef crisis.

The buyers at Thainstone may have been too brave, but there is a level at which keeping cattle are a good buy.

On the bright side, this beef crisis has changed a few ideas about how important farming is to the economy. It has become fashionable to say we have no political clout any more because we have so few votes.

But this crisis in what is after all only a part of farming, has shown that we are very important to the economy. The banning of beef exports and the expected boom in imported food is expected to cause a balance of payments crisis.

As the news unfolded, sterling fell in the foreign exchange markets, forcing up inflation. Government securities fell sharply, forcing up interest rates.

And of course, by far the most serious effect of all from the point of view of those charged with looking after our welfare, the threat of a slaughter policy put the pre-election bribery budget in jeopardy.

If they have to pay for a slaughter policy there'll be no money left for tax cuts.

Mind you, it wasn't all international agri-politics this week. I was carried back 30 and 60 years to the days of potty training.

The Recovery Stock, as I call my elder son to distinguish him from his brother, the Wasting Asset, has slipped a disc.

His wife has to run the cafe and my Breadwinner was away in the Toon winning bread. So, while the Recovery Stock was

NOT A WEE AND NOT A POO!

169

recovering from the surgeon, I had his two Liabilities in my sole charge. Worse than that Gladys, our daily treasure, had a funeral to attend.

I tell you the good Lord was not fooling when he ordained that young rather than old people should have the children. By the time The Breadwinner came home at 6pm, I was tired. And by the time their mother came home at 10 we were just about ready for the slaughter policy.

They were very good as children go, but when you are nearly one and your sister is nearly two, there has to be somebody around. Especially for the potty training.

Now I did do a little napkin work 30 years ago, but things were different then. It is easier now by far; no safety pins, I discovered, and you don't have to shake out the solids or wash the dirty hippins.

And so effective is the waterproofing that you can leave the same nappy on for ages without giving the little darling a sore bottom. You don't really have to change them until the baby gets too heavy. Still, I should have got a lesson.

It was during her supposed rest that I was summoned to help the little Investment first.

I struggled with her garments while the young lady debated whether it would be a wee or a poo.

At last I got her enthroned.

But all we got was a little resounding flatulence.

A grave little face looked at me across half a century, shook her head and said, "Not a wee and not a poo."

April 8, 1996

Tricky times can bring opportunity

THE WORST thing is not knowing where you are. You could go a long way without finding a more self-assured bunch than the farmers who meet to chew the fat at the Salmon Inn on a Sunday evening, but last week no one knew where they were.

Take Big Hamish. He had just been told that his milk quota, which would have been worth not less than £300,000 a couple of short weeks ago,

would be worthless if a cow slaughter policy were introduced. Who's going to need quota if there is a shortage of cows? But then again, is there going to be a slaughter policy? Will they kill all the herds with problems? Surely that is the minimum to satisfy the Europeans when the Irish and the French are already doing that.

Nobody who is daft enough to believe the worst fears is going to be convinced by a policy of killing all the old cows at the end of their working lives. I had a cow which saw 18 summers and Gowkie had one which went to the jingoring at 21. It'll be 15 years before cows like that, alive in the days of contaminated feed, come to the ends of their working lives.

Eradication is the only thing that will work and the sooner the better. That's what we think. But what do we do in the meantime?

The Red Rooster has been looking for an excuse to get rid of his cows for years. "So who do I phone to get my coos killed?"

If only it were as simple as that.

As Mossie says, these are tricky times – but tricky times are times of opportunity. And Mossie thinks he sees a good one. He's in the market for old rotaspreaders.

He's going for the incineration market in a big way.

The opportunity arises because of the imbalance between the numbers of cows some are saying will be slaughtered, and the ability of our incinerators to dispose of them.

Admittedly the weekly capacity rose last Monday from 1000 a week to 3000 a week, but even at the newly invented figure, 4,500,000 old cows are going to take 30 years to incinerate. If, on the other hand, they do as some suggest and kill the lot, it will take them 90 years to dispose of the bodies.

In fact Mossie even doubts whether there are enough old rotaspreaders to make good the shortfall in capacity. He came up to me in the pub on Sunday and whispered, "BSE, CJD, JCB, eh?" and winked conspiratorially.

I understood exactly what he meant. They'll never manage to dispose of all those carcases in incinerators. They'll need to get a safe way of burying them, perhaps in quicklime, or even resort to mass incineration in great funeral pits or pyres as they did with the foot and mouth.

So Mossie's buying himself a brand new JCB to be ready for the contract work.

With his luck he'll likely get it, but the uncertainty of the situation doesn't suit me.

I should be selling 21 of last year's heifer calves in the next fortnight for £500 apiece. My financial controller (another of The Breadwinner's jobs) tells me if I don't cash them I must go for a £50 interview with the banker and get a new overdraft. Farming with the banker's money was never much fun.

My best bet seems to be to kill my old cows. That way I will get full compensation for the worst 21 cows. I would then put the heifers to the bull as replacements.

That should give me more income and lead me into a younger, perhaps better, herd.

But even with all the rotaspreaders and JCBs working flat out it is clearly going to be a long time before the slaughter policy gets round to mine.

After the 22nd of April I should be selling my 20 bull calves for £550 apiece, but in the current uncertainty I might have to take £450 or less. So should I hang on and try to finish them? And should I try to finish them quickly or make them last as long as possible?

I don't know and neither does anyone else.

There will be winners, though. When they eventually get around to slaughtering the old dears Mossie and I will presumably do quite well out of the 100 old bangers we are fattening. There has been talk of between £600 and £1000 a head compensation. If there's a choice we'll go for the top figure but really the lower one would do for most cows at the end of their working lives, and ours are certainly that. Our problem could be keeping them alive long enough to reach the top of the queue for slaughter.

Another winner is Penny Washers. He is also in the food business in a small way – making beef burgers. He was cock-a-hoop at the discussion group on Friday. "My beefburgers are going like hot cakes," he astonished us. "They don't have any beef in them, though they do have some chicken and pork waste. In fact I can honestly say my beefburgers have never had any beef in them."

But we agree that there is one loser from the whole sad business. John Major seems to be decent but that won't save him. The contrast between the Irish who jumped in with a slaughter policy and the way Britain has dithered, is too much. The Irish have Europe at their feet and we are down and perhaps on the way out.

Mossie used to speak about "Doon Major", calling John after the country's most successful neep. But now he's taken to calling the prime minister "Doon-and-oot Major".

And that from one of Nature's Tories.

April 15, 1996

Seeking sympathy over tax changes

AS YOU know, we boys from Aberdeenshire are hard to beat when it comes to blawin. And that's not just true when we are proud of ourselves. It is part of the character of the Lowlanders from the North-east corner of Scotland that we also blaw when we are looking for sympathy – and, like farmers everywhere, we are always after that.

Hilly was at it at the pub on Sunday. He's a bachelor (so far) in his thirties (also so far) who plays hard and works as hard as you have to to hold on to the family acres when you have a brother and a sister who have left you to the plough.

His father had been a fee-ed man who had married a hard-working wife and a thrifty one. Together they built their fortunes until they were lairds of the one-and-a-half pair farm of Hillhead which looks over Little Ardo from just up the hill.

But Auld Hillie's away now and Young Hilly is eloquent on the misfortunes of those who are overcome by the relentless increase in the size of

173

farm necessary to sustain a gentleman. For while his father had 'made it' when he took the reins at Hillhead, Hillie has had to take a job from time to time as well as running Hillhead single-handed. While he is laird of the place to which his father aspired, the Hillie of today has to work on someone else's land to make ends meet.

He was in the process of damning his luck, the weather and the government when he blew out the awful truth about his farm (and mine): "The only thing ye get for nothing in farmin is kittlins and rhubarb."

True enough, but at least this year we got the first making of rhubarb eaten before it went mouldy in the fridge. It was delicious and the farm cat, having been visited by no fewer than four (perhaps many more) admirers is very fat again. You'd think she'd learn.

And the BSE saga has thrown up some new blaws. One such is attributed to a smallholder in one of the bleakest bits of Buchan. He has 80 acres and is currently fattening 40 stots, though he will have more for the grass. He's just bought a £26,000 tractor and given up chain-smoking Capstan Full Strength for chain-smoking cigars.

A neighbour tried to commiserate with our friend about BSE, but he would have none of it. Moving the cigar to the corner of his mouth he said, "BSE hardly affects us. We're mainly arable, noo."

I suppose I could say the same thing. I now have 120 cows and followers, which is all there ever was on my father's 'stock' farm, yet I only have 20% of the place in grass.

That's a mercy, for we are still in the dark over BSE. How many times have we been told that all the old cows are going to be incinerated and at a uniform compensation price of £480? Well, Mossie claims to have it on the best authority that it will be 86 pence per live kilo or 172 pence hung up.

I don't know who Mossie's authority is or whether it is best, but I prefer it to the others.

But the fact that we are going to waste all the good animal protein that once went into feed rations is making the crops even more exciting. Rape seems to be heading for £200 a tonne as the pigs and hens are forced to become vegetarians.

My crops are what we could call 'mixed'. The rape has been ravaged by the pigeons all winter. I have four fields eaten bare and two which have suffered from the frost. Still, I expect there to be 30 cwt by the harvest day and I don't expect there will be any difference in yield between the eaten and the frosted.

174

The barley is looking wonderful, though we have a bit of winter kill for the first time that I can remember. That looks bad but it wouldn't come near to 1% of the area so it isn't important except where it can be seen from the road.

Apart from BSE there was one major topic this week. That was this business of self-assessment for income tax. Big Hamish thinks this is a good idea because he's always paid too much tax when THEY assessed it. "I'll surely be able to make it less than THEM."

But I'm afraid Big Hamish is missing the point.

We used to send in our lies and it was up to THEM to prove that they were lies.

In the new system we will send in our lies and then they'll go back to one in five of us and ask us to prove that our lies are the truth. The whole accountancy world has been turned upside down and the boys don't realise it yet. Lots of people are going to be bankrupted by self-assessment. People who relied on the lack of decent books to keep them from paying up will find they can't prove their lies under the new system.

Our own accountants ("Don't worry about your tax rebate, we'll just add it to our fee") are trying desperately to get the seriousness of keeping records over to their agricultural clients.

The junior partner went to visit an old boy at Rhynie. Had he kept his promise to record

every sale, purchase, delivery, order...?

"Oh aye. They're in this box."

The cardboard box was brimming with totally unsorted bills, reminders, and cancelled cheques.

The accountant was shocked. "This is hopeless. This is no use at all," he said.

"Are ye sure?" asked the farmer.

"No, No. You'll go to jail if you can't do better than that."

Well, if they're nae use to the tax man I'm sure they're nae use tae me," said the farmer, and tipped the lot onto the fire.

Tricky times ahead.

April 22, 1996

Time for farmers to rally round

WHATEVER HAS happened to contingency planning? I thought the excuse for all those big offices in Whitehall was that we needed to be ready for anything.

I have always believed there was a hidden army who worked incessantly on plans to cover every conceivable development in the affairs of the country. No matter what happens, they will have a carefully thought out contingency plan.

Maybe that was always kibosh. Maybe it's just that the Tories' cuts have reduced the civil service so that no contingency can be planned-for. Whatever, the BSE shambles has fairly shown them up.

They have managed the crisis like a squad of little Dutch boys running around sticking their fingers in the holes in the dyke. It is clear they did not plan even for the contingency that evidence would emerge scaring everyone into believing they would get brain disease if they ate beef.

It was always certain the 1995 scare would recur unless and until BSE was eradicated.

Now we all know that you are less likely to get CJD (Creutzfeld-Jakob Disease) from cows infected by BSE (Bovine Spongiform Encephalopathy) than you are to be hit by an RSJ (Reinforced Steel Joist) falling off a building, but it is at least possible that such a link might be established and be strong enough to merit action. You would think the government would have a contingency plan. You'd be wrong, apparently. Isn't it appalling?

In the meanwhile where are we? Don't try to find out from 'the meja'. They haven't a clue. They don't know the difference between the market for cow beef and steer beef. Nor do they know how the dairy herd relates to the beef herd. And the difference between taking the old cows out of the food chain and culling are just a mystery.

I take a paper which told me in three different articles three different compensation levels for old cows.

In the meantime the little farm on the hill is decidedly overstocked. I should have sold 41 stores and a few old bangers. If you say it quick that's maybe not a lot, but counting the feed they're eating, that's £30,000.

And how long will it be before I can cash them? No one knows, but anyone who believes the government (the same lot who told us the export ban would be overturned that first Monday) is in a small minority. It will be at least another month before they can get their cash rolling and, when they do start to kill the old cows, it will be months before they catch up. After all, the queue for the slaughterhouse is growing at something like 30,000 a week.

So how is The Farmer to finance this backlog?

Well, I heard that the banks were to be sympathetic so I contacted the outfit who showed such faith in me in the bad old days that they lent me £1000 an acre on Little Ardo and made my life a misery. I spoke to a very nice young man who would once have been a bank manager but who is now a 'business banker'.

Did the sympathetic approach mean there would be interest free loans?

"Not as such."

So what did it mean?

It meant that the bank was keen for as much business as it could get and was willing to let me have the £30,000 at 2% above base. Instead of £75, because we farmers are having a hard time of it, the arrangement fee would be restricted to £40.

Well, I suppose it's better than a slap across the bare belly wi a cauld fish, as they say in Peterhead, but The Breadwinner has a better idea.

As our beef mountain queues, patiently chewing its way through our retirement fundie, The Breadwinner is operating a queue of her own.

She thinks it is very important that we farming folk stick together in this. As far as is possible, all bills to other farmers and to those in closely allied industries must be paid in full and with the usual delays only.

But all parasites – solicitors, kitchen salespersons, accountants, consultants and factors are offered Allan's choice. They either wait whistling for their money, or show their faith in our beef by accepting payment in kind – at pre-scare prices.

She's not joking, either.

The Breadwinner points to the precedent of Robert Paterson, the farmer from Turriff who made the front page of the London Times before the first world war.

Paterson's brave stand was against the imposition of employers' contributions to their workers' insurance, but the principle was similar.

If the government wanted money from the industry it was threatening it could take it in the threatened currency. Robert Paterson's famous Turra Coo was poinded and put up for sale against his debt for his employees insurance of £3.19s.

April 29, 1996

Carry-out saves sportsmen's day

IT HAS been an interesting week. I have cured a cow of foul-of-the-foot using an ancient Oriental practice and I have come to grips with a new concept in farming: I have been trying to buy 'paper acres'.

But I must tell you first about the boys' weekend.

Some cousins of mine by marriage have been diversifying to such an extent that they now have a clay pigeon shooting venture and a little loch near Dundee teaming with trout and surrounded by chalets.

The challenge is to fish the loch, stay in the chalets and still be able to shoot clay pigeons the next morning.

Mossie accepted the challenge. At the head of the A team, he set out to make a weekend of it. Or to put it the way the tax man is going to hear about it, for an agricultural study tour.

It was quite an itinerary, starting at 6.30 hours at the Salmon Inn with beef sausage rolls and gin.

The two-hour drive saw them comfortably down in the fat lands of Angus in time for the 11 o'clock start.

Ignoring the loch, the lads made eagerly for the clubhouse only to discover the horrible truth – there was no bar.

"Nae bar?"

"Oh that's all right lads. We've bought in some drink for you. It's over there."

"Faur?" they chorused, not able to believe the dozen cans of lager could possibly be it.

The Red Rooster explained. "We had been hoping for a ginny after our journey."

"No problem," said the willing host and soon reappeared from his house with most of a half bottle of Mr Gilbey's finest."

This was an emergency. The captain took charge.

"Right lads, kitty," he said, and a £10 levy produced a gallon of gin and smaller quantities of whisky, vodka and even some mixers.

So the sportsmen warmed up for a day on the loch.

As you can imagine it was a memorable day for those who could remember it.

The main event was a competition to see who could catch the biggest fish. The usual way is to award the prize to the most prolific fisherman, but that was thought to be unfair. After all, anybody could get lucky.

Some fine trout were caught, up to 9lb. It looked as though that would be the winner until Nicol from Keith, unlucky thus far, roared to the ghillie. "Oh Wullie, Wullie. I think I've got a bite."

And so he had, sort of.

The rod was bent double as he strained and lurched like a

man who had had more gin than porridge for his breakfast.

"Canny lad," said Willie, "dinna pull sae hard or you'll brak the rod. Oh my God! I've never seen a thing like this."

And neither he had. Not in a fresh water loch anyway. It was a regular Jaws Four with a huge head and weighed in at 15lb.

It would have been a good enough joke anyway, but Willie the Ghillie was so excited by the discovery of this new freshwater species that he failed to notice it was gutted.

Nicol from Keith had bought a catfish from the Red Rooster's girlfriend's fish shop and sneaked it along disguised as a cairry-oot.

Many years ago I shocked my neighbours at a roup by taking some grass at £90 an acre. But that was in the days before paper acres.

Those arise from attempts to do for the red meat industry what setaside aims to do for combinable crops – produce a shortage. They keep increasing the acreage needed to claim subsidies on cattle and sheep.

According to the man who comes to help me fill in the dreaded forms, unless I find 14 more acres I must forego £1400 worth of subs on my beefers. Any acres will do.

I have no desire to keep more cattle. All I want is to preserve the support a generous government gave me last year.

What about the village football pitch? Or the north side of Bennachie? Perfect, but not on the market.

So it was that I landed at a grass roup last week willing to pay £100 an acre for the paper value alone.

Sadly, everyone else wants paper acres, too. The best fields were snapped up by a dairy lady at £162. Then the beef men got ready to do battle for some mossie hill. It made £172 an acre and I'm still looking.

You will have heard of that Oriental system of medicine where the doctor takes away your symptoms. You are cured and he then cures himself. Well, I did it on Wednesday for a cow with foul-of-the-foot.

She has quite the smallest calf but huge teats and the calf doesn't recognise them. It does lap after lap of the cow, ignoring the four milk bottles.

I have intervened. But sadly my temper is not what it once was. On Wednesday, as this calf did lap after lap, the cow kicked at me again. I lost the rag and kicked her back, just as she was having yet another kick at me.

I was neither brave nor understanding about the pain and the upshot is that the cow's foul-of-the-foot has gone. All I have to do now is cure my own big toe.

Shambles of the incinerator grows

I AM writing this on May Day. That great socialist festival was to have had special significance for the Scottish farmers. This was the day when the first positive action was to be taken by the Doon Major to deal with the beef crisis.

Today is the day when, we were told, we would be able to deliver our farrow cows, those whose working life is over, to the markets or slaughterhouses from which the government would dispose of them and make us suitable recompense.

The Farmer was looking forward to this day. He has decided that the government is incapable of sorting the shambles out. They think it will be over the next time they get a chance to talk some sense into the Europeans.

Remember, Mr Hogg was going to have the ban lifted five weeks ago.

So last Friday The Farmer sold his heifer calves in a difficult market at Thainstone. They made £61 a head less than their sisters did last year. This Friday he is to sell his bull calves and if they're down only £61 he'll be satisfied. Cash is best when you're being run by a Doon Major.

So I was on the phone at the crack of nine o'clock to Thainstone where I was to deliver my old cows. I couldn't believe the response. The shambles goes on.

Thainstone had not been told they can start taking in cattle. All they can do is put me on the list of names of farmers from whom they will take cattle if they ever get the go-ahead.

I put four cattle down on the list. There is the fat Charolais cow who has only two teats and whose calf has been fostered onto a better prospect.

There is the cow who produced a mummified calf. There is a great big fat Simmental which turned out yeld, and an old Friesian. I fear the old Friesian may be dead before she gets to the head of the queue.

The mart say they are referring people to the Department so I ask them how soon I can deliver my old bangers.

Surely the arrangements are far advanced? Wrong again. The Department have yet to look into the Thainstone application to become a collecting centre and report to the Intervention Board.

They haven't even decided whether to recommend Thainstone as a centre. It is just as well they didn't stick to Monday as their supposed starting date.

I phone the Intervention Board. They say some centres in England have started receiving cattle. They have a list of 104 places dealing with slaughter cattle and Thainstone isn't even on it.

In fact now that she checks, there are no Scottish centres listed. "I'll have to check that."

Douglas Hogg, I am told, has just been on the tele. The scheme will open tomorrow. But haven't I just been told it's already started in England?

I phone the mart. They have at last been told that they are to be a collecting centre but they have no idea when they will be able to start.

There are more than a hundred people before me on the list. I have said I want to kill my most desperate four but one man has 60 to kill and most haven't said how many.

There is no chance of the old Friesian living as long as it will take.

The Farmer is depressed.

May 13, 1996

The steers take a pasting

THE BSE scare has cost the tenant of the little farm on the hill £3500 – so far. The steers took their expected pasting at Thainstone on Friday, down £61 a head on the year. That gives a loss over last year's calves of £2600 and extra feed has cost in the region of £900.

That's the good news.

It has been so cold that the grass has disappeared before it has got going. Round and round the fields and the braes go the cattle searching ceaselessly lest they have overlooked a blade or even a buttercup. A cow which had the sense to stand still or lie down and give the stuff a chance would be a pearl without price in a season like this.

The cull has started, at last.

On Saturday those of us who had the foresight to book

in our old cows took part in an exciting lottery. Some would get their cattle disposed of in return for much wanted cash and the others would be allowed a free entry into next week's draw.

The only good news there is Mossie wasn't lucky either.

That wasn't really surprising. The odds are about as bad as in the National Lottery. I have this nightmare where the Chief Executive of the Mart appears at the door of a great celestial float and points a finger at me saying, "This week it might be yoooo."

The latest figures are that they disposed of 600 cattle in the first week and there are getting on for 6,000 in the queue. And anybody who thinks he likes the odds needn't bother

entering his beasts. They are not taking any more into the ballot till they have killed those booked in already.

At the initial rate of disposal that could be ten weeks.

One thing I am happy about is the fact that it is dawning on everyone, even the Doon Major and Hogg-of-the-Hat, that the beef crisis will not be over just as soon as they can give these chappies in Brussels a good earful.

The Farmer and his pals have been keeping quiet about it for fear of being thought to rock the farming boat, but we've been clear from the start that this is going to be a long haul.

Now we've had that confirmed. The co-op which we've formed to help us get our books in on time and maximise our IACS, had a very well-informed speaker at last week's annual meeting.

Mike Dempsey is a farmer and journalist from Eire. He knows all about the EC and sees it from a European, or at least non-British, perspective. He runs his own farmers' magazine and spends a lot of time in Brussels.

Mr Dempsey told us that it will be at least six months before British beef is allowed back into Germany, Holland and Italy. Two years is more likely and, depending on how fast BSE disappears and how slowly CJD grows, it could be five years or forever.

There is more and it is worse.

The Doon Major's anxiety to get the ban removed is play acting. The ordinary people are scared of British beef. They're not going to buy it. Dempsey was in Germany when a professor told a cowering TV audience that there were serious doubts about whether it was now safe to import British medical products for fear of contamination by CJD.

And Dempsey was impressive on the depth of misunderstanding of the situation by the Doon Major and his helpers.

They see this as an unwarranted exclusion of British beef by hysterical and non-scientific Eurocrats. But the Europeans see it the other way round. The ban is a natural step to quell the hysteria caused by the over-the-top reaction of British ministers.

"How can they expect us to accept that their beef is safe when on the 20th of March they told us it was the likely cause of CJD?"

Fear of beef has ruined the European markets. By far the best place to sell beef is Britain, where demand has recovered quite well. Instead of worrying about being allowed to sell to Europe the government should turn their attention to an opposite threat. There is no chance of selling much British beef on the continent today. The British market is likely to be hit by a flood of European imports from countries whose domestic markets have been ruined by the British behaviour over BSE.

"It would be difficult to overestimate the resentment there is in Europe at the way the United Kingdom has handled the crisis," he told us.

We believed him, especially when he surprised us again. For all the money spent by the Irish on trying to establish an identity of their own, the Irish have been tarred with the British brush.

The Irish markets for beef have disappeared along with

the British, never mind any bans.

Their biggest single market was Egypt and CNN news beamed the whole British story right into Egypt and the trade stopped dead. The Egyptians feel the Irish are too close to Britain for comfort and though there was no ban on Irish beef, they just didn't want it.

So why do we watch the news all night every night – at six, at seven on Channel four, at nine on the BBC and ten on ITV, and then Newsnight – just in case there have been developments, in case the ban has been lifted?

According to Dempsey, only the British government thinks that is the point.

May 20, 1996

Farming for the incinerator

SUMMER HAS come at last. We have had a warm day. The grass is growing. The 42 calves are enjoying their freedom and the cows are enjoying the grass.

The Farmer is enjoying having the good Lord feed the cattle.

And yet there is something wrong. We cannot put BSE behind us although we have only ever seen it on television. Perhaps there has only been the one case – the one the BBC shows us day after day, staggering around that disgraceful midden of a farm.

Where do the programme makers get all those dirty farmyards? They must scour the country to find one bad enough.

Perhaps Bojuniak's nightmare is prophetic; some boffin in Brussels discovers that 500 people per year die falling downstairs.

That is 40 times the number with the new form of CJD which may have come from cattle, so it is clearly unacceptable. Something has to be done to stop this loss of life.

It has been decreed that upstairs is banned. All right, it will put 5p on the standard rate of income tax to do away with all the upper floors or install lifts, but the nation's health demands it.

Where The Farmer feels the crisis most is not in his pocket. The worst bit is the futility of feeding cattle for the incinerator.

We are used to feeding cattle for people. Some of our customers are old enough or have travelled far enough to know that food can be in short supply. It can be a virtue to produce beef for the plate. A man can take pride in that.

But here we are with the best of bullocks, fattening them for the incinerator.

One of the troubles with the beef market in recent years has been the cramming of beasts with barley to get them fat at little more than a year old. They taste twice as good after two seasons on the grass. And here we are with bullocks getting a third year at grass but it is illegal to eat them. We are still feeding them up because we get paid per kilo, but no one will eat the meat.

Mossie doesn't mind, of course. His mind is like a balance sheet with a sense of humour. He is delighted.

He's got a court full of old cows eating potatoes and dripping with fat. So far in eight weeks they have eaten more than four tonnes each at as little as £10 a tonne and Mossie's in no hurry to get them away to the incinerator. He'll gladly pour another tonne of tatties into each of them. As long as they put on more than 12 kilos more fat, he'll make money at it.

The Farmer has some on the same deal, but he doesn't like it, and it's not because his potatoes cost an outrageous £12. It just seems so futile.

The most futile deal of all is

REMEMBER MA DEARS WE GET PAID BY THE KILO, SO EAT UP YIR TATTIES!

A MIND LIKE A BALANCE SHEET

Turnbull.

my old Friesian cow, the one which had mastitis and the dead twins. She is such a rickle of bones that she would never have been worth much, even in the good old days when any old rubbish went for pies. But with 86p a kilo on offer at the incinerator she is worth a course of treatment by a team of vets.

If you're in the rat race you've got to run, so I patiently await my turn in the queue for the incinerator. On Wednesday I phoned to find out how they were getting on working their way through the 6000 or so cattle on the first ballot.

They took 600 the first week but on the second week they are down to 480 because the renderers cannot cope.

And where am I in the queue? "Well, there's six pages of names and you're on the third page."

It is just as well the grass is growing.

Mind you there is some good news. The Breadwinner and I are away to Prague for a week.

Potions is getting another chance to look after the place. He may as well get used to the job, and though he doesn't realise it yet the reward may be as much as he ever gets.

A few things had been worrying me about leaving a ship's engineer in charge.

I had a bull, sold for 'an undisclosed four-figure sum' to be loaded for export. He's going to Orkney, to Jim Davidson on Papa Westray. I had a cow with about six inches of hem showing ready to calve and feared she'd let her calf bed down. I had a small heifer coming to the calving. A tenant of one of the cottages had called the sanitary rather than remind me that his septic tank was no longer septic and was overflowing. And the flag leaves were peeping everywhere on the barley.

I got it all done on Tuesday.

I got off my mark in the morning and got a load sprayed before coffee time. When the sprayer was filling, I switched to the tanker and emptied the offending sewer. I was back on duty just as the sprayer was starting to run over.

The Breadwinner had a message that if I could get my bull to Thainstone by eight o'clock they'd take it on Wednesday. So we loaded the horsebox.

When I came home, the cow with the slack womb had calved a super bull calf without incident.

At half-past twelve the heifer had also produced a fine bull calf, although not without incident. She stuck for half an hour at the hurdies and only let go when I turned the calf with a lot of sweat and an iron bar.

Not the way to sell our beef

THE HOLIDAY in Prague was a good idea. A whole week among people who are so poor they can't afford to buy our beef anyway and were too busy coping with capitalism to worry about the chance of getting a disease that affects every millionth person, would be a change and a rest.

But it was spoiled for us the moment we entered the plane to come home.

The waitress offered a copy of the Daily Depression. The front page was half covered by one word. "Disaaaster!" Britain was going to war on Europe. If the Europeans didn't start eating our beef again, and smartly, the Doon Major was going to disrupt the entire working of the European Community.

Sensitive and careful readers of this column will have guessed that I have never been a great admirer of the government's handling of the beef crisis. But standing on the steps of an aircraft on the other side of Europe did heighten the impression that our government had no idea what the crisis was about. They don't seem to be able to see it as a European problem.

Demand for beef has slumped all over Europe because, without much reason, consumers fear it. One of the key markets is Germany and there they fear British beef so much that half as much beef is being eaten as formerly, in case any of it should come from Britain. They can't even eat all the beef being produced by German farmers so they don't need any from Britain.

If the ban were lifted tomorrow and one load of British beef went to Germany, it would kill the demand altogether.

So how would that help us sell our beef? It wouldn't.

Talk about taking a waterlogged horse to the trough and expecting him to drink. And yet Herr Gruppenfuhrer Major is screaming at the Germans, "Ve haff veys off making you eat ze scientifically safe British beef."

Please don't think I'm saying that Hogg and Major's policy is futile. It is much worse than that. If the British beef were to be let loose in Germany the German farmers would lose their markets at home and would have to look elsewhere to sell their product.

Only one beef market in the EC has held up and that is the British. Open the trade before you have satisfied the public on safety and we'll have a flood of foreign beef here.

I don't think that would help us.

What the well-travelled Farmer thinks is that we should leave the Gerries to their own market and go as hard as we can for the British one. In time, confidence will return and it has been shown that there is one way that really enhances that. When the supermarkets halved the price of beef, sales leapt.

The government could boost sales if, instead of wasting a fortune jumping through what it believes are unnecessary hoops and incinerating our best beef, it would return to the old deficiency payments system of agricultural support. Let beef find its own level in the market and make up the farmers' incomes by a direct subsidy.

That was the basis of the cheap food policy that lasted until we joined the common market. It served us well and it is desperately needed now. The mechanism is there in the form of the beef special premium. Just put back the word "Variable".

It was very depressing to be coming back into the EC and to find that, far from beginning to see that the beef problem is a European one, our great leaders and wise teachers are still ex-

189

pecting our European partners to see it as a British problem.

Our partners are baffled and so am I.

But it was a good holiday.

Usually my holidays are spoiled by TA syndrome. (T stands for tight).

Normally, when I am within reach of a shop, a bar or an auction ring, I am a free spender. I would rather buy the first few lots into the ring than hang about all day hoping that the price will fall. I'd rather go to the village shop for my Glenmorangie than wait until the next time I'm near the big superstore that takes a pound off. Rather than get change for the phone call I'd put in a pound and hope The Breadwinner wasn't watching.

But that is when I'm at home. In foreign parts the TA syndrome takes hold.

The Farmer is terrified that he will pay more than 'the right price' for anything. He is afraid he will be done. Being done by Scots is one thing but when he is away foreign The Farmer worries constantly about the price of everything.

No matter how fine the weather, he will always take his coffee standing up inside the cafe because he knows it can be five times as dear sitting out in the Mediterranean sunshine watching the world go by.

Worse still, he may go without coffee because if he waits till he is back in the hotel bedroom he can make himself a cup of tea with no milk.

Well, this time The Breadwinner banned the TA syndrome and it made the holiday. We had beer in the sunshine in the medieval Old Town Square in Prague for ten times what it cost in the wee pub round the corner from the Hotel. When the cheap seats at the opera were gone we just went for the dear ones. Rather than wait in a gathering rage for the courtesy bus to the hotel, we took a taxi.

It made the holiday and made no difference to the overall cost. When it costs you £1000 to get there and beer is 25p a pint, how could it?

Waldie meets his Waterloo

I WANT to tell you about my boyhood pal Waldie because he is one of those who has lost a small fortune by selling his old cows to a dealer rather than marketing them himself.

Waldie got his name (which in our doric means wellington boot) because he was so much smaller than the next youngest in his family of seven.

As was common in such families in rural Aberdeenshire at the tail end of the war, children's clothes only fitted briefly and by coincidence, as they were all hand-me-downs. As often happens with the last of a family, Waldie was much the youngest, by almost three years, and none too well grown, so he was often swamped by his clothes.

And never more so than when the brother two up from him got a new pair of boots to go to secondary school. His old ones were available sooner than expected for the one above Waldie, and Waldie fell heir to the wellingtons which his older brother didn't even fit yet.

He was a memorable sight.

We used to say that Waldie could float across the river Ythan in those boots if only he could keep his balance. They came up past his knees, which caused great distress and inflammation on the backs of his legs until the tops were turned down for him.

They were hopelessly cumbersome, but Waldie never complained. Gamely he struggled on half a lap behind the rest of us, he lugged them up trees and all over the farm in our games of heist-the-green-flag and kick-the-cannie. Waldie had to be goalie because he was so slow in the great boots.

Perhaps his waldies were character-building, but Waldie did well. He served his time as a mechanic and moved to the North of England where, by hard work as a loan shark and property developer in his spare time, he ended up with one of the biggest and best car dealerships in the country.

But Waldie couldn't forget his roots and that led him into spending some of his cash on cattle. He used the magpie system of selection and ended up

with a rather expensive herd of Simmental, Welsh Blacks, Highlanders and Blondes d'Aquitaine. Like 90% of the rest of us in cattle he never made a penny and grumbled a lot, but didn't really mind.

However BSE has sickened him. He rang the other day to say he was selling. At least he was getting a decent price from the government to cull them.

But here's the rub. I asked how he was managing to get them killed. I still haven't got any of mine away. Waldie was delighted to tell me that he had a very good dealer friend who was taking them away and paying him the full liveweight price and that that was a lot because his cows were so fat.

I knew he wouldn't like it

but I had to tell Waldie that this person might be a good dealer but he was not a good friend. The government have offered us 86p a kilo liveweight or 172 pence a kilo for the carcase.

With skinny old bangers from Holstein dominated dairies, for Jerseys or for cows which have been ill, the 86 pence is the one to go for. But with anything that kills out at more than 50% you are better off with the carcase weight. Waldie's pampered beef cows would have killed out at 60% under any system, but for some reason the cull cows are being treated in such a way that more of the carcase is left than if they were going to the food trade. The incinerator seems to like the kidney knob left in, for example, so Waldie's cattle might have killed out at 65%.

I explained it to Waldie using the example of a 600 kilo cow. His dealer friend would give him £516 for the liveweight. But at 60% that would give him 360 kilos deadweight at 172p. or £619. If it killed out at 65% he would have grossed £670.

The phone went quiet as it sunk in that the friendly neighbourhood dealer had done Waldie out of something over £100 a head.

I think he may have had a visit from some of the boys.

Meantime I can report that the culling of the old cows, while still a shambles, can work.

Sadly, it is not me who has achieved success in the ballot but Mossie. He has got a load of the old bangers he bought between the Christmas and March

BSE scares. He won't tell me what they cost but it seems to have worked out well. He claims he put away the worst of them and that they averaged £640. He has been saved by the culling programme.

Reading between the lines he has raised them at least £250 a head, mostly on potatoes. And our man is bewildered. "It's the first time in my life I ever made money out of cattle," he says. "I tellt ye tricky times were times of opportunity."

The Red Rooster has also got the first draw of his last year's bull calves away fat. He had to send them to Somerset to get them killed at all and they were down an average of £184 a head on last year. He's got 100 cows, so count it yourself.

With that and his main business being potatoes at £10 a tonne it is no wonder the shock of red is turning to russet.

June 10, 1996

Wasting Asset to wed

AT LAST the little farm on the hill has reached the top of the culling list.

I got the glad tiding on Thursday and on Monday we

got a load off to Thainstone market. The one skinny old Friesian was weighed with a view to earning me 86p a kilo and the rest made for Edinburgh for 172p per kilo deadweight. No doubt it will be minus a few quid for this and that.

I can tell you that it was a great relief to be putting up the taildoor and seeing the float off.

All this life I have been proud of the fact that my family fed the people. We made two blades of grass grow where only one had grown before. We have made hens convert feed into food in a ratio of 3 to 2 whereas it was once 4 to 1. We grow 20 tonnes of potatoes to the acre where our forefathers grew 4 tonnes in a good year.

When we went into the common market we produced so much food as to be an embarrassment and cause food mountains to grow where hunger had been.

That led to setaside which many of us saw as an affront to the toil of our ancestors. I often feel the weight of their disapproving eyes upon me as I look at the 22 acres of weeds which this year grow on Little Ardo's biggest park.

But that negation of our farming heritage is nothing to the humiliation that BSE has heaped upon us.

Those who once fed the starving are now looking at their heifers to see if there are any hard teeth up yet and hanging onto steers to try to get them to 30 months old. They are not selling them when the beef is best because the best market is to wait until they are 'too old for human consumption'.

That is desperate.

Do you remember the eggs scare? The market disappeared and yet the hens couldn't be stopped from laying.

That was a nightmare and the beef job has been the same. In the course of this scare I have had 44 live calves born. Soon it would have been standing room only at Little Ardo.

So you see I was very glad to see that load roaring up the dusty road on Monday.

It is with a due sense of shame that I turn to my second success of the week.

You will recall that I took this Cadillac off an old friend who had a cash flow problem. With The Farmer's great knowledge of the second-hand market in American cars, he was sure he could give what the dealer was offering and make a profit for the needy friend.

Six months of tax and insurance at 15 miles to the gallon, a new roof seal, brake linings and a paint touch-up later, she is away.

I was worming cows and dishorning calves when the phone call came and I was so excited that I ran up to the house and left the gate open. Naturally the cows followed me. When I had got them out of the barley and out of the rape I

194

wondered what I was good at. That was no advert for my farming and I had dropped 25% in my efforts as a car dealer.

I was glad when the Caddy left for the Derbyshire Downs. "BSE latest: Desperate Farmer forced to sell Cadillac."

Getting rid of the old bangers, bovine and automotive, was good but nothing to the news from the Wasting Asset. He has managed to get a talented, house-proud, sensible girl to agree to marriage.

That might seem unsurprising. He is very good-looking, has a smile that would get the birds down from the trees and certainly attracts them from everywhere else. He has natural good manners and good humour. He has also written a best-selling book described by the New York Times as "by far the best on the subject". The trouble is the subject is soccer hooliganism and the Wasting Asset did some pretty hair-raising research for it.

His curriculum vitae includes: roughneck, nightclub manager in Tenerife, roustabout, nightclub owner and general bon viveur.

He also got the sack from The Farmer over his interpretation of the word 'morning'.

With that history we feared he'd settle for a pretty emptyhead. The extraordinary thing is that my future daughter-in-law is all those good things and is beautiful into the bargain.

Best of all, the Wasting Asset's Investment brings with her two Dividends. The Farmer has two more granddaughters. The netball team now has a reserve.

195

Spring brings plenty

SUDDENLY AND at last, there is plenty for everyone. The grass, which had a sore job keeping up with the mouths, has got away despite the arrival of 45 new calves.

It's not just the cattle that have plenty. The housemartins, always last back in summertime, are chasing the midges around the close as I write.

The birds are fattening up and fattening their little ones. That is good news for the cat.

She has had yet another litter of kittens. The two she had last time died, probably because she wasn't fit to feed them. This time there are four and she takes the scraps from the house but must provide a constant supply of other meats as well. We'd prefer her to stick to rats and mice but why should she when the world is full of young blackbirds and chaffinches?

At the backdoor today there are the remains of a mistle thrush and a jackdaw. The kittens are doing well.

Yes, Nature's bounty is here for all to see. Things even look well for The Farmer.

The rape is in full flower and has had all its treatment. It is just waiting for the swather.

The grain has one or two small holes where the crop has drowned and there are a couple of mysterious thin bits which look like they may have a chemical origin. But the average looks better than I have seen it.

Mossie, from whom The Farmer takes all advice without question, says he likes to be able to throw his bonnet into the crop. If the hat stays on top he is pleased. If it slips out of sight the barley is too thin or weak.

My previous crops adviser had a philosophy which made sense to me. "Sow it right and keep it right," was what he used to tell me. I tried, without much skill or luck.

Mossie's idea is different. "Sow it right but put your crop under stress," he says. "Just when it thinks it is at its auntie's you give it a whack on the head with your sprayer. What happens when you get a whack on the head? You duck, don't you? When you clatter your crop with your sprayer it ducks and spreads out, putting down new roots and cautiously sticking up more stronger and shorter shoots. Keep surprising it or you might have to be content with three tonnes to the acre."

That would never do, or at least we'd never admit it.

I've tried my big Kilmarnock bonnet on the better bits and no matter how hard I throw it it skims along and comes to rest in full view.

The sad thing about these grand crops, and the fine cattle munching away on the grass, is that (with the help of contractors) I have done it all myself. The little farm that used to give a good living to six families and was a kingdom for one farmer, is just a part-time job for me.

And I want to tell you a fine story sent in by someone who signs himself 'A Moray Loon'. It is one of many from the days

when hard work was the supreme virtue on the land and the enforcement of hard work on those who were virtuous only reluctantly, was the purpose of the farm grieve.

Old Mac is the hero. He was grieve at Seapark of Kinloss for many years. Now the Seapark fields march with the railway and it was on such a field that Old Mac faced his first day with a new squad, freshly fee-ed at the May term. First days were important.

They were to be hyowin neeps, or hoeing turnips, depending on where you come from, on a field beside the line.

There was a set pattern to such things. The foreman started first and was expected to set a good pace but one which good men could match without skimping the job. The second horseman would be next, then

197

the third. After the horsemen came the orramen, any cattlemen not involved with their beasts and the grieve took up the rear. If there was a haflin or a loon, he would start last and would soon be half a lap behind.

Strung out across the drills at a forty-five degree angle, the line moved slowly up and down for much of June on the stock farms of Aberdeenshire, when I was a boy.

Beal, the foreman, made as though to start beside the gate but, to the mild surprise of everyone, Old Mac, said, "Na Beal, we'll start at the other side."

And when Beal was about to set off from beside the railway the grieve again stopped him, "Hudd on a minute."

As the squad stood there wondering, a train appeared round the slight bend where the line is crossed by the Forres to Kinloss road.

Old Mac took the pipe from his mouth and said very deliberately – with menace even – "Here's a train. Tak a damned good look at it. This is as near as ye'll get to it and they're aa much the same."

Those were the days – so full of care there was no time to stand and stare. Once maybe, but not at every train if the grieve was looking.

June 24, 1996

His Lordship put in his place

THEY'VE BEEN at it again. They've been telling farmers to diversify. Maybe it is a good idea, but they needn't expect us to like it. When the dentists say they need more money, does the minister of health tell them to diversify? When Doctors want a rise are they told to do a little double glazing?

No. It is just farmers.

I am grateful to Allan Wright, of Farmer's Weekly, for the story of the farmer from Argyll who put Lord Lindsay right on this matter. He told the noble Lord he had nothing to teach farmers about diversifying. They had been doing it for years; marrying teachers, doctors and nurses.

So true. I don't know if I would have managed without the efforts of The Breadwinner.

As soon as she realised what a rocky business we had got into she started teaching at Turriff Academy. The job was made far worse by the fact that she had half an hour in the car each way, with the two Investments and the two Wasting Assets fighting hammer and tongues.

Not many can manage without a Breadwinner these days. But Big Hamish is proud that his wife 'doesn't have to work', unlike every one of his 35 neighbouring farmers' wives. All Big Hamish's wife has to do is look after the house, the kids, the farm books, the books of his contracting and ready-mix concrete business and milk cows on the baillie's day off. It makes you wonder how she fills her time.

So Lord Lindsay and his ilk annoy us when they say we should diversify. It is a huge kick in the teeth for the only industry which is truly necessary for human life.

It is wise of those who can to diversify. But politicians should be aware of our feelings. They would show understanding if they shook their heads gravely as they said, "I fear you'll have to go part-time."

Because that is what they mean. A pig farmer diversifies when he starts a herd of cows. When a farmer installs car parks, toilets and a restaurant and cuts his fields up into little paddocks with various species in them he is not diversifying his farming. He is going part-time. His zoo takes him into the entertainment industry.

The agriculture minister should hang his head rather than suggesting diversification as though he was offering us a new Jerusalem.

I didn't get to the Highland Show after all. On Friday we had to bury that grand old man, my uncle, Sir Maitland Mackie. We planted him in the church-yard of Daviot where we had gathered 36 years earlier to bury his wife Isobel, who had been a schoolteacher. His gravestone overlooks Wester-town where his son and grand-son, both Maitlands, now farm the land he once farmed with his father, Dr Maitland Mackie. It was a moving occasion. It is a stirring example of that to which every true peasant aspires – continuity on his land.

Whereas few people could name their Lord Lieutenant now, every Aberdonian knew his when Mike Mackie was the Queen's representative here. Such was his popularity and sense of duty that he was in the paper every day, often more than once, opening new buildings, planting commemorative trees and welcoming visiting investors, dignitaries or royalty. As well as everything else, Mike was ubiquitous.

Charlemagne is off to Orkney

THE ARDO herd is back in the business of providing beef breeding bulls. For the first time in ten years The Farmer sold a bull for export this spring.

There was a time when it was our main business. Indeed we were the among the first importers of seven breeds of cattle from Europe whose main function was to provide calves for export to the new world.

When the export boom subsided it became apparent that to survive in the pedigree cattle business you had either to be a lot cleverer than me or a lot crookeder. As there was nothing much I could do about the former gift and as I hadn't the bottle for the second vice, the Ardo herd went commercial when we came back from Kenya in 1989. Since then my bulls have been grown for their beef and their subsidies rather than their genes.

For all that, I have kept up some pedigrees. So when an old client phoned needing a bull I was able to help. Jim Davidson bought cattle from me when they were scarce and

dear, so I could surely oblige when, thanks to Mr Dorrell, you can hardly give them away.

Jim's requirements were simple. He wanted a damned good bull, ready to work on the first of June and "No too dear, ye ken."

I had just the thing. I had a well bred pure calf among my barley beefers. He would be 13 months old on the first of June.

I did my best not to oversell the bull. I pointed out that he had had no fancy feed, just plenty of barley like the rest. I thought he'd manage the cows but wanted my buyer to take the risk. "He's not that big."

Jim wanted him anyway so we called him Charlemagne and off he went to Orkney as his siblings went to the store sale at Thainstone. I don't suppose he had any idea how lucky he was to be taking the boat.

Now, Orkney is no different from any other farming place. Your neighbours take a great, and not altogether friendly, interest in your affairs. The arrival of a new bull is a moment of some importance. All the neighbours want to see if there is a fault to be found with the new purchase ... after all, the bull is half the herd.

So Jim had prepared for the worst. He told the neighbours the bull was only eight months old and that he hadn't had any feeding. It was nearly true. He'd just left out the word 'fancy'.

He need not have worried. Charlemagne was the biggest in the pen and, by the time he left Little Ardo, I knew that the next biggest was 535 kilos. When Jim's new bull got off the boat at Orkney we can be sure he was not less than 11cwt. He must have been a sore disappointment to the neighbours. The only comment to reach my ears was: "That's a calf has so been fed."

Anyway, my buyer is delighted. And by the end of Charlemagne's first day on Orkney, a big black cow was delighted too.

I enjoyed my day at the top end of the beef market. But my big news today is from the opposite end. I refer to the old cows which once went to make hamburgers, sausages and mince but which nowadays are deemed too low even for that. We have now been paid for the old cows which we disposed of under the government's slaughter programme.

All right, if it hadn't been for BSE, I've no doubt I would

have got more for my farrow cows, but in the circumstances, I think it would be churlish to bite the taxpayers' hand over this. Our deadweight cows averaged £528 a head. That doesn't seem too bad for the old dears which didn't owe me anything anyway.

But what about the cows we bought in the farrow cow ring with a view to taking a calf and then putting back to the sale?

There were three in that category. A coloured Charolais cow was bought in February for £555. She had a heifer calf which went to a cow that lost her calf. She realised £534

There was an old Friesian which cost £385 and had two dead bull calves. She made £468 liveweight. That was so nearly a success. But it would have been bad had it not been for the incinerator. She would not have made good pies.

And finally there was a black Hereford which was bought for £395. She turned out not in calf and sold for £494 after deductions.

That hardly looks like a triumph for The Farmer. There is no evidence there that buying farrow cows for the calf they might have inside them is the way forward. After all, to those figures have to be added two floater's bills and a small mountain of potatoes.

But the figures are better than they seem. All the remaining cows have calves at foot. I have to keep them until they have done their mothering bit before I can find out if I've got it right. And the snag is that by then they'll be heavy with their next calf.

I couldn't see how those cows got to the farrow cow ring when they were in calf. I see now.

July 8, 1996

Bargains shift beef

MOSSIE AND I have been testing our theory that the way to shift beef is to reduce its price.

We were trying this view on The Butcher in the pub last month. He got quite excited about the accusation that butchers are trying too hard to keep prices up when the best policy would be to take a smaller margin to sell more beef, keep the market intact, and develop the beef-eating habit.

"It's amazin' how the wifies will forget BSE if they see a bargain. The supermarkets proved that when they slashed prices after March 20th," Mossie told The Butcher.

The Butcher was furious. "Right ye little *****," he challenged. "I'll sell ye sirloin roasts at £1 a pound. How mony do ye want?"

This was a windfall. Beef for less than the price of pork? This was the way forward. Times of opportunity had arrived. Mossie took four 20lb roasts and soon the beef was melting from The Butcher's store like snow off a dyke.

Now I wouldn't like to give the wrong impression. I wouldn't like to cause a riot at your local butcher's, so let me explain. The Butcher not only has a shop but a large wholesale business. He supplies the hotel trade which needs a lot of the top quality cuts to spoil for weddings and annual dinners. That trade leaves him with the sirloins from the less desirable end of the beasts. With those sirloins you have to take a covering of tougher meat which is really better stewed. The catering trade cannot cope at the front end of the sirloin, so that gives those who can a chance.

According to The Butcher, the beef was fully hung and ready for the rotisserie (Mossie's rotaspreader which is now a barbecue). But our man hung the beef for a full three weeks longer before inviting 25 of Aberdeenshire's finest to a day's mayhem among the clay pigeons, pink gin and 40lb of sirloin roast at less than the price of mince.

There was a certain scepticism. "Is this some of your tough auld coos that should have gone to the incinerator?" roared Big Hamish, though it would make no difference to him, for he never takes time to chew anything.

It was absolutely wonderful. More than four weeks of hanging meant it was tasty and tender. A contented silence fell over the sportsmen as they tucked into their sirloin, daintily served in a bap. The chorus of praise was started by the Red Rooster who said in wonder, "You ken Mossie, the toughest thing about this is the bap."

Anyway, at the right price and with the right cooking the beef will go. We ate the pound and a half per head. On the following Sunday The Breadwinner and I had the family round to share a 20 pounder and effected a total clearance.

If the government would spend its money on a temporary return to the policy of cheap food instead of on burning the best of beef we'd preserve more of our industry and be the readier for the great day when we have eradicated BSE.

One part of the industry which has been devastated is the small family butcher. Three butchers within reach of here have closed in the last year and the town of Ellon, in the great beef producing Earldom of Buchan, doesn't have a single butcher's left. The small shops are the main hope for producing well-handled beef so it is serious.

But I have one success to report. Potions, who saved the butcher's shop in New Deer, has found a bright young man to take it over. He has great plans for it. He is willing to work all the hours it takes towards his dream of his own business and good meat, properly prepared. Everyone who believes in 'The Village' should wish him well.

I'm not so sure about the Doon Major, though. Now I find he is doing me out of a pension.

The Breadwinner and I are building ourselves the Death House just up the hill so the next generation can get on with it. This willingness to remove the tired old men standing between agriculture and progress would entitle us to a nice little nest egg if only we lived in one of the other European States.

A farmer giving up in his fifties can get a golden boot of up to £30,000 to encourage him to get out. Thank goodness we have the Doon Major to make sure we're not in that.

We still contribute to the scheme in other countries, but at least British farmers don't have to enjoy such shame.

Credit where due

THAT'S IT. Everything is tidied up. The last of the crop of 1995 is sold and we've done all we can for the crop of 1996. Now we have a couple of free weeks before harvest and the reckoning for another year.

When I was selling my bull calves on the Spring day I had to bring some home. The Breadwinner was adamant that I should not sell any at below £1 a kilo.

She didn't care if the market had fallen. If that was all I could get I wasn't to take it.

You can't argue with her when she's like that so half a dozen came home. I had been bid 98p and, while £10 a beast didn't seem worth getting steamed up about, I did quite enjoy saying to the buyers that this time they had offered too little – that I had my price and my pride.

For weeks after that it looked as though 98p a kilo wasn't that bad for the bottom end of my consignment. Then it started to look like great riches as the prices of young bulls plunged into the 80 pences.

However, I have been able to get them away at 171p a kilo deadweight, which should be worth over £1 liveweight because those young bulls do kill out well. And ten weeks on potatoes at £10 a tonne (delivered) has put a lot of weight onto them for small money.

The Breadwinner was right again. In fact I am thinking of finishing all my bull calves next year, depending on what the cheque for this lot looks like when it arrives.

I may even have the market to myself. This year, when bulls were much the weakest part of the trade, has put a lot of farmers off. It has been a bad year for testicles. Farmers, who for years left their calves entire to get the benefits of faster and leaner growth, have reached once more for the knife.

The signs are that harvest will be heavy and the prices good. The barley is going to be very heavy. I am sure that the best of our Pleasante is going to be as good as we have ever had. There will be four tonnes there in several fields.

The only question remaining is, can we get it out of the field in good order?

There are a couple of mysterious poor bits in one field . There are stripes which look as though the old sprayer has managed to spray some sort of weedkiller out of two or three jets only. It has to be chemical damage because it is so regular, but what, and how? Even Mossie is baffled.

The rape is such a hard crop to judge. It keeps letting you down when you think you have a bumper crop. When you think you have slipped up it will give you a most delightful surprise.

By that token I could be in for a good rape crop, for it doesn't look well to me.

Much of it is very weedy, for a start. I know why that is. I have abandoned my policy of spending half the winter trying to chase the pigeons off it. Last year we had one field stripped completely in March and yet in August it was only four days behind the rest and we could see no difference in the yield.

I suppose that may yet happen this year, but it doesn't look likely.

The trouble is that, by laying the brown earth open in the springtime, the pigeons let the weeds in. They are normally smothered by a lush rape crop but wild flowers can be a real pest if they get off first on the Spring day. I fear I may have to go back to a winter of hunting.

And finally, let me tell you about the farmer who lost his credit card.

It is refreshing, in this time of political correctness, to know that there is still life in the old male chauvinist piggery. It's not that The Farmer is a male chauvinist, you understand; financially dependent on The Breadwinner and surrounded by ten daughters, daughters-in-law and granddaughters, how could he be?

But The Farmer is a traditionalist. Just as it is with Victorian architecture or Highland cattle, it is good to preserve a little male chauvinism as a reminder of the past.

It's a serious business, losing your credit card. A thief can go on a spending spree and cost you a fortune. I once had a narrow escape from the bill for an ocean-going yacht. When we lived in Glasgow a conman adopted my identity. Luckily a smart salesman noticed this 'university lecturer' had difficulty producing joined-up writing and spelling his (my) name.

So, as soon as you know your card is away, you must report it ... usually.

But this farmer, (I can't name him because his wife can read) didn't bother to stop the card. It had been gone for some time before he noticed it and phoned the company immediately. But they were able to satisfy him that the thief wasn't buying as much with his plastic as the wife had been.

As Mossie says, "It's nae just the money ye save. It's the money ye dinna spend."

Death House needs a new name

THE FARMER has received an ultimatum. If he doesn't stop calling the retirement home 'The Death House' The Breadwinner will refuse to live in it. Worse than that, she will stop winning bread. Instead of going off to the toon to make a bit more for our retirement fundie she'll stay at home to see that I don't nick down to the Salmon Inn and spend any of it.

She means it. She's furious.

As usual her fury isn't entirely fair. After all, it is some months since I changed the name to 'Glowerindoon'.

But it is hard to put a genie back in a bottle. Glowerindoon wouldn't stick. Even the architect's plans were entitled Plans for Death House at Little Ardo.

Now The Breadwinner is roused and a new name that will stick is required. We have found it.

It does not perhaps have quite the same smack to it, but it is a suitable name and we both like it. The Postie will be instructed not to deliver mail addressed to any other house.

Our new house will have a name that reflects its history, and its geography. It even has a sense of humour.

We don't want to be a sore thumb in the countryside, so the design of our retirement house is that of an old-fashioned H plan steading. It is to be built of stone and slate. The arched cartshed doors are to become French windows and garage doors while the midden is to be glazed over for a sitootery. From there the old man may observe as much as he can for as long as he can in as much comfort as possible.

This mythical farm's two nearest neighbours will be Backhill of Ardo and Hillhead of Ardo so that, had it really existed as a farm, it would undoubtedly have been called Something Hill of Ardo.

But what?

Well, like every other exposed part of the ancient Earldom of Buchan, there are whins along the dykesides on the hill, so something to do with whins would be appropriate.

What really sold that idea to The Breadwinner was that she had been very taken with a passage in the autobiography of Sir

Maitland Mackie. He had described the early part of his second marriage as "20 years of fun". She would like to think of our new home as being the place to which we left for 20 years of fun. She even suggested Fun House but that seemed a bit naff.

Then it all came together. The Doric pronunciation of wh is f. What is fit, where is far – and whins are funs.

So there we have it. Our new home is to be spelt Whinhill of Ardo and pronounced Funhill, locally at least.

We have many daft stories about non-Doric speakers being thrown by our mother tongue. Like the expat who was told to wait for a lift beside the whin bush. He waited and waited for fun bus to arrive.

I rather like that simple story, largely because I am fascinated to know what the poor chap expected a fun bus to look like. He can hardly have expected it to contain clowns. Or did he expect a sort of bouncy castle bus? Did he imagine a bus full of ladies of the night?

The name's settled then, and I have moved on to weightier matters. To build a traditional steading you need stones, not cement blocks, and Welsh or Scots slates, not MFI tiles. To save a lot of money I would provide the stone and slate myself.

Now Little Ardo is no more than a little humus and some sand set down on rock so stone is not in short supply. We've even got two quarries on the place, though neither of those has operated in my lifetime.

But the trouble is that the quarries are rottenrock, and the great brutes which have broken ploughs and generations of ploughmen's hearts are the wrong shape for building. What we need is granite which has already been in a wall.

So far I've bought two unwanted farm buildings and Mossie has offered me an old washhouse he's taking down to extend one of his cottages. I found two lintels among stone gatherings by the side of the road leading down to the village. Gowkie has had seven nice corner stones lying in his close for as long as he can remember, so I got them.

Every farm has a few stones like that and The Breadwinner has a plan. At weddings and funerals or wherever we meet other farmers she tells them the story of Whinhill and asks them for a stone or two. And she gets them. The heap is growing. She rather fancies Whinhill of Ardo as a sort of friendship house built with a small contribution from a circle of good people.

So do I – it's cheaper than buying them.

July 29, 1996

Vive la difference dans la cuisine

WE COULD hardly believe it. Our holiday had just been spoiled by the news that the nervous systems and spleens of sheep were to be removed from the food chain. It wasn't that we eat much sheep's brain or spleen, of course, but the fear that another food scare was set to pound our poor hill farmers.

We had broken out and gone to a restaurant well above our usual price range off Parlia-ment Square in Bordeaux. The Breadwinner is pretty good at French so we managed most of the menu, but we were stumped by Cervelle de Veau. The waiter was only too willing to help. They were offering us calf's brains and he promised us that they were delicious.

"I don't believe it," exclaimed The Farmer, in Victor Meldrew style. "In my country it's illegal." There was a good

209

deal of merriment around the restaurant which a profounder student of French than The Farmer might have understood.

So there you have it. While we are spending hundreds of millions of pounds removing potentially infective material from the food chain the French glory on regardless.

We won't feed 'specified offal' to cattle (and hens and pigs which have never had BSE). But the French are happily eating the most potentially infective material, lightly cooked, without putting it through another animal first.

The Farmer and The Bread-winner were on a tour of the vineyards of a part of France which sounds like a wine list. Centred on Bordeaux, they went to St Emilion, Entre deux Mers, and Haut Medoc.

The idea was to visit various vineyards, study how the wine is made, sample the wine from the cask and bottle, and so put themselves in the enviable position of knowing when they are being taken to the cleaners in British restaurants.

The team was eight strong, and all pronounced it a most successful trip.

All, that is, except The Farmer. He enjoyed the tasting of the wine, but after you've seen how one wine is made only an expert has anything to learn from the tour round the next

chateau. And the trip from chateau to chateau was by bicycle which did displace rather a lot of drinking time.

And The Farmer doesn't know one good wine from another, so he would have been happy to stay and continue to taste the wine at the first place.

Mind you, I had been looking forward to seeing a bit of the French countryside. I wanted to check the rumours that, while we were setting 10% and more aside, you couldn't find any setaside on the Continent.

I was disappointed there. I didn't see any setaside, right enough, but then I didn't see much grain. And the system used to control wine output is production limits. They can grow scrubby little vines or run round with a shears before harvest cutting off all the less promising grapes.

A chateau is no more, and often much less, than a farm. They grow their own wine, design their own labels and get the mobile bottlers in. The smallest chateau we visited has only six hectares of vines and yet we shouldn't be too sorry for them. Chateau Lanote is a premier cru and so sells at first division prices. They make 32,000 bottles a year and, if they sell to everyone else at what they took from us, that brings in a third of a million pounds.

And we got a pleasant surprise near the other end of the scale. At Chateau Mouton Rothschild our guide was a most impressive young lady from Dirlton, near Gullane. Christine Dakin worked in Oddbins when a student and now she and her husband are both working in vineyards in France. They're doing a course in viniculture and, should they pass, they'll gain access to 20 hectares of land of their own and finance at 2.5% to work it.

With government assistance like that no wonder there are so many vineyards.

Anyway, Christine explained everything with such clarity that subsequent explanations were superfluous. After her I would have preferred more "work experience" in how it is drunk. But it was a magical tour.

The method of transport was particularly good. Temperatures ranged from 30 to 35 degrees in the shade and there wasn't much shade on the open road. And yet we were never too hot. The great thing about the bike is that even on a still day the cyclist enjoys a gentle breeze as he pedals along.

There had been worries that The Breadwinner might find up to 60 kilometres a day too much, but they needn't have worried. As The Farmer watched her pedalling away out in front he recognised the neat, balanced and focused style that had first attracted him to her on the running track at King's College 37 years ago.

Party blows the PHT blues

I TOLD Mossie PHT wasn't a good name for a party.

But I can't deny that Pre-Harvest Tension is in the air. Big Hamish has taken to painting doors that have done without paint for 30 years. And to take our minds off the moment of truth we're having a massive slimming competition. I know farmers depend on food consumption, but there you are. That's how tense we are.

Everybody at the Salmon Inn put in a tenner at the weigh-in and the one who sheds the most pounds will take home some £200 with which to put the weight back on again. That is except Antique Robbie, the second-hand furniture dealer. He lives on cigarettes and black coffee so he has no fat to lose. He will win if he puts on more than any of the slimmers lose.

The usual way to cope with the wait is to go on holiday and we've mostly done that. But the harvest is late. The less heavy crops of winter barley should be taken in the last week of July in Aberdeenshire and the farmers who panic will usually be cutting even the best of stands.

But when we came back this year, eager to put nature's bounty in the bank, it was just too soon. The grains were there but they were still full of moisture. Harvest will start at least a fortnight late in 1996.

According to Mains, a man full of country wisdom despite having seen no more than 30 summers, "We always start the hairst at Turra show time. The trouble this year is the show's a week later." Isn't nature a wonderful thing?

The waiting has been worst for Mossie. He's so excited about his harvest that he refused to go on holiday. He would stay at Moss-side and watch the grain turn to gold.

Mrs Moss is a wonderful wife to our man. She lets him go anywhere, any time. And if he is delayed by some important deal, she keeps his supper warm (rather than her wrath) and waits patiently for his call to come and drive him home.

Or at least she used to. Even the nicest of worms may have turned.

"Well, I'm booking up a holiday whether you like it or

not," she told him. Mossie called her bluff. "Well, please yersel."

Except that it wasn't a bluff. The next the poor farmer of Moss-side heard was that the wife and the Irishman's wife were off to the Costa Fortune with their buckets, spades, suntan oil and dancing pumps.

That made Aberdeenshire sit up. "Mossie's wife's awa fae him, ye ken. Oh aye, the place'll have tae be sellt." Ambitious neighbours made discreet calls to their bankers and the bankers promptly told anyone who would listen.

And anyone who saw Mossie that week would fairly believe the worst. While most farmers would fine like rid of the wife for a week, Mossie was miserable. He's not easy to feel sorry for but there was something pathetic about the brave smile and the, "Nae supper to go hame for and nae wife to drive me. This is hopeless."

So the PHT party was necessary.

A distinguished company of 50 gathered at Moss-side to shoot clay pigeons and make another major contribution towards the support of the flagging beef industry. Two enormous sirloin roasts were spitted on the muck spreader.

Also, in recognition of the magnificent breakthrough those scientists have made in getting the BSE agent to stick to a sheep by injecting infective

tissue direct into its brains, half a sheep was also roasted. Hilly provided the strawberries and the boys provided a bottle and can loch.

Pre-Harvest Tension was blown to smithereens, as was a fair skelp of Mossie's barley. You see one of the layouts is what he calls 'the settling geese'. The clays come from a high tower and settle gently on the field, which happens to be barley. Indeed it happens to be the crop that Mossie has been deaving us about. If this crop doesn't yield five tonnes he'll eat his hat.

Well, some of us would like to see that, so we let every clay come down to ear level before firing. You could say harvest is over on that bit of the crop.

A member of the distinguished company was Freddy Duncan, Chairman of the Grampian Food Group. Thirty years ago he was calling at Moss-side to sell lime to Mossie's dad. Now he's something of a local folk hero. He pays himself over £300,000 a year as boss of the largest supplier of frozen chickens in the UK and employer to 3000 men.

I can't vouch for the truth of this story but it was given out at the prizegiving that Chairman Fred had been hurrying to Edinburgh for a meeting with Lord Lindsay. He was late and, unimpressed with the progress of his chauffeur, took the wheel.

That helped and when they were making their way through Edinburgh at 90 miles an hour they surprised two policemen. "Who the hell's that?" said one.

His partner, who happened to come from Turriff, couldn't help much. "I dinna ken who it is but he must be pretty important. Chairman Fred's driving him."

August 19, 1996

Harvest's Glorious Twelfth

THE PHT has been dispelled at last. After a false start on the sixth, harvest really got going on the twelfth of August, just eleven days later than last year.

The Pre-Harvest Tension had been mounting steadily. The barley heads went down a good three weeks ago. That meant they were ripe and only had to dry. But grain won't dry if it is raining and so it did, for most of the three weeks. When it didn't rain the haar, which can be such a blessing to Scotland's east coast in dry seasons, made sure the moisture contents never approached the 19% which is the magic figure for members of Aberdeen Grain.

This co-op, which dries, stores and markets 30,000 tonnes of grain including mine, makes a handling charge which is supposed to cover the cost of drying the grain to under 15%. Drying costs the same up to 19% so there is not much point in getting it below 18.9.

Well, I don't know what it was like on the grouse moors, but it was a Glorious Twelfth at Little Ardo.

At 6am Peter the Swather appeared to cut the rape.

At 7.30 the Man of Few Words arrived to sow next year's rape.

"What a use the setaside's been for letting us get an early entry into rape," I chatted. "Here we are with no barley cut and yet we can sow 23 acres of next year's crop."

"Aye," said the Man of Few Words.

At 12.30 Mains appeared with his combine and we agreed that, much as he would have liked the £25 an acre all to himself, we had better get help.

So Young Ochyoch was summoned. He farms in the bleaker Buchan lands of the New Pitsligo Triangle and his harvest isn't ready yet.

Gowkie, who doesn't have a harvest as he is a genuine claimant of Hill Cow Subsidy, was available to drive one tractor and Potions the chemist came down to drive the second.

That left The Farmer free to do that most rewarding of jobs – loading the lorries taking the precious grain on the first leg of its journey to the pub.

It just struck me as I was waving goodbye to the first load that we might meet again at the Salmon Inn some Sunday. Much of the grain will undoubtedly be made into strong drink. And while I'm not as bad as Mossie, there is no doubt a decent whack of the money I get for the grain will find its way back into the liquor trade.

We had cut 40 acres by the time the haar came in at 8.30 that night.

It's too early to say that the results were glorious. It looks to me as though the first field didn't make three tonnes and the second didn't make four tonnes to the acre, but that is all I can say – except that the first two loads had moisture contents of 19.4 and 20.6, which means both will suffer extra drying charges. With harvest so late I will be glad to pay them.

You may be as shocked as I am at The Farmer complaining that the middle of August is late for harvest. After all, my father would seldom have seen any harvest in August, if you don't count oats cut green to ripen in the stook. With the advent of winter-sown crops the harvest is earlier nowadays.

But the hash is really on because we need to get the barley off the fields so we can get the winter rape in for next year.

It really was fun having all that action about the place. It was just like the old days when farming was a major employer in the land. In the hairst we would have had six men, the farmer, a lady to drive the tractor between the stooks and a hairst man – nine in all.

On the Glorious Twelfth we had two combines and two tractor drivers in the harvest field. We had three men ploughing and planting the rape. There was one man swathing last year's rape and The Farmer loaded five lorries, relieved everyone at meal times and ran to the smiddy with everything that broke.

For one glorious day Little Ardo was back to the days of the fermtouns when a farm was a major employer and population centre.

Sadly, at night they all went home bar me. There are still three farm cottages but the tenants don't work here. And of course none of them has a child. That is the big difference, there are no bairns now on the farm and that makes me sad.

It also makes me wonder who will look after the present couples when they are old?

Anyway, that day's harvesting made quite a change from The Farmer's Friday. That was spent haring away down to Castle Douglas to address the Holstein-Friesian Society's dinner.

I was a bit self-conscious about swishing south in the Jaggie when all my neighbours were harvesting.

"Oh aye," I could imagine them saying. "Charlie's fairly letting go now – awa gallivantin in the middle o' hairst."

And the beef producers of Buchan would have been even more shocked had they known that I was driving 500 miles to entertain the Holstein part of my audience.

It was a good party and it was nice to find some people who recognise that BSE isn't all bad news. The £90 apiece or so that they are getting for their slink calves (as they call their unwanted bulls) for slaughter, is a very good market.

And the beef boys in Buchan should be pleased, too. This way they can't be caught trying to fatten beasts with conformation like cricket bats.

August 26, 1996

Poor harvest gets in Potions' way

THE GRAIN is a disappointment. We'll have averaged three tonnes. That is 15cwt less than last year and a sad blow to The Farmer's retirement fundie. He may even have to stay on for an extra year to make up the shortfall.

And that highlights one of the age-old problems on the land; the plight of the young as they struggle through middle age waiting for the old to give them their turn of the overdraft.

Poor Potions. He's not the local chemist because of a lifelong desire to sell drugs. Since he was a boy he's had nothing else in his head but tractors.

He wasn't brought up on a farm, nor is he of farming folk. If he had been he might have understood that life on the farm is not an oil painting by Constable. But he went to a rural school and had to listen to all the ploughmen's sons arguing the relative merits of the tractors their fathers drove.

I know something of the

intensity with which these discussions were carried out because my sons, the Wasting Assets, were at the same school. When their biology class was to visit they begged me to hide our two old Fordson Majors so that their pals might not see them.

"My father has a Fergie."

"Nae use bize a John Deere."

"There's naen o them can reverse like a Nashie."

"Aye, bit the Ford'll be worth twice as much when you come to sell it."

If you didn't understand much of that you will know how Potions felt at school; barred by his ignorance from the intellectual conversation of his peers. The frustration of that burnt into the boy an inextin- guishable desire to be a farmer which no argument or agricultural disaster could relieve.

And he's done well. He has married the Elder Investment. Better than that, it has been decided (even trumpeted) that, when The Farmer retires, the Investment will get her inheritance early and Potions will at last have the key to a life in the service of the Clydesdale Bank.

Gone will be the terrible dilemmas of his current life – what will he do today? Not until he is an old man will he ever again have to worry about what to do with his money.

All that is assured. And the joy of looking at a fine crop of suckled calves and knowing that it will soon be pressing down upon his overdraft.

But when? How soon will

218

The Farmer retire? And that's where Potions' luck starts to run out. The Farmer has the poor chemist running hither and thither. Potions has been so busy farming during this harvest and The Farmer's recent health scares, that he has barely had time to open the shop in the morning and till-up at night.

And if he so much as hints at wages The Farmer smiles a guileless smile and says, "Oh aye, of course, Potions laddie. How much would you need? But mind, it'll have to come out of my retirement fundie."

That stops him. Potions knows the fundie needs to be large enough to protect The Farmer against having to rely on the love of his children or the support of his sons-in-law in what he intends will be a long retirement.

So, you see, the shortfall in the barley crop, some £70 an acre, is bad news for me but it may be even worse for Potions.

The reason is not clear unless you believe Mossie, my (thankfully) honorary crops consultant. He says the poor crop is down to The Farmer being so efficient last year.

When the monsoon struck, stopping everything for three weeks after barely a week of September, The Farmer had all his harvest in and nearly all his new crop sown. That was just too early, according to Mossie.

All that early growing gave the disease more time to get going and in the end, despite frequent spraying, the disease won.

His evidence in support of that theory is that the one field that was sown in the last week of September was clearly the highest yielding despite being one of our least fertile.

I have an altogether more Machiavellian explanation.

Last year Little Ardo grew more barley than Moss-side. It wasn't as much as a whole cwt to the acre but there was clear golden water between us.

And that is surely the worst mistake a pupil can make. Mossie's advice had punted The Farmer up, from one of those who struggle to a position among the top boys. Mossie took full credit without a hint of modesty or embarrassment.

But when the Little Ardo crops beat those at Moss-side – look out! I don't know what he did but I am firmly in my place.

I did notice one thing, though. While I have persevered with the Pleasante which has served me so well, he has moved on, almost exclusively, to blends. For next year I am preparing to blend Pleasante and Pastoral. At least that should avoid this year's indignity of an average specific weight of below 60 kilograms per hectolitre (whatever that means in pounds per bushel).

219

Harvesting the goodwill of friends

THE FARMER has been at a low ebb though the tide may be turning at last. It is not considered quite proper to tell what has been wrong except to say there is 'trouble in the waterworks'.

Two Mondays ago he went to the doctor with the minor complaint that making water was like passing 100% proof whisky – not that he'd ever done that though he must have been close often. Some cheery words, an antibiotic and The Farmer entered a period of steady, even alarming, decline.

I mean when you are too ill to watch Coronation Street, that's ill.

The trouble is the waterworks doesn't just consist of a tap. Soon the germs had crawled back up all the piping and invaded the reservoir. Then round the back to the purification plants.

And there has been more. I don't wish to be sacrilegious but it was surely a design fault that the good Lord didn't keep our urinary and genital systems apart.

Anyway, the germs soon found the connection and got into one of the generators, causing a spectacular explosion there and leaving The Farmer distinctly lopsided.

And all in the middle of harvest.

Once again it has shown how unstable my business is. For perhaps five days I could no more drive a tractor than ride a bicycle. The farm had to do without me.

That is not sound business practice. I can see the time coming when it will be illegal to keep livestock unless you have employees on duty 24 hours a day. Never mind every five days. Where will the farmers of 250 acres be then?

The only hope is to have a Potions. He can't afford for The Farmer's illness to cause losses. He did his best.

Through the fevered ears I heard the tractors buzzing about.

I heard it whispered in the hall, "The digger's knackered" and "The old tractor's packed it in." And yet, despite having his own business to run, he coped. Indeed he did so with a flair which may be described as promising.

Gowkie my crofting neighbour who, luckily, is off his work as a mason having had a second bionic hip inserted, was the mainstay, but anyone who called was roped in to help.

Three old friends will probably avoid Little Ardo if they ever vacation here again. The first came from Corby, where he has lived and prospered since he gave the son of the farmer of Little Ardo a hiding at the carnival in Methlick in 1948. He wasn't even allowed to visit The Farmer (he might have come to apologise) and yet he spent the afternoon driving in the last of the barley.

The hospital police would have been better to let him in than the pair from New Zealand. They got through long enough for the wife to assure The Farmer that she was an expert and that he would never recover unless his treatment was changed. That didn't help a lot but Potions did manage to get the Kiwi to load stones in the field the contractor refused to plough and plant. It has to be stoned first.

And Potions got a whole day at the stones from another old friend. He works all over the place by the hour and was happy to put in a day despite being underwhelmed by the going rates at Little Ardo. Apparently he looked incredulously at the flutter of paper in

BEST GET A MOVE ON IN CASE YOU'RE TOO LATE!

THE RETIREMENT HOUSE

his hand and said, "I've worked for more, but it's grand to be home."

So despite the fact that The Farmer hasn't done a hand's turn for ten days, he's not far behind. And the main reason isn't Potions' gallant efforts. The weather has been so bad that no-one else has got on either.

And the weather's been a blessing in disguise to Mossie's brother. He was very proud of his new drier. Whereas Mossie has to rise several times in the night to feed his drier with its pathetic 20-tonne capacity, and where Mossie had to be sampling and taking the temperature of his grain the whole time in case he should over-dry any, Will had gone state-of-the-art.

A snip at £80,000, this machine was fully automatic for everything. It needed neither rest nor sleep. "Get yoursel organised," he said in triumph to the brother who had often said the same to him.

Will went to bed happily in the not unreasonable expectation that by morning the grain would be dry to perfection.

But automatic systems, while they are grand when they work, are dangerous when they don't.

This shiny monster had a sensor which told the intake to stop when the 20-tonne capacity had been reached. Unfortu-nately the sensor failed in the night. The great augers churned away, stuffing more and more barley into the giant until everything seized in a pack of compressed barley and twisted steel.

It was under warranty so the £80,000 didn't come into it, but what Will didn't need was a visit that day from his big brother and the Red Rooster.

But he got one. The two cynical grain barons found him when they went to inspect the new machine. From inside came thuds and "language" and occasionally out through an inspection hatch would come another small shovelful of compressed grain.

Will was not delighted when he eventually stuck his head out for air only to be met by the two pals chorusing, "Get yersel organised, Will."

No, he wasn't pleased, but his silver lining is that with all this weather there's been nothing to dry anyway.

Even The Farmer's health has its good side. They say there has been tremendous progress with our retirement house. The foundations are in, the water is there and walls of best Aberdeenshire granite are rising fast.

Apparently Mossie went round all the tradesmen telling them they'd best get a move on in case they were too late.

Rum doos are back

THE FARMER has made a remarkable recovery. He is not yet fit for the bicycle but at least he is back to worrying about the farm on a full-time basis.

And he has been worrying to effect. There is to be an almost complete change in farming policy.

At least, the policy will be the same. We'll continue to grow half winter barley and half winter rape, and keep our 40 cows. But the tactics are to be overhauled.

Take the barley. Mossie has three tonnes and three quarters and good bushel weights. We have only three tonnes and penalties to pay for low weights on some loads.

So what went wrong? Well, first of all we drilled it far too soon. It looked well but it was all show and no dough. The early growth let in the fungi and we never really got rid of them. So no more drilling before the third week of September.

Then I'm getting a bit fed up of our seed. It is at least sixth generation and that's only if I was told the truth when I bought it. It could be getting tired. Certainly Pleasante has been a good yielder here but it does produce small grains.

Also, it netted down this year and though we got all the heads over most of the fields the tram lines were full of enough heads to show what a disaster it might have been.

So I have bought new seed and I've blended it with Pastorale which should give a bolder sample and may help it to stand.

You may have noticed that this is a belt, braces, safety pins and string approach, so I'll never know what the fundamental problem in 1996 was – but who cares as long as it works?

The rape is in for a shake-up as well. We have about 30cwt to the acre this year, which is less than we are used to. Mossie has 5cwt more on average. But his real success is with the new hybrid variety, Synergy.

There has been much fuss about Synergy and for once that seems to be justified. Mossie has over two tonnes to the acre so I cannot resist following. I have sown all my 95 acres with a blend of Synergy and Rocket.

Sowing all one variety would have been a huge risk. We did it in 1990 when we thought that Tapidor was the way forward for the North-east. That was a disaster. Sclerotinia

Signs in image: "CUSHIES LAND HERE ↓", "KEEP SCOTLAND TIDY EAT A PIGEON", "Turnbull"

SO IT'S BACK TO WAR ON THE PIGEONS and SLUGS B.WARE

made sure we had barely a tonne to the acre.

But we are covered against another such disaster by the blend. Rocket, which is shorter, is there primarily to give a greater depth of flowers and to help hold the Synergy up. But if the Synergy fails there will be more than enough Rocket to give us a crop.

Then there's the pigeons.

I used to spend all winter with Willie the Hunter shooting pigeons to try to keep them off the rape.

Then setaside came in and the pigeons stopped eating the rape because there was so much good stuff on the setaside. But the number of cushies has risen.

Three years ago they reappeared on the rape but only for a month or so in early spring and there was no noticeable effect on yields. So we let them eat, convinced they made no difference.

That complacency has been shattered. By 1996 there were so many in the blue clouds that half the crop was eaten quite bare. And they stayed so long that they let the weeds in on the spring day. Half our rape crops were a mess of shepherd's purse and giant daisies.

That is bad from two points of view; the weeds compete for food and light, and in a wet year, weeds can make drying a dirty crop impossible. We got away with it this year but we might not another year. So it's back to war on the pigeons.

The slugs are in for a hard

time, too. We always sow a couple of kilos per hectare on the rape after setaside "to give them a feedie" as Mossie puts it with fine disregard for animal welfare or the principles of organic farming. Setaside seems to be particularly suitable for slugs so it is a must there.

But this year we have taken the additional precaution of going once round the outsides of all the new-sown fields in case of invasion from overgrown dykesides. As with the pigeons, the aim is as much to keep the weeds out as to protect the marginal rape plant.

September 16, 1996

Mossie's philosophy and the CSC man

MOSSIE, MY guide, philosopher and neighbour, has a saying with which he deflates the moaners. When righteous indignation is being expressed by a cattle finisher that he is losing £200 a head and the 'mak-up' isn't nearly enough and how unfair it all is, or when one of the lads has been stopped from running his business as five separate firms (one for himself, one for the wife, one each for the children and one in the name of the bothy cat) in order to claim extra sheep quota, and he's sounding off about it, then Mossie says it. "Aye, the worst losses are always in the pub."

I think he means that, when the final sums are done, most 'disasters' hardly register in the books. Certainly my oil seeds this year are a case in point. The weeds that the pigeons let in looked dreadful and could have prevented the swath drying, but in the event we took 31cwt to the acre. That is less than we like but way above the national average.

On the other hand, there have been some pretty spectacular 'disasters' this harvest. Like that which befell the Young Laird. He went to town and bought a new combine, the top line for which is £175,000.

If you don't even know how much money that is, join the club.

I've been trying to make sense of it but the nearest I can get is that it is almost twice what I paid for Little Ardo when I bought it from my father

225

and 44 times what he paid my grandfather for the place in 1945.

Well, well. The Young Laird was combining one of his steeper fields, the one that runs alongside the road to Auchnagatt, when one of his shooting pals came past. In excitement to blow about his purchase the Young Laird jumped down and rushed over to the fence to converse.

Unfortunately his pride of ownership had swamped his natural care and attention and he forgot to apply the handbrake. When he turned round to wave expansively at his new status symbol it had vanished. There is a very deep ditch at the bottom of that field and the combine was quite out of sight.

But Mossie's right again. That won't even show in the Young Laird's books. It is the insurance company's money that went down that drain.

And I had a little disaster of my own. It was when I was putting the pre-emergence weed spray on the rape.

My old Hardie sprayer has a wonderful array of taps at its front. Those let you spray with anything from the full 60 feet down to 15 feet. In order to operate the taps and to adjust the pressure and attend to other technical matters to do with the accurate application of the sprays, The Farmer, at considerable risk to his fragile health, operates the rig with the rear window of the tractor open.

This had caused an acci-

dent. In turning sharp right and plunging down a hole, the rear door had bashed one of the taps and shut it off.

The Farmer never noticed. Gayly he sprayed up and down the field, missing a 15-foot strip. He was surprised at how well the chemical seemed to last and kept increasing the output from the remaining taps.

The error was only discovered when the gushet was reached. In order to reduce plating The Farmer reached for the outside tap to turn it off. Only then did he discover that it was off already.

Consternation reigned. The Farmer foresaw a winter of striped rape crops and a summer of looking at stripes of gowans which would give his crops a tartan look – and it's right beside the road.

The only hope was to load up with more chemical (a three-figure disaster in itself) and go over the field again with the one tap on and the other three off. But where to start?

As luck would have it there was another in the field. A man from the Comical Spraying Co. was laying down slug pellets. Had he noticed anything funny about my spraying?

Yes. He had, as soon as he came in the field.

So why hadn't he said anything?

He had once told a farmer that there was a bit hanging off one of his implements. The farmer told him to mind his own business. The man had sworn never to interfere again. What a pity that farmer had so little sweetness in him.

However the CSC man's belated advice enabled me to work out where the tap had been shut off and I went over it all again. I am still fearful but at least I haven't killed the crop by plating it.

Let us hope Mossie is right again, and that, beyond the wasted chemicals, there will be nothing to show in the books.

There are some disasters which you cannot hide. With the crops getting overripe in the fields, memories have been put to the test round the watering holes of the North-east.

David Jack, the cereals man, recalls 1966 when many crops were stripped by the wind. He was combining at night and seemed to be making fair progress on a shiny new combine with no cab but no less than an eight foot cutting bar.

Eventually, against the distraction of the hurricane, he became aware that though he was hacking the field down he didn't seem to be filling the tank.

The trouble was the grain had a one foot drop into the tank and it just couldn't make it. The wind was whipping it all away.

September 23, 1996

Sunny smiles as depression lifts

HE IS 75 now so it must have been 61 years ago that old Jimmy discovered just how hungry farmers in the Northeast could be. He was employed on a farm in Donside for the princely sum of five pounds and five shillings per half year.

An epidemic of flu' had left the Laird short of beaters so the factor had asked Jimmy's employer if he had anybody who would beat. "Jimmy, de ye ken how tae beat?"

"No."

"Well, ye won't be able to say that tomorrow."

So Jimmy went to the beating. He enjoyed it – walking along in line making a noise by banging a dry stick against the trees or on a stone. And he was absolutely delighted when he not only got a good dinner but got a tip – in hard cash.

And remember, those were the days when farm servants signed on for a year or a half year and worked all the hours they were told to and were only paid at the end of the contract. There was no overtime paid though plenty was worked.

So when the farmer asked Jimmy the next day whether the laird had paid him for his day's work, Jimmy was still loaded. "Aye," he said enthusiastically and whipped out the four shillings he'd been paid.

That was a mistake. The farmer took the money from the outstretched hand. "Of course this is really all mine, James. I have ye for the half year. Still, here's two shillings for yoursel'."

The saying 'hungry farmer' still has a special meaning for Jimmy.

I've been thinking a lot about Jimmy and his like who, by the sweat of their brows, created the fertile land of Buchan which has been my inheritance and will be my legacy.

You see, we have been allowed by the planning authorities to build ourselves a house so we can let the next generation get going.

But we must not build a nice cheap-and-cheerful kit house. To get planning permission we must build in stone and slate and look as though we belong on top of Ardo's hill.

Fair enough. But where do you get all that stone and slate? And remember any old stone won't do. Little Ardo is mostly stones with a wee bit of mould squeezed in between them. But we need stones with flat surfaces, and especially with two flat surfaces forming a right angle to make the corners of the building, the windows and the doors.

It costs an arm and a leg to get a quarry to cut stones nowadays so realistically the only place you can get that sort of stone is off another building. The great stone chase is on.

The Breadwinner and I can't pass a heap of stone gatherings by the road without leaping out to see if we can find any to take home. But mostly our stones are second-hand.

The Young Laird had a fire in his grain drier and had to take down that shed. He was able to spare us a few of his beautiful (aristocratic) corner stones. Mossie is extending one of his cottages which means bulldozing the old washhouse out the back. So he's bulldozed it into a cart and we got two lintels and forty-one corner stones there. Then Gordon Stephen, who created a new record for land in the North-east when he reputedly paid over £3000 an acre for Muirton near Oldmeldrum, proved it was the land he was after by knocking down a big

shed there. A few more corner stones came over to Little Ardo.

Gowkie had to widen his steading door to let the tractors in ten years ago and he still had the stones that came out of there. Mains had a building the roof of which was falling in. He was happy to sell me the slates at 20 pence apiece and use the money to replace the slates with metal box section.

We're going to know the provenance of every stone on this house. "This is the Mossside wing. Here we have the Muirton corner. This is the Mains gable."

The Great Stone Hunt is good fun. But it has dawned slowly upon The Farmer that he has not struck a blow for traditional building methods. He is not helping to stem the tide of alien tiles, bricks and pebble dash nor leading the countryside back to native stone and slate.

Because he is relying on second-hand materials his new house will represent the total or partial demise of at least seven traditional buildings.

The Farmer is all right. He is happy he has kept his inheritance intact for the family. He is glad his great great grandfather will be able to look up and see that the family still hasn't been blown off the hill. The Farmer will be happy his grandchildren are playing on the braes. But what about the farmers of East Kinochry Farm?

That 30-acre place became uneconomic in the 1930s. The family sold it after the war. The big farmer who bought it sold the house off during the oil boom of the 1970s. The new owners changed its name to Snowdrop Cottage.

And, the final insult, Charlie Allan bought the steading and carted it all away to make a retirement cottage for himself and The Breadwinner.

It doesn't pay to think too much.

September 30, 1996

It's an ill wind ...

DAMN THE weather but double damn the weather forecasters. Who are these people who are making a whole new branch of show business out of presenting the teleweather and presume to tell me what sort of weather is good for me?

Here sits The Farmer. His late-sown rape crop may yet be saved if rain comes soon. Breathlessly he waits at five to seven for news of life-giving precipitation. On comes Heather looking like the head girl on speech day. After a few brief, embarrassing and irrelevant words with Jackie she turns to The Farmer and says "Hallo there. And the bad news is that rain is sweeping in from the West."

Bad news? What is the head girl talking about? It is the best news The Farmer has heard since Britain was forced off the ERM on Black Wednesday.

Or it would be if the rain materialised. But they even get that wrong. Sitting on the cold shoulder of Scotland that sticks out into the North Sea and is sheltered by the Grampians, we in the North-east lowlands have to put up with disappointing rainfall. Every second shower promised by the head girl is hijacked by the Grampian mountains. The only sight we get of it is when it swishes down the many rivers between the Esk and the Spey.

But it is not that the forecasters get it wrong. What gets right up The Farmer's nose is the arrogance of these children. Good weather, they should surely realise, is in the eye of the beholder.

I like a good snowstorm in

winter because it covers my crops and protects them from the frost and the pigeons. The skiers like it, too. The fishermen are always looking for rain, and farmers with muck to spread like a good frost.

Think of the worst weather you can and it will suit somebody. Gales and a foot of snow? That will be ideal for the young man who is spending the weekend with his girlfriend in a wee cottage up a glen. He has plenty of food and drink in. The peat stack is just at the backdoor and he doesn't fancy going back to work on Monday.

And then the head girl comes on and tells him "the bad news is ..." he's going to be snowed in for a few days?

Come on BBC. Get a grip of these people.

If you think The Farmer is being uncharacteristically petulant this morning it will be because of the trouble we are having with our last-sown field of rape. We have been hit by downie mildew. That attacks the first leaves of the rape plants soon after emergence, covers them with white fungus and usually kills them.

We are not alone. All over the North-east there are crops which have great patches which have died. The key seems to be the dry weather though, most oddly, it is not the knaps and knowes that are hit hardest but the low-lying parts of the fields.

A spray in time kills the downie mildew and as soon as real leaves appear the danger is over – provided it is not too dry. Little Ardo is too dry. I have sprayed the plants twice and the downey mildew is gone but, with the cotyledons dead, there is not enough water to develop the true leaves. It is so dry and so windy that the tiny rape plants are being tormented by the wind until some are even being blown out of the dust which passes for soil.

And the head girl tells us the bad news is that rain is on its way.

Anyway, it is clear that I am going to have to be as good as my word and keep the pigeons off the rape this winter.

It will be a belt, braces, tie (my father used his to support his breeks), string and chewing gum affair. My machinery will be left out in the fields with music playing. Willie the Hunter will be given a thousand cartridges and told to go and start world war three. Scarecrows will be erected and I may even try Mossie's triple-banging gas gun.

It is well understood that everything works to some extent. My theory is that you've got to keep varying it.

But now I am told of the ultimate pigeon deterrent. It is a

giant hawk that flutters above the fields and scares the doos off up to 30 acres, depending on the shape of your fields.

Well, it's not a hawk really, but the pigeons react to it as though it were. It's a helium-filled balloon.

It's an old trick which seems to work. A neighbour has been using one for several years and swears by it. But the trouble is that when the wind blows the balloon gets blown down to earth – and it's when the wind is at its best that the pigeon is at its worst.

That's why some people have been flying kites above their rape crops. The trouble there is that the kite falls to earth when the wind stops.

The innovation in the Allsopp Helikite is that it combines a kite and a balloon. When the wind blows the kite keeps the balloon up and when the wind drops the balloon keeps the kite up.

It's worth a try.

Mind you, I had a nightmare the other night.

I had got my the farm quite covered by the contraptions. No sooner had I filled the sky with kites and colourful balloons than Mossie, the Red Rooster, Nicol from Keith, Crookie, Hillie and Mains arrived, followed by a line of other over-powered vehicles.

"We saw the balloons Charlie. When does the party start?"

Working to satisfy the incinerator

TOMORROW IS the day. The beef farmers of the North-east are having our day in court to get justice for our local mart. We're out to get the Secretary of State to let us continue to kill our cull cows in Edinburgh under the programme to eradicate BSE.

I don't suppose Michael Forsyth will be there in person and it's not a case of Big Hamish, the Red Rooster and The Farmer going there to chin him. The battle will be fought between the £1000-a-day boys in wigs. But we are involved and it is important.

The system had been working very well. A thousand cattle a week were collected at the Thainstone Mart. They were then killed in Edinburgh, where a whole slaughter line was dedicated to culls. We got paid in a week. Everybody was happy. Our mart got organised first and was held up as a model for others.

Until Friday 27th September. Then it became apparent that the Edinburgh plant would not be allowed to kill on the Monday ... or thenceforth. No one told the staff at Aberdeen and Northern Marts. They were left to guess that they were out of that business when the weekly fax failed to arrive.

That was a blow to our mart, and after the collapse Buchan Meat we're taking a much closer interest in our co-ops.

But it is also a blow to The Farmer. He has had ten cows in the queue to be killed for 14 weeks. The Farmer could have been doing with getting the money in, but at least they were feeding their calves and, though it is false economics, it never seems like it is costing much to feed cattle on grass.

But now we are feeding our winter keep to those cows. Now we really want rid of them. So do the owners of the 7000 cattle in the Aberdeen and Northern Marts' queue. There is nothing more depressing than feeding cows for no other purpose than to incinerate them.

And it's worse than that.

Something like half the cows that are 'retired' are culled because of bad feet and I have one which has been in

need of attention now for ten weeks. She's a cross Limousin and a good mother but we decided that her feet were a mess. She wasn't in any pain. She had no infection, but the horn on her feet had grown to such an extent that it was interfering with her mobility and, perhaps more important, she didn't look well. Trouble could develop.

We never did anything about it because she was always on the point of going to Edinburgh.

But now that the Edinburgh door has closed, I have had to spend a whole morning paring these damned feet. All the skill I developed when I used to show cattle came into play. It's not for me to say but I did a fine job. When she gets used to be-

ing so near the ground she will look far better of her surgery.

How frustrating it is that all that work, including borrowing the Red Rooster's turntable crush and taking it back, is just so she can walk a few steps to the incinerator.

And while I've had useless extra work to do, 57 men in the slaughterhouse in Edinburgh have had light pay packets because useful work has been taken away from them.

The trouble is that there isn't enough capacity to get rid of the carcases. We could soon kill the 28,000 cattle queuing in Scotland but there isn't enough rendering capacity. So the available capacity has to be rationed between the slaughterers who want to enter what has been a lucrative trade. One of the things we don't like is the way the allocation is done.

There is pride that this is an 'industry-run scheme'. That may sound good but it is run by your competitors. Put like that it doesn't sound so clever.

The conflict is about dedication. That is the excellent idea that all this culling of animals reckoned to be at risk of carrying BSE should be done in abattoirs dedicated to that purpose.

It's a Scotland-only idea and the supermarkets like it. If we ever get anywhere near getting back into the European Market before the English we expect the European buyers to be impressed too.

The fact that Aberdeen and Northern had so many abattoirs was what enabled them to get off to such a prompt start to the slaughtering of cattle over 30 months old. They were able to dedicate a whole slaughterline in Edinburgh to the job.

But now they've changed the rules. Because ANM still slaughters sheep and pigs in the other two lines in Edinburgh they can no longer count themselves dedicated. It matters not that the three lines were once owned by separate companies and that they can be separated physically. It matters not that in the rest of the UK they are not dedicating at all.

So we're in court. There is to be a judicial review, by which time the whole OTM business is likely to be over. In the meantime Aberdeen will have missed out on a lot of money. Tomorrow's action is to try to get an order returning to the previous definition pending the revue.

It's worth a heap of dough to the marts and a small heap to The Farmer. They are reducing the compensation for OTM cattle by about £50 a head from the 14th of October, so it is worth £500 to me to get my culls away before then.

October 14, 1996

Mossie gets lost

I AM afraid I've lost my pal Mossie. He's sprinting up the social ladder so fast he's about out of sight. He's been up on the grouse moors with the aristoc-racy. He can hardly speak about anything else. There's no way I can keep up.

It was all a bit strange for our man. There were Porsches

and Range Rovers everywhere and he had just the Jeep. And there wasn't a welly boot there worth less than a week's wages while Mossie just had Harbro's best at £25 a pair.

And our man realised that he was really breaking new ground after the first drive.

"How many did you shoot Mr Moss?"

"Three."

"Oh very good. That's excellent for a man who hasn't shot grouse before. I bet you didn't shoot six on the first drive of your first pheasant shoot."

"Maybe no," said Mossie, puzzled, "but I only shot three birds this time."

"Oh I see," said the head keeper, snobby-like. "That's one and a half."

"But I shot three, I tell't ye," shouted Mossie exasperated by the very thought of shooting half a grouse.

"And that's one and a half brace."

Not used to being wrong Mossie was ready for them after the second drive. "Two and a half," he said, quick as a flash, and as to that manor born.

He had a great shoot. "Don't listen to them if they say there's a shortage of birds. My gun was about red hot. I was up to my knees in cartridges. They were shouting at me one time "bird over, bird over" but I just tell't them I was too busy muckin oot the butt."

And how did Mossie get in amongst all that wealth, smoked salmon and champagne? Well, it was a return invitation following his Pre-Harvest Tension clay pigeon shoot and barbecue. And at that event Mossie had charged his guests £25 a head.

That's a return for you. That's an investment!

And Big Hamish has been cashing in his investments too. He's rumoured to have sold his milk quota for not less than £65 a litre. Now, I would be the last person to praise the big man's acumen, but he must be in for our Businessman of the Year award over this decision. It takes guts to sell the herd your father milked but it takes a brave man to hold on to the cows in present circumstances.

All right, the dairymen are making money just now, but there is so much capital involved and more than half of that capital has no intrinsic value at all. The quota system could disappear overnight.

You may think that unlikely but it happened with potatoes.

It is not to gloat that I tell you again about my potato quota. I had 15 acres which was once a lot of spuds. But by the late eighties anything less than 40 acres was uneconomic – just

236

a pest. So I sold them to the Red Rooster for the best part of £10,000. That saved me a lot of backache and a lot of headache and the Rooster did well enough out of his investment for a few years. But what it his ten thousand worth today?

Well, I've invested it wisely so it is worth quite a lot, but the potato quota is now worthless. If the EEC goes broke or if the Eurosceptics take us out of Europe or if there is a drastic cull to get rid of BSE, the value of the milk quota will disappear overnight.

A hundred cows could cost £100,000, the buildings and machinery necessary for milking them about £200,000 and the quota over £400,000. Hamish has cashed all his quota value and he must be right.

So should everybody be trying to cash their quotas?

Well, no. That wouldn't work. You can only sell if there is some fool who wants to buy.

So am I saying everyone who wants to buy quota is a fool?

Wrong again. It makes perfect sense to be expanding if you have plenty of money and your retirement fundie is well swelled. Such a man who likes getting up at four in the morning to milk cows on Christmas day is quite right to keep quota. Some farms won't grow anything but grass and are too small to sustain a high enough income without dairy cows, so their farmers are trapped. Then again there are farmers who love their cows.

But Hamish isn't like that. Buying a baronial castle and every machine that's known to man as soon as it comes out has ensured that he's better off taking the money. Hamish doesn't love cows. He loves machines.

And here's one for those who fear that our weather is becoming more extreme. The Red Rooster has had cloud bursts of the sort not normally seen outside the tropics. In two 40-minute spells his parched fields were transformed into raging torrents. Fields of newly sown rape were washed away leaving channels a foot deep along all tramlines and other wheelmarks. An unmade farm road was rendered quite impassable by gulleys deep enough to hide the Rooster himself and he's six foot four in his stocking soles (even the ones with the holes in them).

A dam was burst, the water supply polluted and the tanks silted up. A thousand tonnes of stones as big as footballs were deposited in one heap alone.

Yet at Little Ardo, not a mile away, we were still crying out for rain. The Rooster couldn't move for mud and The Farmer's grain wouldn't germinate for dust.

October 21, 1996

Champagne tears at a hellova party

THE MARRIAGE of a son to a good woman is indeed a happy event. But the wedding can be a harrowing experience. So it was no surprise for the congregation that The Farmer's shoulders seemed to quiver and The Breadwinner's hanky was on overtime at Methlick's Auld Kirk.

While the Wasting Asset and his bride were signing the register a sympathetic hand fell on The Breadwinner's shoulder. "Are you crying for your little boy?" a guest asked.

"No," she said, "I'm crying for that poor lassie."

I think she didn't mean it, for the young couple did look well; she in her flowing robes and he in the kilt, which looked well with the earring.

A big wedding really is a bit of nonsense. What has all that posing, speechifying, hat-wearing and over eating, drinking and dancing got to do with a marriage anyway? Not much.

And if there is anything more ludicrous than an Englishman in hired morning dress which is too long in the trousers, rigged out for an afternoon wedding, it may well be a Scotsman, in full evening dress with a hired kilt that is too short.

And yet it must give the young some pause, in these days of fast food and quickie divorces, to stand up in front of all their friends, relations, the minister and perhaps even God, to make a public commitment to one another.

At any rate it was done and it was done well. It was a mixed wedding so we sang about England's green and pleasant land. And while we were singing our favourite psalm I couldn't help hoping the shepherd would show his legendary compassion to this bit of his flock.

Not that any seemed to be needed. The Wasting Asset took his bride with transparent joy as she took him.

After a few quick photographs in the rain, Mains tuned up his pipes and marched us through the village to the reception in the Public Hall. I was rather proud of the idea but when I saw the rain I suggested that we could drive.

"Take the cars if you like. We're walking whatever the weather," said the newlyweds. And they did. And so did everybody else. The village turned out and waved and a lorry driver stopped his big artic to let the procession cross the road, and gave us a ribbald blast on his horn.

In welcoming the guests to the village where the groom's family had farmed for six generations I felt it no more than fair to say a bit about the man whose portrait hangs there.

Mr Beaton was the farmer of Breemies in the middle of the 19th century. That was a modest place of 30 acres and yet he was able to move to Middlethird, where he had 250. And off that he was able to make a gift of the hall which now bears his name.

It is a wonderful facility. Granite built, it has a magnificent facade, reception rooms and a hall with oak beams which are at once elegant and sturdy – fine enough to have graced a great castle.

"And," I asked the company, "what farmer could so endow his village today? Yes, yes," I said, "we farmers are going through another sticky patch."

Nevertheless we had killed the fatted calf for our prodigal son. Mossie roasted a pound a head of sirloin-on-the-bone in the mobile barbecue made from the old rotaspreader.

We also offered a quarter of a pound a head of salmon. I told The Breadwinner she was daft ordering all that salmon but she wouldn't listen. Half the salmon was left but, despite the fact there were nine vegetarians in the company, there was just enough of the beef left for one pot of stovies.

It had been hung for a month, turned on the spit so that none of the juices ran out and lightly cooked. Perfection!

The speeches weren't perfect though, at least The Farmer was not altogether pleased. You see it was the unanimous opinion that the best bit was when I tried to give the groom some tips in the middle of his speech. "No, no," said the Wasting Asset. "This is my speech. You can speak later."

I preferred when, in what was really a handsome speech delivered with the sort of energy he used to show towards the opposition at football matches, the Wasting Asset turned to The Breadwinner and me and said, "I know it wasn't easy being my parents."

Amen to that, but at least it was never dull. It has only just occurred to me in writing this that my heart no longer jumps when I see a police car within a mile of the farm.

The bridegroom also delighted the guests by thanking the minister, in the most powerful and heartfelt way, for what he described as a "hellova good service, hellova well done". The Breadwinner and The Farmer sank down into their seats. But, good man that he is, the Revie greeted this extraordinary tribute with good humour which looked to me like incredulous glee.

The star crack of the day came from the best man. He and the Wasting Asset set off to make hay and their fortunes around the world after being disciplined by Her Majesty for over-enthusiastic support for Aberdeen Football Club.

On that tour, which lasted several years, the best man said: "Jay bailed me out of some tricky situations and I bailed him out of a lot of debt." Turning to the bride, he said: "I can warn you, Angie, this guy's expensive."

As we danced the night away I reflected that the Wasting Asset would never give up the champagne tastes. Luckily he's started to do something about the Irn Bru income and he's got a strong woman to keep him at it.

October 28, 1996

Female famine in the countryside

THE FARMER is still bathing in the afterglow of the marriage of the Wasting Asset, his second son. And it is no wonder. For farmer's sons, especially farmers' second sons where the expectations are that much less, getting a lass to marry is quite an achievement.

The lassies hereabouts don't want to marry. Why should they?

When the lads were all worrying about their tractors or the onset of manhood, the girls were sticking in at school. So they left the boys at home with their tractors and went to universities and business colleges where they learned that there were other men in the world, men who weren't up to their necks in grease and to whom a 'pick-up hitch' was something altogether more alluring.

And if they do fancy the boy who used to be next door, these modern young women find they can have them ... but why marry? They are all better qualified than their brothers so they definitely don't need support.

We hear a lot about the urban underclass of young men with no jobs, no education, no hope and plenty of mindless aggression. Their sisters don't need such men – not on a permanent basis anyway.

But what about the rural underclass of young men? They're doing the only job in the world which is truly indispensable – producing food. They are good at their jobs and yet they are dispensable. The rural quines don't want them.

As far as rural Scotland is concerned women's liberation has arrived for this generation. It is the boys that need a boost.

Things have improved in my circle in the last year or two. There were at least a dozen young men getting through their 30s at an alarming rate and no signs of matrimony, but suddenly it is coming right.

Crookie nearly made 40 before marrying and becoming a father but has been making up for the time which had seemed a big loss. He has managed a child per year since. His third is a boy and Crookie's joy is unconfined, even by his overdraft. He swithered a long time before buying the place next door but his first comment on the arrival of his son is said to have been, "Thank God I bought that fairm."

The Man of Few Words, Davie the contractor, is to be married next year as soon as his father gets his retirement house up. And there's Mains. He went off to Canada this year supposedly after a farm on the prairies. He was hardly home before he met this fine lass from New Zealand. Her world tour ended in the North-east. Another wedding looms, though I think maybe New Zealand is too far.

And the Wasting Assets have both gone for outcrosses, to Holland and England. It is all working out for those, but I'm sad to say there are a heap more.

Hilly's still available and there's Watery too. Thirty-five and never been close.

Mind you, life for the bachelors of the rural underclass is not dull. The smart girls who escaped to the town do come home – sometimes to play. And there are the White Settlers.

We have a lot of them here because of the oil boom. That has meant that every croft and cottar house which is no longer required for modern agriculture is full of incomers, many of whom are rich and some of whom are bored.

The young men are handy for the wives of oilmen who work two weeks offshore at a time. OMO is such a wife. Her husband is very rich so she has no need to work. She gets bored when he is away, so she puts a packet of OMO in her kitchen window. The farmer of Waterside who knows that OMO means Old Man Offshore.

I think they should change their brand to Persil, for everyone is in on that code now except the husband, and he's never at home to read it.

And while I'm on rural affairs, I have to report that the new Aberdeenshire Council which is replacing Grampian Region has closed the public waterclosets beside our bus shelters.

This is a severe blow to the prestige of the village, for whom the erection of these amenities just after the war put us far ahead of our neighbours.

The villagers are not pleased. We now have a pleasure park used by picnickers from all over but no urinal. It is a scandal. What will we do if we are caught short while in the village? How can it be that we were rich enough to build the toilets after the greatest war the world has ever seen, and yet after the Thatcher Revolution we can't afford to keep it open?

It threatens to become a cause celebre like Clochmerle.

And I do feel for the residents. One of their problems is that the teenagers have "nothing to do". As with nearly all teenagers, that includes sleeping at nights and so they congregate at the bus shelter which, until last week, was handy for the toilets.

Now, apart from the noise and the amazing amount of waste paper they produce, the teenagers generate a prodigious volume of urine.

It is feared that the amenity of our village will not be enhanced by this change. It surely cannot be called progress.

243

Paid for not producing

DESPITE THE disappointing harvest and the continuing expense of building Whinhill of Ardo, The Farmer's bank balance is looking quite sound. There was even a sum of £13 and some pence for interest this quarter.

"That's not much," I hear you say. I disagree. That judgement depends on where you start from.

I judge my bank interest by reference to the bad old days when I used to have to pay £8,000 a quarter in interest and that was just to one of my two banks – and it didn't include interest to the mart for anything up to 200 big cattle.

Compared with that £13 on the positive side of the register is a magnificent sum.

And there is better news even than that.

At last I have got my ten farrow cows off to the incinerator. Those old dears who would once have graced the school dinners, the sausages and the hamburgers of this great country, went off to be burned in case they might be harbouring BSE, though there would be no reason to suspect such a thing. We have never seen that disease at Little Ardo.

It seems quite hard that they have to die for nothing. But it is hard on The Farmer, too. The price was right at £1.666 per kilo but The Farmer wasn't happy with the cheque. Those cows had just been weaned and they had not been being fed on the grass so they were quite lean. They only averaged 282 kilos deadweight or £448 cash-in-hand.

Now there is no doubt I could have had another £100 apiece if I'd been willing to feed them on tatties until February, but I couldn't do it. It is just too daft for a proud provider-of-food-for-the-masses to fatten cattle for the incinerator. I want to produce food, not greenhouse gases.

Still, the cheque added to The Farmer's happiness even if it did make him reflect sadly on the way his rewards have become divorced from the noble task of filling bellies. My grandfather was intensely proud of making two blades of grass grow where one had grown before. I wonder what he would have thought of using it to fatten cattle to burn.

The other reason for the unaccustomed health of The Farmer's bank balance is that the "rape cheque" is in. At least, that's what I was trying to tell the boys at the Salmon on Sunday. I was shouted down.

"Na, na, Charlie. You got the rape cheque ages ago. This latest cheque's the Arable Aid."

I think it is so much per acre for all the barley I grew last year and perhaps the money I was paid for not growing anything on my setaside.

At all events it was a cheque for £11,000 and it could hardly have gone to a better cause. It is safely into The Farmer's retirement fundie. But isn't it sad that all The Farmer's cash flow has been quite unrelated to his skill in producing food?

That arable aid is paid (almost) irrespective of how badly I grow barley and anybody can grow setaside. I find it sad. I am glad that retirement looms.

And while I'm on retirement, I know you are wondering how the building is going. It is going well.

Most of Whinhill is up to the eaves and though I am still scouring the countryside for suitable stone, it is more out of habit than of need for we are just about ready for the joiners.

When we decided to go for a traditional stone and slate house we wondered where we would get masons to work with

stone. In fact it is amazing how quickly they have relearned the skill after years of cement blocks and pebble-dash. Five firms priced for the job. Indeed so fashionable has it become to build with stone that the Peterhead quarry is opening again.

Perhaps progress does not have to mean everything becoming shoddier after all.

Mind you, it does look huge for a retirement house. Mossie says it is far too big. "You'll never be able to afford carpets for this lot," he says. "

You'll just need to tarmac the lot. You'll need a door big enough to let in the Barber-Greene." (I didn't know that was what they called a tarring machine either)

November 11, 1996

Leaving the land in safe hands

THE FARMER has been enduring criticism over his arrangements for retirement. He is handing over the place to the elder of his two daughters.

The Investment and her husband, Potions, will move into the farmhouse as soon as our retirement home is finished and into the business as soon as The Farmer thinks he has wrung all he can out of the situation.

Some people are shocked. "But what about the boys? Was neither of them interested?" And "Your daughter'll have to buy the others out."

Of course the Wasting Asset and even the Recovery Stock were interested. Who wouldn't be interested in an asset valued by today's market at half a million pounds?

But the peasant's first duty is to his land. He is only the custodian of his acres. He must do his best on it and leave it fit for the next generation. He must pass it on to someone who will accept a similar duty and be capable of looking after it.

In these difficult times it is very important to pass the land to someone who will be willing to stick with it and work hard at it with tiny financial rewards in relation to the farm's alleged value.

That's where the Senior Investment has it. She is careful and Potions knows all about working hard for little or no reward – I've seen to that in the last seven years.

That £500,000 valuation is mere finance anyway. I have always said the land is worth nothing in itself. Only if they farm it well will they get a living from this small place. Unless they farm it much better than The Farmer ever did they will never make as much out of Little Ardo as they can out of a well-run chemist's shop.

And it is just nonsense to say that value should be split four ways between The Farmer's children. To be fair, they have never even hinted at such a thing. They know full well that if they were all to get a share then none would get the land. That would sever a connection that goes back to their great-great-great-grandfather.

If we had a great estate we could consider dividing it in four but 250 acres divided into four parts leaves everyone with nothing but money.

So let them be shocked. Let them call The Farmer a feminist. It will be the third time in five changes that the female line has been favoured.

Of course I could have done things differently. I could have done as Digger Peter's father has done.

Old Pete called his son in the other day to tell him about the arrangements he had made for his succession.

You'll remember that Peter is the member of the discussion group who sells diggers. He is the one who explained the whole second-hand market. I couldn't see how he was able to keep going considering he had just sold me what seemed like a good digger at a reasonable price and had taken the old one back at the same price as he had sold it to me two years earlier.

It works like this. When Big Hamish goes to buy a digger for £30,000, Peter doesn't just get his £2,000 out of the deal. Hamish trades his old one in for, say £24,000 and Peter sells that and makes another £2,000. And so on until he has pocketed virtually the whole £30,000.

He was telling us on Sunday about selling a digger at the lower end of the market to a white settler who was trying to make a living out of small croft on the Moss of Byth.

Not having the language skills, he had not known that "Moss" in the North-east meant "peat bog" so he really is struggling. According to Peter he was a bit deficient in mechanical skills too.

Peter had confessed to this chap that although this machine he was selling was in all other respects wonderful, it had lost

its door in the course of its 25 years at the sharp end of the building trade.

"No door?" said the White Settler. "Oh dear! How shall I get out and in?"

Peter learned his trade as a dealer to get away from helping Old Peter on the farm. He found the rewards meagre, especially when they were still in Orkney. He hated the way Old Peter insisted that everything had to be done in the most difficult way possible. But what he hated most was the wind.

"If it wasna tied doon it blew away and sometimes it blew away even if it was tied doon.

"Like the henhoose. It was tied, yet efter a gale she was gone, hens and all. Old Pete thocht nothing much of it till he was going across on the ferry to the mainland. Here's the hen-hoose floatin in the Firth wi a sad-lookin hen on top of it."

Peter was prepared for a shock, for Old Peter never did things by the book. He was once banned from going home to Orkney for the County Show so he cadged a lift to the airport and was gone. Why should it be any different with Old Peter's 'arrangements'.

I take it the main objective in ordering one's affairs towards the end of one's days is to avoid the sort of unseemly wrangling which is so common among 'beneficiaries'.

There was clearly scope for error. Apart from Young Peter there are three sisters and a brother.

"Your mither and me has made a will," Old Peter announced. "We've jist left it all to your brother and you till sort it oot."

Caught out by the weather

IT'S CATCHY weather. If you don't know what that is, try to spray your crops in mid November when you are a couple of weeks behind the top men and they are beginning to ask you in the pub if you have given up farming already.

My excuse for being two weeks behind? Well, as you know, I had better barley yields than Mossie two years ago and he has been making sure it doesn't happen again. After a spell of ideal weather he phones up and gives me the recipe for the next brew. As I glance nervously out of the window at the gathering clouds he says, "Get it on right away, now. I finished mine three days since."

If you had nothing to do but paint byre doors and sweep the close you could look forward to a thin sun peeping down, bright and cool from a November sky. But get behind with the spraying and be sure you'll get catchy weather.

Now, that doesn't mean rain, frost and wind. What Heather the Weather would call "bad" weather is all right. At least you know where you are if

it is blind drift. Then you batten down the hatches and make an excuse to get on with some office work, especially if there is a fire and a comfortable old armchair in your office.

But if it is catchy weather you're kept on tenterhooks.

That's what it's been like.

It looks as if it could dry up enough to let me get spraying in the afternoon, so I fill the old sprayer first thing. I put in the chemicals when it is 80% full as that is best for making sure the stuff mixes properly.

It takes about an hour and a half to fill and by the time it is up to 80% the rain is on. Nothing is lost except that I have hung about all morning and it is now too late for the trip to town.

At least next morning I won't have to fill the tank.

But that doesn't matter because it is a dull morning and the crop is quite soaking. With not a purr of wind, there is no hope of spraying.

And yet, by dinnertime the wind has risen. The leaves are still soaking. You wouldn't dream of spraying if you weren't so far behind.

249

At two o'clock the crop is still wet but you can stand it no longer. There is a sticker in the cocktail which means you'll do some good if the rain stays off for ten minutes after you start. In goes the chemical. You start to top up the sprayer and on comes the rain.

Now, this brew is one of the most complicated cocktails known to man. We fear that it will go into one 1500 litre lump and be the end of my trusty sprayer.

There is £400 worth of stuff in her so we can't just empty it out. The tractor engine must be left running all day and night, agitating the brew, until the crop is dry enough.

The next day threatens rain but never quite delivers. In mid afternoon the crop is drying but the dew is expected in another hour or so. The Farmer gives up.

But he is wrong again. The wind rises. The dew is very slow to come down and we could have sprayed quite well.

The next day The Farmer is nearing the edge. He will go today if at all possible.

There is a very heavy dew and no wind. Heather the Weather has promised Jackie that there will be showers. The Farmer goes off to town. He takes the Jaggie by way of consolation. He will see the accountant for as short a time as possible as he costs £100 an hour. Then he will buy a new

250

jacket. This is not extravagance. The Breadwinner has pointed out that there is a hole in The Farmer's old one.

When, at a cost of almost £200, he emerges from the accountant's, The Farmer is met by sunshine and a gentle wind. The jacket with the hole will have to do a turn yet.

He rushes home. The rape isn't dry. There are some droplets of water still on the oily leaves, but it is drying. An hour later The Farmer is on the last gallon when, out of a clear sky, there is a sharp shower lasting perhaps a minute.

It will have washed all the chemical off the most recently sprayed leaves, and some of it off all 30 acres. The Farmer doesn't know where he is.

That's catchy weather. It is the weather which has made life miserable and left my 93 acres of rape in a mess.

Not that some of it wasn't in a mess already. I have told you of the field which got a severe attack of downey mildew. It is still very thin and there are two tiny patches which show no growth at all, not even weeds. If it survives the winter it will likely yield better than the others on the "all show, no dough" theory. The thinner it is the better the plants seem to perform.

But the real disappointment is the rape which was sown first. It was out of setaside and got off to the usual very good start. But it looks terrible. It has the biggest infestation of skellagh I've ever had and I have only once before had more dead nettles. Round the outside there are bits where it looks as though we are trying for a crop of meadow grass. It is short of something.

Can that be Mossie's final revenge?

November 25, 1996

Man in a suitcase

THE FARMER has been living out of a suitcase. In seven days he has spoken at four dinners and a lunch from Aberdeen to Ayr. It has been exhausting. The Farmer will never do it again. But he has learned a lot.

For a start he has learned what it is like to be gridlocked in Glasgow in what passes, in that douce green place, for a snowstorm.

The aim was to be in Ayr by six for dinner with the

251

Blackface sheep breeders. I would then give them a talk at half past seven. I left Little Ardo in glorious sunshine at just before two and was on the motorway just south of Glasgow at five, stationary in a snowstorm.

I am told that I should not have tried to cut across through East Kilbride to the Kilmarnock road and I believe it. By the time I made it to the Fenwick moors it was half past seven. I had almost disappeared forever in the Clarkston Triangle.

Two and a half hours to go ten miles is too much. In the days when I ran marathons I could have run it in an hour.

I knew the route roughly but all the signs were obliterated by snow. I sat behind a lorry, I knew not where, for several minutes before I realised that he was stuck. When I got past I had the road to myself, but where to go? There were no signs to tell me but I did sense that I was wrong just before I got right onto the wrong carriageway of a motorway. I sat in one jam for at least ten minutes reading a sign which I thought proclaimed "Tay". Surely I wasn't back in Dundee? When I got near enough I could see that it was a housing development by Tay Construction.

The frustrating thing was that while I was jammed I could ask directions. "Ayr? Oh God, you're a lang way fae there, Jimmy." But as soon as I got going I was lost again because it was far too dangerous to stop in the traffic.

Eventually I arrived two hours late for my dinner and half an hour late for my speech.

However I had learned another thing – the value of the mobile phone. I've had it for four years and used it maybe 20 times, but it was a godsend. I was able to keep in touch with my hosts and Jim Ritchie the secretary was able to talk me right to the door of the hotel, when I did get to Ayr.

Next day I was at the East of Scotland Grassland Society Silver Jubilee Dinner in Edinburgh. I told them East of Scotland and Grassland was something of a contradiction in terms and though it was said in jest I wasn't far wrong. It seemed that about half of the members are all arable now. That is a damnable thing about the EEC. It is making us grow crops to which our land is not always suited. CAP has been very hard on grass.

On Thursday I was learning again at the 90th birthday dinner in honour of Betty Forbes of Slains Park, on the cliffs of what used to be Kincardineshire but has now been gobbled up by Aberdeeenshire. A won-

derful homemaker, Betty produced four sons who have shown the way to make money in farming from Dundee to Elgin.

And the man for whom she made that wonderful home was some guy himself. Alistair Forbes went to college in Aberdeen to learn farming and when he graduated he went into partnership with the Principal of the Rowett, Sir John Boyd-Orr.

Anyway, Betty was in a mood to teach me more. I was not half as good a writer as my father had been. I am afraid I have come upon more proof that she is right. The Breadwinner was tidying and came across a copy of John R Allan's diary 'Day in Day Out' which he used to write for the Department's quarterly journal 'Scottish Agriculture'. That's what Betty used to read.

It is full of wit. I offer you this example "18.12.55 – calves now being put on dry feed after a week or two. The results seem good for the milk saved is paid for by the Board in the middle of the following month and the food goes into the file marked 'accounts rendered'; an excellent system when you have to scrape a living from the second class lands of Scotland."

Then on Friday we had the Ythanside Farmers' Dinner. There I learned that there is still

253

at least one male chauvinist left in the piggery of Scottish Agriculture. George Rafferty is the vet from the Highlands who was the hero of a television series a few years back. Most ladies remember it for his kitchen, which was worse than antiquated. I remember there was a tap in it but not much else. Every woman who saw that series remembers that his wife, in the nineties and in the middle class, had no washing machine.

George is unashamed. He started his speech to this mixed gathering something like this. "I know you'll be wondering so I'll tell you. My wife still has no washing machine. Now, her vital statistics are 36-25-37 and ladies, unless you can shape up like that, go home and throw out your washing machines."

I also learned that the worst speech to give is the vote of thanks because you can't really get stuck into the hospitality until it is all over. If I come back in another life I shall be a minister. After I have said grace I'll be able to have a rerr terr.

And when I was nearly home I was given, for the umpteenth time, a lesson which I will surely never learn now. Never go unprepared into the Scottish weather. At the end of the road I ran into a snowdrift and got quite stuck. I had not prepared for this. In sweater, slacks and trainers I was snug enough in the Jaggie. But it was blowing hard and I had no coat.

There was nothing for it but to get out the suitcase. I put the trousers of the good suit on above the slacks, then the kilt and Prince Charlie jacket and topped it off with the suit jacket. A pair of Y-fronts was all I could find to keep the wind away from my lugs. I may have looked like a flitting, but by the time I won home I was glad of every stitch.

Hotels are biggest threat to beef

THERE BEING little doing on the snowbound farm and the lads having been prevented by their wives from storming London for the Smithfield Show, The Farmer has been thinking. It has done him no good at all.

His thoughts include that the threat to our beef industry from BSE is nothing compared with that posed by Scotland's hotels.

Nobody who recognises a steak or roast beef as the ultimate culinary treat is going to stop eating it because there is a tiny perceived risk of getting CJD, one of the rarest diseases known to man.

But what if they only eat beef in Scotland's hotels? Worst of all, what if their main contact with roast beef is at the Farmer's Ball, the Agricultural Show Dinner and Dance, and weddings?

There they will be lucky if they get beef which has been hung for more than one week and they may even get some of the stuff that is rushed from byre to plate in two days.

They will be very lucky indeed if their roast beef has not been cooked the day before, pre-cut, microwaved and served with bisto on top.

They will be lucky if they get a decent thick slice off the roast. It will very likely have been put through the bacon slicer and for that you have to have it cold.

Because of the torture the hotels put our roasts through you will be lucky indeed if you are offered roast beef which is not dried out. You will go far to find a bit of the pink stuff with juices and flavours still there.

I am especially conscious of this appalling set of truths because of my recent tour, when I ate four such dinners and two of what we used to call dinners (luncheons), in a week.

And there is worse. It is not that the cooking in those hotels was all bad. There was a choice of chicken on five occasions and that was very acceptably cooked. I know because I was usually sat beside a lady who was watching her figure and so could spare a little for the disappointed beefeater.

Worse still, they mostly had a generous choice of lightly

255

cooked vegetables which were anything from acceptable to delicious.

So why do they make such a bog of beef? Can it be malice?

Aberdeen and Northern Marts recently donated the beef to a prestigious gathering at a very up-market venue. Eddie Gillanders, who looks after their public relations, made sure they got nothing but the best and telephoned two days before the event just to make sure all was well with the beef. "Yes, beautiful. We cooked it yesterday." Eddie doesn't have much hair to pull out these days which is just as well. How can they be so ignorant?

One of my dinner partners last week is a fairly aggressive vegetarian, a cousin of a cousin of mine and an impressive person on many counts. Soon she will be a minister.

But she was a disappointing dinner partner, being unable to mitigate the horrors of my very course-grained, tough and tasteless beef, with any chicken. I didn't fancy any of her vegetarian lasagne.

And The Farmer found her disappointing also as an adversary in debate about diet. She took refuge in the bible and that put The Farmer at a distinct disadvantage.

The Farmer isn't an atheist, but at the same time he didn't pay sufficient attention during bible studies to make much headway in debate with one who is studying hard for the priesthood. She said that Daniel was the world's first vegetarian and that his encounter with the lions was some kind of proof that vegetarians were best.

Well, The Farmer was for none of that. "Och well, if Daniel was a vegetarian there'd be nothing on him. Lions don't kill for fun you know. They only kill for the pot, so to speak. So they wouldn't bother with a bag of bones. They'd be looking for a nice fat meat-eater."

But that wouldn't do. The contrary was the case. For Daniel had already taken part in a controlled scientific experiment which showed clearly that meat-eating was bad for you.

He had persuaded Melzar, Prince of the eunochs who were looking after him and his pals, to feed half of them on pulses and water and while the other half partook of the King's meat and wine. "And at the end of ten days their countenances appeared fairer and fatter in the flesh than all the children that did eat the portion of the King's meat and drank his wine."

The Farmer did his best. It was the wine that had done the damage. Those children should not have been boozing at their ages. No wonder they were off colour.

Sadly, the poor Farmer was shown up again. The 'children' in question weren't children at all, but the Children of Israel, which anybody who has read the Old Testament knows are, of course, adults.

There is another possible explanation. Perhaps Melzar didn't cook the King's meat properly. Perhaps he contracted the supply out to one of Scotland's hotels – one that specialises in catering for functions.

December 9, 1996

Plenty cooks to do the devil's work

MY EPISTLE of last week caused quite a stir.

Robin Geyer, who farms in Fife, faxed me right away with his support. He had been brought up on a beef farm where one of the sayings was, "God sends the food and the devil sends the cooks."

I'm not sure that I would go as far as that. After all, where would God be without us to "till the fields and scatter the good seed o'er the land"?

There is an old Aberdeenshire story which makes that point. The minister was shocked to find one of his flock feeding his beasts on a Sunday. What was he doing barrowing turnips to his byreful of stots when he might have been at church? "Remember the Sabbath and keep it holy," the farmer was advised.

"But Minister, what about the beasts?"

"The Lord will provide," said the minister with the faith that gives so much strength to so few nowadays.

"Well Minister, I'm sorry, but I'll continue to look after my stock on a Sunday and go to the kirk if there's time. The Lord may be a good enough baillie in summertime but he's nae much use in the winter."

Of course it's a lot easier nowadays. But wintering cattle is still onerous and it is still a duty of care. It is still seven days a week and calves still prefer to be born at night. You need a fair reward. With BSE that is not at the moment available. So it really is adding injury to insult when our final product is so badly cooked that it is less than a treat.

I thought perhaps it was only The Farmer who felt like that, but letters from the Black Isle to the Borders have assured me that many beef producers feel the same frustration. If there is only turkey on the menu he is furious beef is ignored. And nine times out of ten, if beef is served, he is even more furious because it is spoiled.

I was telling Potions all about it yesterday.

"What about pork?" he said. "We were at a wedding last week and we had reheated, thin slices with gravy poured on them, served on a silver platter. Talk about 'fur coat and no knickers'. I thought it was beer mats they were serving us."

Yes. Beef gets the worst mauling, but I have to admit pig producers have cause for complaint, though at least they've been well paid recently.

From my speaking tour I can report that the great English breakfast is in deep trouble. It too is under attack from the devil's chef and his microwave. Never have I had such a soggy mess as I was served under the title of the "full English breakfast". The point is that bacon must be grilled till the fat has some crispness and you just cannot get that in a microwave. You just get a limp white disaster. Sausages showed no sign whatsoever of having been grilled. They looked as though they had been steamed.

Yet most of the places that have ruined the English breakfast have come along in leaps

and bounds as regards providing, cereals, muesli, fresh fruit, yoghurt and brown toast. It is only the meat and eggs (Oh! the warmed-up rubber eggs) that are ruined.

I have complained a lot about all the livestock farmer's work being ruined. But farmers did not provide the raw material for the worst culinary disaster I suffered two weeks ago.

As a change from the full English breakfast I chose, in Ayrshire, that undeniably Scottish breakfast, kippers. I hadn't had any for years and really looked forward to them as they are a real favourite. I once bought a whole box in Mallaig, straight from the kipperer and, grilled slowly for a long time, they were kings among breakfasts even if they did speak back to you for the rest of the day.

What must our tourists must think of us?

'They' turned out to be 'it', and that turned out to be just as well. It looked nice on the fleshy side but the skin side hadn't even been shown to the grill. That side was totally raw. The nice waitress told me the plan was to cook breakfasts in the oven and then grill them up before serving. She offered me a fresh full English breakfast. I should have known to decline.

So we farmers have a grievance. But what about the fishermen? I hope they were well rewarded financially for that herring because it was destroyed before it got to the plate and it ended up in the cat's dish.

And do the people who run that hotel not know the old saying, "That's nae herring you're eating, that's men's lives?"

No beef for the sheep man

THE FARMER has to watch himself in writing this column. He must remember that this is the diary of a farmer, not the political commentary of a journalist. There is no call here for balance or to give a careful account of the other side of the story, for this is The Farmer's diary.

All the same, he has had to sing a wee bit dumb recently, on the horrors that are said to have befallen the farming industry as a result of BSE.

"Oh yes," we say, "we farmers are going through tricky times just now." And because of all the publicity BSE has engendered that sort of remark goes unquestioned. It is nice having so much sympathy.

The truth is that those who make their living by producing beef alone have suffered badly. But the beef men who produce other food as well have won a little as they have lost a little. And most of the other farmers have made money out of BSE.

The flight of consumers from beef has done wonders for the sale of sheep.

Do you remember the Armstrong? He was the man I used to get from the machinery ring to help at Little Ardo.

I remember him best as the lad who, while in the navy, slammed his foot so hard in saluting the deceased at a military funeral that the ground gave way and he landed in the grave.

Anyway, about April when the roof really fell in on beef producers, the Armstrong's wife got very depressed about the red meat sector and insisted that Jim get rid of all these damned beasts, no matter what the loss.

So the three stirks had to go and the 50 broken-mouthed ewes. They'd been bought in the backend for a song and were lambing good-oh.

Not a man to waste time reading the papers, the Armstrong had no idea how prices were going so he was absolutely gobsmacked by the price he got for his sheep. When the Armstrong took his cheque home to his good lady his credibility as a farmer was totally restored.

It's the same with the

pigmen. They have never made money like in the last couple of years, thanks to BSE. My goodness, Mossie, the only pigman in our discussion group, doesn't know where to hide all his money these days. He has to go shooting three times a week.

It's the same with poultry farmers. The people have eaten less beef but they haven't done any less eating.

Then there are the dairymen. To produce milk they have to produce calves. The half of those calves which are bulls were worth between nothing and £100 before BSE. Since the government started buying those bull calves to slaughter them they have all been worth the guts of £100. To most dairymen that has been a considerable bonus of BSE. To those

using Channel Island breeds (true value at birth negative) BSE has been manna from Brussels.

This point was brought up at the Aberlour discussion group I visited last week. I was speaking at the home of Walker's shortbread, which is handy for several of the best Glenlivet malts. It is an area where nearly all the farm income comes from red meat.

I asked my hosts how they had fared with BSE. The beef producers are suffering dreadfully, and that's most of them.

On the other hand the sheep men have done very well, though it was pointed out that as the market prices go up so the support comes down.

But what about those who have both? Well there we got an

interesting guesstimate. If you were two thirds sheep the losses on the cattle would just about balance the gains on the sheep.

Mind you, even in this red meat area it's hard to get a bit of beef. The lads were entertaining me to a meal in the Station Hotel and I'm afraid they got a red face.

We would all have beef. There wasn't a steak on the menu so we all went for the stew. That was off "but the salmon's nice". The chilli con carne? "You can't have that till chef arrives and the beefburgers are off too."

All right then, I'd wait for the chilli con carne. When the chef got up from his rest he was able to confirm that too was off, "but the fish fritters are nice".

Was the fish fresh?

"Oh yes. We had some the other day. Best haddock we've ever tasted."

The Farmer had the salmon fritters,which were not bad at all. But I don't think my hosts will be taking their guests there again.

Mine hostess was Welsh and a vegetarian, which may be neither here nor there, but it does seem likely that the pub being for sale was in some way relevant.

December 23, 1996

Grave business of whisky collection

PENNY WASHERS, the white settler, has been over to Islay to buy cattle. It can take several days and is chargeable to expenses.

He told us about it at the discussion group at the Salmon on Sunday. We knew all about the on-farm sales and the apres-la-sale which, on an island group famous for its distiller-ies, can be very tough going. But he did have a couple of good stories which he collected on the Jura leg of the safari.

The first concerned a lady from the south who was taking the peace-and-quiet cure in Jura. It seemed to be working, especially when the local farmer started sniffing about. The lady was asked if she

would like to go walking. The farmer had to go and see the stirkies. Would she like to see them too?

Indeed she would.

When the lady returned from her trip, her pal and hostess was agog. How had she got on? Oh, it had been very nice. The only disappointment was they had hoped to see the Starkeys. She had hoped they might be invited in for a coffee or something. But they hadn't seen the Starkeys so she was dying for a drink.

Penny Washers was amazed at the gang of dealers who had been robbing the islanders for years and yet were lionised by their victims, as they swished round the islands paying as little as they could get away with for as much as they could get.

Chief among the lions when I last went, 20 years ago, was the great Aberdeenshire dealer Willie Low. He certainly was popular. I will always remember the reception he received at one farm where they were selling some hundreds of handy-weight steers.

When we arrived at the farm at nine o'clock for the sale at half past, Mrs Epps had a magnificent spread ready in the kitchen for the invaders. It was not surprising Willie was a bit later as he'd had a very sociable evening. But when he did arrive Mrs Epps was ecstatic.

"Oh Willie, you've come

back to see us," and he got a big hug. "Now Willie, will you have a cup of tea or a wee dram?"

"Oh," says Willie, "it's jist some early in the mornin for tea."

Anyway, Penny Washers found out that you get a great welcome on those islands if you are willing to fill a float. And he got a splendid story of an island funeral.

This farmer had two passions. One was for his land. And he managed to persuade the laird to sell him a small plot on the farm so that he might be buried there.

His other passion was his collection of island whiskies. He had not been a poor man and had pursued his hobby for 40 years, so it was with great reluctance that he approached the day when he would have to leave all that nectar behind.

In the event he left a will insisting that the whisky was to be drunk at his wake. The guests were to drink as much as they wanted but any left over had to be poured into the grave.

So they had the extraordinary vision of the open grave with the coffin already at rest and an open Ifor Williams trailer standing by, tail-door down, laden down with whisky bottles and surrounded by grim-faced farmers, crofters and estate workers trying to minimise the amount that would have to be wasted.

December 30, 1996

Creaming it with Jerseys

I HAVE news which will amaze you. Mackies, the Aberdeenshire firm who are among the biggest milk producers with over 400 cows, are planning to sell their black and whites.

Yet this is not the retrenchment which cynical neighbours have been predicting for many years. For Mackies are only changing breeds. They are going in for Jerseys. The Farmer is claiming full credit for this change of strategy on the part of his cousin. Was it not The Farmer who pioneered the Jersey beef herd eight years ago?

That was a hair-brained idea which came from taking a look at the problem from the

point of view of the scientist and the accountant. What was required was milky mums with wide pelvises for ease of calving. The Jerseys had both those characteristics.

Then we needed beefy calves, so we would transplant those from pure beef animals and get the best mothering available for the best calves possible. How could we fail to make money?

Now Mackie's have taken a cool scientific look at their milk requirements and decided that the Jersey is a better bet than the Holstein/Friesians.

The key to their logic is that they do not require water. They do not sell their milk in liquid form to the public and so get no benefit from producing a sea of blue from each cow.

They make their milk into ice cream and for that all they need is the cream and it is well known that Jerseys produce more cream per gallon than do their competitors. Fair enough, but what really gives the wee Jerseys the edge over their enormous counterparts is the quota system.

Farmers nowadays can't just go ahead and produce all the milk they want. They have to pay 65 pence a litre for a quota for every drop their cows produce. A cow producing 8,000 litres of milk a year would be useless without £5200 worth of quota.

So with their Jersey cows

Mackie's reckon they will get more cream for their quota.

And the story gets better.

One of the big snags with the black and whites is their genetic strength. Since the Holstein has come completely to dominate the trade, the surplus calves which used to be so good for producing beef are now not much use except for bones for soup. Even if you put the best of Charolais bulls over the Holsteins you are liable to be left with the pointed shape so prized among dairymen.

But the Jerseys are so weak genetically that you can put a Belgian Blue bull over them and get calves which have the best attributes of a beef beast – put crudely, a long strong back and big round backside.

I hope it works. My beef scheme didn't, mainly because the Jersey cowies weren't fit to compete in our mixed herd. Mackie's don't intend to make that mistake.

Mr Mackie told me of his plans at the Harbro Bonspiel and Barbecue, where Mossie was roasting the beef on his converted rotospreader and I was one of the carvers. Mackie had had a good day. Having been in a winning rink he had been presented with, I thought, an above average golden statue on a wee plastic plinth.

Unfortunately, Mossie got hold of the trophy and to our horror started scratching at it. "It's all right," says he, "I'm only tryin to get at the chocolate."

It was one of my maternal grandfather's boasts that he could put a hen round twelve people and keep them all laughing while he carved.

At the bonspiel the contract was to put three 24lb roasts round 65 people. And they were already so well stoked-up there was no need to try to keep them laughing. It would have been a job to get them to stop.

Of course there would have been even more to go round had Mossie's knife not slipped three days earlier.

You see he hangs the beef for a month in his own chill and he'd been showing it to the Red Rooster and me when he was overcome with pride. "What about a steak, boys?"

He nipped into the house and returned with a great butcher's knife. He sliced a whole fillet off, wrapped it hygienically in newspaper and marched us to the Salmon Inn.

Mossie slapped the fillet on the bar and challenged the landlady, "Foo much corkage are ye goin to charge me on that?"

It was delicious. As we tucked in the great man enthused: "This is the way forward, isn't it? Bring your own. You canna be too careful nowadays."

266

January 6, 1997

Immune to germs

THE DISCUSSION group has a fervent wish for 1997 – no more food disasters.

And it isn't that we care more about our profits than about the people who have suffered from food poisoning in recent years.

As the scare moves from eggs to beef, to lamb and to precooked meat, the people don't eat any less. They just eat more of other foods. And who produces those? While one farmer's bank balance suffers, another's benefits.

Even the tough guys in the discussion group are wounded by the food scares. We pride ourselves on feeding the world. Sixty million people in Britain can manage without the heroes in the New Year honours list, but farmers are indispensable.

So when we are told that the food we produce is dangerous we are much more than sad. We are bewildered.

One thing is sure. The boys in the discussion group are not willing to accept any of the blame for food scares.

Take the suggestion that it was dangerous to feed cows grain mixed with high protein derived from offal from slaughterhouses. It is agreed that that was dangerous, at least at the low temperatures that were being used to cook it in England. The boys are quite happy that the government has banned that. But with all its scientific advice it still took the government ages to make up its mind, so how was an individual farmer to know any better?

It is the same with antibiotics. It is said that their overuse in farm animals risks the development of superbugs. Perhaps it does. It is a matter for scientists to research and governments to act upon.

All a farmer knows is that if he has a beast that is ill it will do better with antibiotics and if he adds things to their diets his stock will grow more economically. He cannot sort out the science. He can only use what gives the best results within the law or go out of business.

In any case, individual action by farmers can do no good. Freedom from superbugs is what economists call a public good. The bugs will develop unless everyone acts together. Public enforcement is the only way to get near that.

Peter the digger salesman thinks all these scares are the fault of media hype. His theory

is that there has always been an outbreak of something somewhere but we didn't worry because we didn't get to hear about it.

"When I was a bairn you would never have heard if 20 folk had died in Aiberdeen never mind Lanarkshire. Forty years ago we didna even ken where Lanarkshire was. Where is Lanarkshire anyway?"

There must be some truth that media interest has fed our hypochondria as a society.

But the consensus of biased opinion concentrated around the ideas of Big Hamish. His philosophy goes like this: "There's far too much hygiene nooadays. You're supposed to eat a tonne of muck afore ye die

and we're all so clean that we're nae eatin hardly any."

There are two things wrong with Hamish's theory.

First it's 'a peck of earth' you're supposed to eat, not 'a tonne of muck'.

And second, you're not supposed to eat it all at once.

But the Big Man has surely got a point. We have put up many barriers to stop us from taking in microbes. To infect us germs must swim through oceans of disinfectant, scramble round the layers of latex, and penetrate the shrinkwrap that seems to come with all our food nowadays. Most of the time they don't make it and we're safe.

But when one batch does

get through, they take us completely by surprise.

The child brought up on a weak solution of Savlon instead of mother's milk and bathed in Domestos has built up no immunities. It has no idea how to do battle with the microbe hoards.

Everybody who has worked in an old-fashioned byre of cows has had a smack across the mouth with a wet sharny tail. He would wipe his face but never wash it until he got home. Yet it never did him any harm, despite the fact that the E coli were always there.

And I remember the chronic salmonella we had among our calves. They all scoured. Some died but not many. There were always plenty left to infect the next batch.

So every day we took the temperature of each calf. Then as the vet-approved hygiene measure we took a pinch of the calf's hair and drew the thermometer through our fingers before moving on to the next calf. We then injected ailing calves and staggered on until it cleared up at last.

But the point is that we never got salmonella poisoning ourselves. And yet Gordon, the stockman, smoked throughout the entire exercise and none of us would have dreamt of washing our hands at piece time.

On second thoughts, maybe a tonne of muck was pretty near it, but we're sure it helped build up our resistance.

January 13, 1997

Cavalier attitude to drink driving

LAST YEAR it was the weather that kept us safe from the Bobbies at the New Year. There was such a storm that the only way to go first footing was by snowplough.

There was no such luck this year. While the rest of Britain seems to have been hit by winter we in the North-east corner have had it surprisingly mild. I have only had one burst pipe despite being 400 pigs and 200 cattle below the carrying capacity of the place.

And worse than that, the authorities have had a very dangerous new line in their worthy campaigns to have revellers pay more attention to their driving and less to their thirsts.

A poster has been sent to the owners of the area's watering holes encouraging boozers to phone a special number and report anyone they feel may be drunk and likely to drive a car.

Northsound, the local radio station, is never stopped giving out the number and an invitation to snoopers.

Now there is no doubt that the way we have adapted to the Draconian attitude to drunk drivers is a good thing.

Some of the boys who have been men long enough to have children old enough, get them to come to the pub and drive them home. Then there are the wives. The Breadwinner always says there is no need for men to fear Women's Lib: "After all, we'll always need the boys to drive us TO boozy parties."

Even in the roughest of company, nowadays, someone stays within sight of sobriety. That's all to the good.

But I'm not sure I want to live in a society where we are all encouraged to phone the police when we suspect the civil law is in danger. It smacks of the societies which have been swept away in Eastern Europe.

And it isn't just that. The quality of information the police get is bound to be a bit biased. People who are popular are less likely to be reported. Those who have annoyed their neighbours are likely to be reported for spite. Heaven help the farmer who has left his gas gun on all night.

The police can only process a tiny number of cases per night so surely it is better to have them use their traditional methods of selection rather than going where Tom, Dick or Harry points his jealous finger.

Of course there are those who think the new system of beggar-my-neighbour is a godsend. These clever people will drink to excess and then, when they are ready to swerve homeward, phone the snoopers number and send the police on a wild goose chase. That will clear the way for a 'safe' drive home.

Anyway, this Hogmanay we all managed somehow. We had a great party at the Salmon Inn. All the wives were there, unlike on Sundays for the discussion group. Mossie's wife decided early in their marriage that her husband would easily handle all the drinking required and the Irishman has the opposite arrangement with his wife.

Unfortunately, The Breadwinner and I do not have such complementary tastes and they kept asking: "Who's driving? You Charlie. An orange juice?"

"No thank you, I'll easy

drive. And make mine a double."

We had a great night. A superb three-course meal of stuffed mushrooms, sirloin steak (thick, well hung and rare), sticky toffee pudding, Irish coffee and port (make mine a double).

Of course we didn't approve of the disco. On Hogmanay there should surely be enough genuine jollity without having to add electronic noise.

Worse than that, they had imported a smoke machine, as though the Red Rooster's pipe wasn't enough. I'm sure that Bas the landlord didn't get enough fireworks when he was a boy, for he took great joy from enveloping himself and the dancers in this awful stuff.

"Mair smoke, Bas," shouts Mossie, "We can still see your lang face."

I thought that was an apt, if cruel, call but we had no time to dwell on it. We were just slipping onto the drams – "Ach, make mine a double." "And a chaser?" "What use is a half pint to man who is half cut?" – when Mossie gave me nudge.

The bill was on its way. He grabbed The Breadwinner and I grabbed the Irishman's wife and we were off jiving enough to put the young to shame, if they had any.

What a success. When we came back the bill was paid.

In no time it seemed we were at one for the road, one for the ditch and a clochendichter (Ach, make mine a double). It was time for The Farmer and The Breadwinner to go home to

Little Ardo to see in their last New Year in the farmhouse.

And they needn't have worried about The Farmer being done for miraculous driving. We tottered round to the back of the Salmon, held the barbed wire for each other as we negotiated Little Ardo's fence, got into the old Cavalier and drove home through the frostbound rape.

The Farmer may have been drunk but he must have been fairly capable for the evidence next day was that he had either kept exactly to the tramlines... or flown home.

January 20, 1997

You can't teach a gundog new tricks

AFTER NIPPING through the rape fields to avoid breaking the drink-driving laws, we prepared to spend our last New Year in my family home. Next year we should be in Whinhill of Ardo.

The prospect of spending the rest of the evening alone with The Breadwinner was not an unattractive one. After 36 years she still laughs at my jokes and I still crave that approval. But I couldn't help thinking, as the strains of the disco faded mercifully behind us, that John Yull would have thought the blood was getting a bit thin had he seen his great-grandson leaving the pub with his own wife before midnight on Hogmanay.

Certainly our intention, to have a quiet night in, would have been inexplicable to the old boy. He never had a quiet Hogmanay. The records of our general merchants show that one December 31st he bought two gallons of whisky. And yet, on January 1st, he had to go back for another gallon.

When midnight came this time I turned off the box and The Breadwinner and I sang the song we all (in rural Aberdeenshire) used to sing at midnight:

"A good New Year tae ane and aa'
And mony may ye see
And during aa the years tae come,
Happy may ye be."

We were just about ready for the stairs at one o'clock when there was uproar at the

272

door. I hid the good stuff and got out the Grouse. In they all came, a motley crew who wouldn't know the difference sober, singing "Come in, come in, it's nice tae see ye. Foos yersel? Yer lookin grand."

And I have to admit it was nice to see them. Especially as my sons – the Wasting Asset and his big brother, the Recovery Stock – were among them.

I know they must be fed up of people saying: "Did you not want the farm, that your sister's getting it?" So it was poignant that they were our first feet.

At half past two they took the road and The Breadwinner and I took the stairs for the last time on a Hogmanay. There are no stairs at Whinhill.

Whether it was the enormity of the occasion or not I do not know, but New Year's day was a first. It was the first first of January that The Farmer had enjoyed without a hangover.

And 1997 is off to a flying start, with a candidate for most pathetic story of the year.

Penny Washers has a new enterprise and a new gundog. Each was quite a good idea but they didn't mix.

The four bantam hens and the cock would provide our man with the most delicious fresh eggs. They would be costless, because, in common with Penny Washers' normal husbandry, they would peck about for what they could get.

Gustas is a beautiful black Labrador, superbly trained and well bred. The seller told Penny Washers it was a snip at £1000 and then sold it to him for £700.

Anyway this hound was also allowed free range upon the farm and therein lay the trouble. The dog was trained to pick up and deliver to his master small flightless foul. For all he knew the splendid bronze bantie cock filled the bill perfectly.

When Penny Washers next saw his banties, there were the four hens in refuge on top of the combine but there was no sight of the cock, who, he remembered being told, couldn't fly.

Then round the corner came Gustas with the bantie in his mouth.

Now, a good dog is trained to have a 'soft' mouth. It does not eat the quarry but gently brings it to his master. So the bantie was only shaken. But what to do with Gustas? Penny Washers thought that stern words would do. He explained to Gustas about the differences between bronze banties and pheasant cocks and told him not to do it again.

That had about as much affect on Gustas as stern words have on the human youth of today. In no time he was back, eagerly wagging his tail, presenting the bantie to his master for execution.

Penny Washers decided on a dose of what used to tame teenagers. But then again, he couldn't give Gustas too much of a leathering or it might put him off pheasant for life.

The best solution would have been for the bantie to learn to fly but despite the encouragement given by Gustas, it was all over by next morning.

Penny Washers' flying bantams were short of a helpmate in their work of producing eggs. The wee cock was undamaged but I guess he just gave up.

January 27, 1997

The Farmer breaks duck to save face

JAMES FOWLIE, farmer of Auchrynie and one of the cattle Barons of Buchan, is that rare combination of gentleman, farmer and gentleman-farmer. I don't doubt that he had a pair of tackety boots in his younger days, and a pair of wellies, but they were abandoned early in his career. James's contribution to his farming empire concentrated on what could be done with a pencil, a telephone and, most importantly, the almost imperceptible twitch of the hand with which he bought several thousand forward store cattle per year.

That is the way I would have liked to farm, but here I am, right at the end of my stint, still with the alarm set for seven and the frozen wellies waiting for me in the back porch.

Yet I could hardly be doing less. This is the openest winter anyone can remember. No snow to clear. No feed to get in through the drift. No burst pipes to see to. Apart from the hour or so seeing to the beasts in the morning, it is more or less the life of a gentleman.

The Farmer has even been to a shoot, and a 'driven day' at that.

It's an odd thing, the shooting. It seems to be very much a part of the farming life for the A team. It's an uncertain business trying to get Mossie, the Red Rooster, the Young Laird and Crookie at home these days. They and the aristocracy of the agricultural supply and food trades like the Butcher and Chairman Fred, seem to take turns of entertaining one another to a day at the pheasants.

Small farmers like Hillie, Mains, Waterside and myself simply can't afford it.

Except for once a year. That is how I pay Mossie for his work as crop consultant. He books a day and I pay. I bring the port and the stilton.

"That's a small price," I can hear you say, "for supervising the spraying of 180 acres of crop." You're right, too, but it's not that cheap. It costs £250 each and an extra £20 per bird for any above 150 shot by the ten guns.

Now, you don't need a degree in economics to see that this is a lopsided deal. The guests like to shoot as big a bag as possible, but it is in the interest of those who are paying to keep the death rate as low as can be achieved with honour.

As one of the hosts you don't want, as happened to The Farmer last year, the lady organiser saying in a loud voice: "Charlie seems to be having an off day." However much it is costing, you must shoot a few.

And that is a problem for The Farmer.

He has been brought up on rough shooting for the pot. There the best shot is the one who gets a couple of pigeons for the dog, a hare for the soup and a brace of pheasants for Saturday night, and only uses four cartridges.

Not so in the Laird's driven day at £250, plus VAT. Here it is bad form to shoot at anything below the level of the trees and

it is a hanging offence to hit them on the ground. The best shot is the man who brings down a bird in which the rough shooter wouldn't dream of investing a tenpenny cartridge.

But the biggest cause of his embarrassment is that The Farmer just can't shoot. His idea of a perfect stance is one among high trees where he has no hope of hitting anything and no fear of being seen missing.

The embarrassments started early. The Farmer forgot that he had a pair of moleskins and could only find one legging. He would certainly be the only one in corduroy flairs. The fore-and-after was lost and the only headgear he could find was an old ANZAC hat given him by an Australian Caber-tosser in the days when The Farmer was an athlete.

My guest showed his disapproval by saying to the sergeant-major, "I hope Charlie disna have another off day, though he looks like one."

The old side-by-side, which comes out once a year, proved so rusty the cartridges wouldn't eject. I kept forgetting to put off the safety catch and I'd be sure to be loading when the best chances came.

They thought The Farmer wasn't trying, but they were wrong.

At lunch time he was the only one without a kill. Mossie rubbed it in. "Charlie was £100-a-bird last year but this year he canna even work it oot. He hasna shot anything to divide the cost by."

Disapproving glances were shot at The Farmer.

In the penultimate drive all started to come right. The unluckiest woodcock in Buchan came swooping through the trees. In raising his gun, The Farmer caught his cranny in his pocket, the gun went off and the woodcock dropped dead.

And then in the last drive The Farmer hit a purple patch.

A pheasant came out between him and Drew Phillip, a renowned shot. To The Farmer's horror Drew missed the bird with both barrels. There was nothing for it but to blast off, in full view of everyone, despite the fact that the bird was now well over his left shoulder.

He missed with the first barrel and, quite unable to turn he tried to follow the bird over until the arthritic back was arched double. Just as the bird was disappearing over the trees, the knee that used to throw the hammer gave out. The Farmer gasped in agony. The trigger went off and the pheasant fell among the pines.

After that The Farmer could miss nothing. He lost count and damn the expense. And at the dinner he was presented with a handsome hip flask for the shot-of-the-day.

With retirement looming I may escape having the fluke revealed for what it was.

Daft controls begin to bite

NO ONE can remember such an open winter. We had a couple of flurries of snow in December which caused us to put the snowplough on the tractor. There was a bit of frost in early January, but by the end of the month it felt like April.

The grass is even growing on Scotland's cold shoulder, and the 35 cows which are going out and in are getting sufficient grass to be content with rather less than one bale of treated straw per day and only two and a half pounds of cake.

If fodder becomes worth anything again the fine weather will have saved me a fortune.

Another bright spot is the calves. I have 45 of them to be sold when the grass really gets going and The Farmer's expectations are rising. Not only are the stores looking dearer, not only are they thriving better than last year's, but the price of their feed is down.

Cheap barley has helped the price of cattle cake, we have at least twice as much first rate straw as we can ever hope to use, and potatoes are already at £12 a tonne delivered and ex-pected to go as low as the cost of delivery.

At this time we'd normally expect to get a few rejects from the dressing process but Big Hamish is only able to get £7 more than we're giving him to cover the cost of dressing and bagging his ware for human consumption. So he is selling them to us off the undressed heap.

Our cattle are dining on the best Wilja which I remember making £350 a tonne many years ago when money was worth something.

Some feeders even expect the big potato growers to be willing to deliver free to anyone who will give them a dump free of landfill charges.

I dare say that is outrageous optimism but if they weren't outrageous optimists they wouldn't be in cattle.

Anyway, it is all making The Farmer consider keeping his stores and finishing them at home. His retirement fundie needs every boost available, and the beef just might provide it this summer.

That was the good news.

On the other hand The Farmer was really shocked at the proposal which Professor Hugh Pennington is said to have brought forward in his report on the Lanarkshire E coli outbreak.

One of his measures, designed to avoid cross contamination, is that butchers who sell both cooked and uncooked meat should have separate staff and separate counters for the two categories of meat. That may make sense for large urban butchers but it is not on in small villages.

How can the young man who took over the butcher's shop in Potions' village cope? There is no other staff but him. And he cannot survive without his pies, haggis and stuffing.

And there is more cause for pessimism.

You will recall The Farmer's sadness a couple of years ago when one of the Wasting Assets' daughters emigrated to Australia with her mother.

You will remember Turnbull's cartoon of the gallant seven-year-old standing on a chair at her farewell party and making her speech: "I am happy about going to Australia but I'll be sad because I'm leaving youse."

The Farmer had hoped that the young emigree would benefit from a more robust atmosphere in the Colonies. He had hoped she might be freer of daft controls such as on the curva-

ture of the banana and the contents of the haggis. He had hoped that political correctness would be taken out of the debate on how much meat to eat.

Well, the blonde-haired beauty of nine was back for a month at Christmas. She came all the way herself and seemed to think nothing of it. She stayed with us for a couple of nights and helped me feed the beasts.

But now she tells me she doesn't eat meat. She learned what a bad thing that was from children's television.

And I'm having trouble with another of my women.

The Breadwinner is afraid that I am going to give myself a heart attack with all the training I'm doing on my fancy exercise bike. I try to do 30 miles a day and it is no good me telling her that it is precisely to avoid heart disease that I am doing it.

She came into the bothy the other day when I was at about 25 miles. The floor was awash with sweat.

"Stop that, for goodness sake," she said. You'll get dehydrated."

"No dear," says the athlete, "you see, I take a sip out of this bottle after every two miles."

She looked doubtfully from the bottle to the puddle on the floor. "Would it not be a lot safer just to pour the water straight onto the floor, instead of getting yourself into a state like that?"

February 10, 1997

The Farmer warms to income statistics

WHEN I go to the shop for my paper in the morning or the pub for a pint in the evening, people will ask: "How are you?" or even "Fit like?" I use the opportunity for a bit of propaganda.

"Well, as you well know," I say, with that misunderstood look for which I am becoming known, "we farmers are going through tricky times at the moment."

And do you know, they don't believe a word of it. They even think I am joking. They never saw a poor farmer yet.

Well, thank goodness, it is now official. Farm incomes were down 19% last year. I don't know if they've got better

280

statisticians on the case this year, but that's the sort of statistics we want – something we can relate to and none of that rubbish like what they dished out last year, saying farm incomes were up 50%.

This year, when the nurses and the teachers complain about getting 2.5% or whatever, we can howl out, "What about the farmers? We've had minus 19%."

And it's going to get worse.

It depends who's growing them and it depends on who's counting, but I reckon it costs £70 a tonne to grow potatoes and yet the market is flooded with tubers at £10 a tonne delivered. And no one believes even that price can be maintained. If

Big Hamish has to sell all his potatoes at that it should come to a loss of £1200 to the acre. (That is at 20 tonnes to the acre, by no means a huge yield nowadays.) Luckily Hamish doesn't grow as many tonnes to the acre, which also means he has less money tied up in tattie boxes, but even so he will have a colossal loss.

I'd be sorry for him were it not for the fact that I am feeding them to the cattle.

Our latest deal is 20 tonnes of potatoes for my old untestable Vauxhall. We both like the deal. I reckon I am getting £200 for the old wreck and Hamish thinks he is getting £20 a tonne for his potatoes.

Hamish needs the car for

Young Hamish who, being ten now, needs an old banger to learn about skids and bumps in the fields. He has a series of soft obstacles made of big bales on the setaside and the lad is set to find out all about crashing cars without hurting himself.

He has learned two important lessons already. The first is to make sure there isn't much diesel in a machine when you sell it. And the second is never to assume that, when you buy a car, you are buying a full tank as well. The seller is liable to be older and wiser than you (especially if you are ten) and have heard of rule one. Poor Young Hamish ran out of juice on his first expedition.

But Mossie is scandalised at the deal. He blames me for trying to talk up the price of potatoes. The way he counts it, with the £7 dumping tax to get rid of their surplus, the growers should be paying us to take them away.

Mossie's not pleased about the pigs, mind. When I was in for my coffee and to criticise our neighbours on Friday, he showed me his latest returns. He had 94.6% in the top grade and yet he was below £70 per head, while a few short months ago he averaged over £100.

And what about the grain? Last year we were looking eagerly forward to getting £105 for our feeding barley at har-vest. Now we are fearful that £85 may be more than we'll get for a tonne of barley this time.

Malting barley contracts are unattainable and it is my guess that they will be worth-less at harvest anyway. What is the value of a contract without a price attached?

And now that the Germans have got BSE in a Galloway calf we can kiss goodbye to that market for our beef for at least another two years.

So if the price of everything is down, what hope from the subsidies with which our indus-try is blessed? Do they not rise when prices fall to ensure that the great British public die of obesity rather than hunger?

Well, that was what I thought, but there is talk of the subsidies being frozen until 1999.

In fact here is an interesting conundrum.

As I have been saying, we farmers are going through tricky times. The prices for bulls may have been up at Perth last week but that's just farmers buying from other farmers. Everything we sell off the farms is down or struggling, yet the price of land is rising.

How in hell can that be? Who wants to pay more and more for this asset which is pro-ducing less and less?

Meanwhile costs keep ris-ing. Take the shooting. Mossie

and his pals in the A team have taken to supporting the Young Laird by paying £80 a night for duck shooting. For that you get to shoot duck for the ten minutes or so between the time when it is too early and the time when it is too dark.

They were out again last Friday and ten of them shot a grand total 22 ducks. That's about £40 a duck or £480 an hour, depending on how you count it.

With income falling, I'll tell you, tricky times are here.

February 17, 1997

Mains finds a wife

WE ARE full of admiration for Mains. He has taken his life by the scruff of the neck. He has been to New Zealand for an out-cross. The better half of the village is girding its loins for a great banquet and dance to welcome a new Mistress home to the Mains. (Mossie and I agree that "the better half" is any half which includes us – and our invitations have arrived.)

It's only a few short months since he introduced Susan, a Kiwi on the world tour who paused just too long in Aberdeen and Mains hooked her. Any other lad might have slipped over to New Zealand to check out the folks before marrying, but not Mains. One of the few Doric speakers of his generation, he sold most of the livestock, got Old Mains to look after the place for two months and set off to the Antipodes to claim his bride. "When you're in your 30s and mak up your mind you dinna hing aboot."

Now our meetings at the Salmon Inn are usually devoted to the criticism of the government and our neighbours, and the swapping of information on who might have a bull available or who might have a man spare for a hour or two on Monday.

But on Sunday night the boys were all looking at the wedding photographs from New Zealand.

It's summer there, so while we were shivering in the warmest winter any of us can remember, Mains and his bride were married in her parents' garden, she in white and he in the kilt, in glorious sunshine and under a bower weighed down with hydrangea and rose blossom.

The Farmer thought they made a gallant couple.

And he was absolutely gobsmacked by what Mains

283

had done. He had travelled half round the world totally unsupported. He had no one with him from home and yet he seems to have carried it off with aplomb.

I don't know if it is a sign of how well the New Zealanders treated our man or of how hard he normally works, but he put on almost a stone a month while away. We'd never have recognised him if Mains had stayed away much longer.

"And did ye tak the pipes with you, Mains?"

"I did that. I had to pipe mysel intae my ain wedding."

So having had a New Zealand wedding, Mains now plans a Scottish wedding breakfast in the village hall.

Now I have told you of the lengths our young farmers are going to get their brides. The other traditional problem with farmers, one that affected the present lot's grandparents, was the wait for dead men's shoes.

Many a farmer's son missed his chance or wasted the flower of his youth on endless courtship, waiting for his father to die and give him his turn of the big bed in the front room.

But there will be no such problem at the Mains. Old Mains is far from dead but he has grabbed his chance, bought himself a bungalow and skedaddled. He has willingly exchanged the plough and the barrow for the bowling green.

My Breadwinner and I now have tentative date for moving into Whinhill of Ardo.

Am I wise to stay here

where I can feel the cold breath of my ancestors as they peer over my shoulders and down in wonder at what young Potions is making of the place upon which we have laboured for 160 years? Am I right to stay close so I can compare the young man's every move to my own brilliance as a farmer?

Or has Old Mains got it right as he prepares to leave his hill for pastures new? He'll be too far away to hear the crash as the tin comes off the old byre roof, too far away to be of any assistance when the stots break out in the night.

Old Mains and I have probably made the best decisions for ourselves, though we'll probably both go through spells of thinking the other got it right.

Finally I must just tell you that I have seen Mossie embarrassed at last.

His was just about the last shoot of the season. He invited the A team and laid on a splendid spread with the best roast beef, stilton and port. Everyone turned up except the pheasants.

Mossie apologised and doubled his lifetime consumption of humble pie. In desperation, he invited Aberdeenshire's finest to ring the old steadings and he would flush out the tame doos for them.

Surveying the bag of seven pheasants, three woodpigeons and 43 feral pigeons afterwards, The Butcher said to his host, "Would you like us to come over next week and do your rabbits?"

February 24, 1997

Good job I'm off

THE FARMER is quite right to retire and let his son-in-law have his turn to struggle against nature on the family acres.

Previous generations of my family on both sides hung on, usually out of economic necessity. Their sons and daughters, because there were too many of them and they couldn't bear the wait, made for the Empire.

The Granny with whom I lived during the war saw all her brothers leave. Two went to Australia and one to California. Her mother had a wish, well into old age, that she could just hear once from Jimmy before she died. There are two versions of what happened. One is that a letter did eventually come and that she died happy. The

285

other is that no letter came and just as well, for Jimmy had died in the gutter in San Francisco.

All my father's uncles and both his parents emigrated, leaving the boy to be brought up by his grandparents who stayed in their farm till the old man died at the end of the Great War. There was no one left to carry on. One Allan who went to Canada married an Indian princess (in a native ceremony) when he tired of his first wife. Then when his first white wife died he married another.

At any rate I am going before my 60th birthday and it is a good thing. I will enjoy being on the land but not responsible for it on cold mornings. And the farm will benefit from a fresh mind worrying about it.

I've an example already.

I have been paralysed by fear of upsetting the brave men who built the steading in the 19th century and perhaps before. Rather than knock useless old buildings down I have left them there and built new ones.

Jimmy Low, who arrived here as grieve in 1931, said the old byre was done then. It was still done in 1975 when he left. It was to The Farmer's great shame that the old stable roof fell in in 1987. Replacing the slate roof on the old shed was out of the question. It would have cost many thousands and it would have remained a useless building for the 21st century. So down she came.

Mossie pleaded with me to take down the rest and put up something useful in its place, but I couldn't do it. Well, the new man can do it. And he will.

Or at least he would were it

not for his wife. She is not for her great-great-grandfather's barn being bulldozed. The new farmers are to re-roof the old steading and hang the expense. They have even started, even though I am still in harness.

But the really good news is that it isn't going to bankrupt the new owners.

The trick is that they are giving up on the slates. They will re-roof the old steading in green box section. They already have an estimate for doing the old byre. It will cost £1500 for the tin and renewing every second truss.

That is a fraction of the money I have spent my entire farming life worrying about.

Indeed, with the demand for second-hand materials for building "traditional" stone and slate dwelling houses, it isn't going to cost a penny. The 2000 slates are worth £1200 once they are off the roof. Four fancy granite spur stones are worth £15 apiece. There are 90 feet of coping at £2 a foot and 16 granite skew stones at £6 each. If Potions can just get £24 for a heap of firewood, he'll have a new roof for nothing.

Had I stayed another 20 years the old steading would have fallen about my ears, the slates wasted.

If you have a tumbledown steading, have a good look at what might sell on the second-hand market. While looking for the materials to build Whinhill I have been asked £10 for sandstone coping and 75 pence a slate. I am trying to buy two chimney cans identical to those which disappeared when the old stable fell down. With £10 off they will cost me £120.

Mind you, it isn't all good, having the new man pulling the steading down about my ears. I'm blaming that for the trouble with one of our young bulls.

It seemed like he had picked up a bit of slate or a nail. At any rate, he had damaged a foot and it was decided that a cleat would have to come off.

Now you know that I prefer my vets middle-aged, fat and chain-smoking. So I wasn't pleased when a skinny youth who looked like he was on work experience turned up. The Farmer's faith was not enhanced by the tourniquet that would have been pushed to keep potatoes in a sack. When it came to the sawing you'd have thought the cheesewire was cutting a bit of mature stilton. The lad lacked the brutality of an old-fashioned vet.

And then again, when the job was done, admittedly much later, it was neatly sewn and thoroughly clean. A week later we can say it is a job well done.

That's another reason why Little Ardo may be better under a new hand.

Heavy mob has a good moan at show

ON TUESDAY we had the Aberdeen Spring Show in the glorious sunshine we in the Northeast are beginning to regard as normal winter weather.

It's a growing show. More than 5000 paid admission and they came from all over Scotland.

The Farmer had a particularly jolly session in the Bennachie Bar with some who had travelled from the Wild West. They had come to follow the Clydesdales and included David Picken from Kirkcudbright, who entertained us with a story of Smithfield Show. He had given a likely lassie a dance and opined that she was quite a good dancer and fully up to his own standard, only to be told that she was one of the Tiller Girls' chorus line.

He obviously got to more upmarket parties than The Farmer ever did at Smithfield. And there was Alec Kerr, who I think of more as a Simmental man because he was one of the early importers. He swished around Europe in a loch of white wine with such stalwarts as Gerry Rankine, Jim Swanney and Willie Allan, choosing cattle to open up the British market.

The second prerequisite was an eye for cattle and the first was an iron liver. Alec was the man who after a particularly jolly evening at Smithfield was taking a pre-breakfast stroll and offered his hand to a yappy dog, saying: "Bite it if you like but for God's sake don't bark."

My pal Bertie Paton from Kirriemuir was there. He is another of the original Simmental importers. He was a most welcome visitor, for he bought the reserve champion commercial beast for the top price of the day – £2000.

Then there was George Sinclair, who started life in Glasgow but found himself feeed to a farm in Aberdeenshire in the 1940s. Like every other feeed man at that time, he told us, his breakfast was brose – not porridge, mind, just boiling water and a pinch of salt on his oats.

But unlike most farm lads, George was lucky. He had taken the eye of the farmer's wife and once a week he got an egg and a slice of toast – not a whole egg, mind, but a pullet's egg – one of the younger bird's first attempts. So small were they that George used to put a piece of toast in the bottom of the egg cup to hold the eggie up to the spoon – or so he told us.

I'm pleased to say that there was one young man in the company. He was wearing a Scottish Agricultural College sweatshirt. He didn't want to be named but made me promise to tell you that he felt that the staff at the college were now so busy being consultants, and earning their big fees, that they had not sufficient time for their students. If that is true then it is a black mark for privatisation.

But mostly it was senior citizens 'heavying'. That means damning the weather, the government and their luck. And there is plenty to criticise.

Take all this fuss about Dolly. That is the breakthrough by Edinburgh scientists in cloning a sheep. Dolly, unlike every other sheep in the world, didn't get half her genes from each of her parents. She got the lot from her mother. She has the same intelligence, which isn't much, and she is exactly as likely as her mother was at her age, to develop bad habits and die young.

But as far as the heavy squad at the show was concerned, clever as it may be, this piece of science is useless. We are all interested in improving our animals by careful selection of parental characteristics

289

and mixing them up in the hope of getting offspring that are better than their parents. With clones there can be no progress.

We also had fun with the antics of the Hogg, the Doon Major and the other Neeps over BSE. Funnily enough, most farmers seem to think the government deserves about eight out of ten for trying. But their incompetence makes us laugh.

It baffles us poor farmers that the Neeps can't see that BSE is two problems. First there's the disease, and second there is a hysterical fear of food poisoning on the part (mostly) of the Germans. Instead of concentrating on the disease, they keep trying to cure the Germans' food hysteria, and that is quite out of British control.

Professor Hugh Pennington, the scientist whose proposals would shut down half the wee butchers, is a bit more popular with the farmers this week. He has pointed out that E. coli can't just be caught from uncooked beef.

Organic vegetables, those that are manured with 'good honest muck' instead of 'chemicals' are a potential source of infection.

We have nothing against the organic farmers, but that might just make them a little less holier-than-us.

Big Hamish isn't at his best on politics but he did offer us that the Chinese would be all right on that score because he'd heard they were going to have to manage without dung.

March 10, 1997

Spring is in the air

IT WILL all be to pay for. This fine open winter will finish with a terrible storm that will make 1946 look like a snow flurry. And if by any chance the storm fails to turn up, the wells will all run dry this summer. So say the old men.

It has been wonderfully mild. The cows have got a picking on the grass all winter and now, in the second week of March, spring is in the air.

The partridges have been pairing since the end of February. I even heard a chaffinch trying for a mate this morning. The lapwings are back from Africa and The Breadwinner wishes we had gone with them, back to the clear mountain air of Nairobi and the Rift Valley.

In the heronry across the Ythan, nesting is well advanced and the rooks would be well on with their home-building if they would concentrate on getting building materials for themselves instead of stealing from their neighbours.

On Monday The Farmer counted ten unattended hen pheasants in the Piggery Park. "Vacancies for ten healthy cocks" – news like that soon gets around. On Tuesday there were two males and no sign that they wanted reinforcements. By Wednesday there were at least three brilliantly showy chaps and they were starting to fight for the harem.

I haven't seen the five roe deer which have been wintering the wood. They grazed my rape up until a few days ago. I like to think they are lying low and quietly producing another generation.

Even The Farmer is stirring early this year. He has put a little spice on the barley and has already been over the rape twice with jumping nuts and sulphur.

All this pleases The Farmer. You might think that harvest, when we reap what we have sown, would be the best time of year. But it lacks the excitement of the spring. At harvest you know how small your crops have turned out. But, as Mossie says, in the springtime everybody has four tonnes to the acre.

And The Farmer is not the only one who sees it that way.

The woodpigeons are not willing to wait till harvest.

It's the leaves of the winter rape they're after.

The increase in rape growing has been a great blessing for the doos. They used to have to winter on what scraps they could glean from the aftermath of the previous harvest. And when that was ploughed in the spring they had a very thin time indeed until they could pillage the spring barley seeds to keep them going until the clover came in May.

Now they have the rape. They will leave as soon as there is an alternative, but it seems to keep them going from January on and they can strip a field bare in a day or two. For they do not come in ones to feed. They gather into great clouds and descend like a biblical plague.

Last year they stripped two of The Farmer's fields bare. Though the rape plants were as healthy as ever, the crops were spoiled because the weeds, normally smothered by the rape, got an ideal start on the spring day and never looked back.

The Farmer's main job this winter has been to ensure that the same doesn't happen this year. But how?

Those gas guns just don't work. Scarecrows do but you need at least one to the acre and to keep moving them.

Shooting is useless. Pigeons are like that nightmare where you are being attacked and every time you kill an opponent two more take his place. Shoot as many as you like, you can't reduce their number so that you notice.

Mind you, it does make The beleaguered Farmer feel better to gun a few of them down. And in that I am claiming a world record.

I had been for a bit for my sprayer and returned to find the park in front of the house being attacked by perhaps 5000 pigeons. They were grazing within 40 yards of the dyke.

I could have gone to the dyke and waved my arms. They would all have flown off. But The Farmer had hate in his heart. He sneaked into the house for a gun. He scuttled crouching across the lawn and peeped over the dyke. The field had turned a greeny blue. They were busy.

There was no need to aim. The hunter fired. The 5000 jumped. He fired again, blowing a hole in the blue cloud.

The Farmer was able to retrieve no fewer than 17 pigeons, and you never get them all. Still, The Butcher gave me £6.80 for my right and left.

For the record, which may never be recognised, The Farmer was using a Fiocchi cartridge, which delivers over an ounce of shot.

The Young Laird cops it

THE YOUNG Laird is in trouble. He forgot the golden rule; If you drink and drive – don't breathe.

It was bad luck. He's big in the Union and was at a particularly jolly annual meeting down country. He'd had one or two before the formalities. He'd had several to celebrate his election as junior Vice President. And he'd fairly done justice to the excellent claret at dinner.

No harm done, he decided it was time to go home. But where was Madeleine? Where was that necessary component of civilised living, the little wife, the chauffeuse who quietly sips orange juice and longs for the time when she can collect the remains of her husband and drive him home?

She didn't seem to be nagging at him to come away. Too late he remembered. Madeleine had declined to come. He was alone and 30 shark-infested miles from home.

Now, you might think a man of the importance of the Young Laird JP would have nothing to fear from the Law.

But again he was out of luck. The Bobbies who stopped him were the same two who had stopped him last spring.

Then the Young Laird had wound down his window and asked imperiously if they knew who he was?

When he told them the Bobbies had said, "Well, sir, either drink less or drive straighter."

But this time the Young Laird had drunk more, was driving squinter and the Bobbies knew exactly who he was.

So the young toff has a two-year membership of the bicycle club. The Rolls and the Rangie wait patiently in the garage while their master pedals around the estate on his mountain bike, seeing to things.

And he makes a brave site, panting down to the village for his papers every morning in the fore-and-aft bonnet, the tweed plus fours and the body warmer. As the overhang subsides over the next two years I'm sure his bad luck will prove to be the best thing that ever happened to him.

I'm glad about that because

the Young Laird's a nice chap, even if it is his woods from which the doos swarm down to pillage my rape.

I have been tearing round my crops on Honda the four wheeled Dog at least four times a day to scare them. It doesn't keep them off but it does seem to stop them gathering into the dense blue clouds that can devour an acre in an hour.

All my neighbours are using those infernal gas guns which shatter the peace every few minutes. I believe the doos use the noise to guide them to tasty fields. Certainly where you have a badly-eaten field there is usually a gas gun advertising it. Nowadays most of those guns are fitted with photosensitive cells which put them off automatically when it

gets dark. At least you get a few hours of uninterrupted rest until first light. But there are still a few old-fashioned ones left.

That was what led to the row I had with the farmer of Waterside.

Watery opened up with this cannon on the 3rd of January. Usually gas guns don't bother me, but this one did. It seemed to be pointed at my bedroom window. It went off every four minutes all night and when it did The Farmer's heart leapt.

The Breadwinner slept the sleep of the just but The Farmer had to make a bed on the floor of the cellar to get any rest at all.

As soon as was decent I was on the phone.

I should have told him to get that noise stopped or I'd have the police on him and banged down the receiver. But you can't do that with neighbours unless there's a chance of them leaving.

"Aye Watery, very nice morning."

"Oh aye. If this keeps up well get sowing before long."

"Aye Watery, I was just thinking; that gas gun you've got outside my window – the photocell doesn't seem to be working?"

It's funny how you can feel refrigeration coming down the phone.

"That gun hasn't a cell. I can't afford £100 for all my guns – there are six in that field alone. Hairy Sandy's nearer than you and he hasn't complained."

"I canna help it if Hairy Sandy's hard of hearing. You'll need to shut it off at night – the doos only fly by day."

"Yes," said Watery struggling to maintain his cool. "But what about the deer? They graze at night and there are six of them in my wood."

That was a new one on me. "Well I don't think deer do any harm and I like to see them."

"Well if you like them that much you can have mine an aa," Watery shouted and did what I should have done in the first place – he hung up.

It seemed like a declaration of war. The Farmer was ready. Every time one of Watery's gas guns went off in the night he would get a phone call telling him so. If he left the phone off the hook he'd get a fax and if he switched the fax off it would be the environmental health and the police.

There was no need for all that. The guns fell silent that night and though all hell breaks out each dawn, the nights have been still ever since.

March 24, 1997

When eggs were money

ON THE boys' first annual outing to the salmon fishing on the Spey I heard a farming story about the Good Old Days.

The Good Old Days to which I refer are the 20 years or so after the outbreak of World War Two. True, they weren't good days for everyone. The war years were a bad time to be

Jewish or a Gypsy in Europe and it was dangerous to be of fighting age even in Britain.

But it was a time of food shortages.

Those were the days when they used to talk about farmers being "featherbedded". We were exhorted to save the country by "digging for victory" and producing "food from our own resources". Best of all, they paid us very well to do it.

In the Good Old Days my father gave a decent living to six workers and never did a hand's turn himself. Now his son does all the work himself.

In those days you could get a seat in the one-and-sixpenny cuddlies at the Laurencekirk picturehouse for the price of three eggs. The nearest cinema now would charge you the product of 100 eggs ... and no usherettes!

I knew a man who got two tickets for a show in London's West end for a dozen eggs ... and it was supposed to be sold out at the time.

My story is of those Good Old Days. Despite being heir to one of the finest herds of Aberdeen Angus cattle, despite being related to the founders of that great breed, young Charlie McCombie, like most of the loons who played, had the dream of becoming a professional footballer.

Indeed McCombie was making progress. He was an outstanding full back for Huntly (the Highland league champions of today), earning five shillings if the team won.

It was in 1945 that Huntly played in the Aberdeenshire League against the professionals of Aberdeen Football Club. If he could impress the visiting manager, the young right back could maybe leave the plough and the currie comb for the bright lights of the city. He would enter the life of the professional athlete. And remember, the Aberdeen players were paid more than £10 a week.

The young farmer had a good game. As he walked off he saw the visiting manager in conversation with the home officials and they pointed at him.

Heart in mouth, the young man walked towards his destiny, trying not to look expectant. Sure enough the Aberdeen manager beckoned him over: "Aye McCombie, ye wouldna have ony eggs, would ye?"

Charlie's life might have been so different, but then he might not have won the senior championship at the Perth bull sales in 1983 and the female championship the year after.

I only heard that story because Henry Gregson, a pal of Mossie's, was invited to a day's fishing on that prince among salmon rivers, the Spey. Not to be outdone, Mossie was deter-

296

mined that we would all go. We would all take our rods and the Red Rooster would take the bandie net he used to use in the mill dam.

I managed to persuade the boys that 'a rod' on the Spey meant one rod on the Spey. We might get a cast with Henry's rod when he was having a refreshment, but it was not a question of come-one-come-all. This was way up-market from dangling a worm in the Moss-side burn. Anyway a day out sounded like a good idea to break the pre-calving tension.

It was a wonderful March day. The headquarters was a little bothy down on the banks of the fast-flowing river and nestling in to the steep banks which were covered by a great show of the biggest snowdrops that I have ever seen.

There was a jolly company of maybe 12 toffs and half a dozen ghillies. The demon drink was there but there was some nice-like orangeade so The Farmer, remembering previous mistakes, stuck to that.

Jack Sleigh, the former President of the Highland, was there. He caught a salmon which had to be thrown back because it had been up the river too long. But Bill Phillip, a retired farmer from Bennachie, got a fresh run fish. It weighed over 10lb.

I had a couple more delightful orangeades on a bench by the water with a most engaging Englishman. Mack taught me a bit about the economics of fishing. He gets all the fishing he wants because for every fish caught the value of the beat goes up £10,000. The laird was pleased to let Mack catch all he could.

So Mack got a partner for his drapery business and spends six months of the year on the Spey, adding value for the laird. The business flourishes too. Turnover rose from £1m to £65m. Just think how rich Mack could have been if he'd spent all his time fishing.

I could be like that next year. With Potions doing the work and doing it well, I could be on the Spey. But I think I'll stay away from the orangeade.

I remarked to Mack that "This stuff's almost as good as booze.

"It should be," he said and lent me his glasses. "It's alcopop for the children of today. It's far too strong for grown men."

It was called "Cirrhosis" and was 6% alcohol.

Next time I'm sticking to the devil I know.

Another family wedding to plan

I CAN'T say that life is dull, despite the election. The boys in the discussion group are nearly all natural Tories, hereditary Tories, but they are either changing this time or keeping very quiet. As Big Hamish put it, "Major's going to see what setaside feels like."

But The Farmer hardly has time to think about great affairs of state or care about the doings to which Mickey Hirst gets up in his own time. Hardly has he got the Wasting Asset safely married off than the Younger Investment announces she is to make an honest man of her long time bidie-in.

The whole circus has to be gone through again.

Mossie is to spit roast two cwt of the best Aberdeen Angus beef. I tried them with chicken and then pork but they would have nothing but the best. What a boost that the price has been so badly hit by BSE. The hall and church are booked. The minister is bracing himself for another noisy invasion.

The fighting over who is to be invited is proceeding in its usual bloody fashion but I have had two important victories. The accountant and the banker are not getting. With retirement looming The Farmer won't be using them so they'll be needing all their time to make up the shortfall in their accounts.

The squabbling over which of the bride's nieces is to be a flower girl has been settled. We're getting a job lot of summer dresses from British Home Stores and having all six.

Oh dear! Is that a tear? It seems only a short time since the Youngest Investment was saying "I'm Thoothie and I do not have a lithp."

It's not all joy. Pleasures have to be paid for. It is The Farmer who has to do the paying. It could have come at a better time, too. With the Wasting Asset's wedding just past and the Dea... the retirement house... gobbling up cash, The Farmer's retirement fundie is taking a severe beating.

Thank goodness The Breadwinner is still winning bread from Aberdeen.

And the farm is doing its best. The unprecedented mild, dry winter has meant the crops

are looking wonderful. I hate the way our crops consultant Mossie walks through it. It is so thick and so crunchie that his great footprints seem a shame. I stick to the tramlines.

And if the barley is good the rape is in new territory altogether. The weather has been ideal but the key may be the fact that we are growing the new hybrid variety, Synergy. No one has ever seen such vigour.

Most rape crops at this time of year are disfigured by senescence – the lower leaves die off and give the field an ill-thriven, yellowy tinge. But in our five fields of Synergy there is no more that a handful of dead leaves. They are deepest green, like an ad for nitrogen fertiliser.

One of the critical times for rape is when the crop reaches the tops of your wellies. Then it is ready for the secret formula which regulates its growth, provides mineral boosters and kills all known disease. Well, our crops this year got their wellie boot spray exactly one month earlier than last.

With this Synergy sprouting in the warm sunshine all winter, the weeds just have not had a chance. Neither have the pigeons. They've been eating but they have made no impact. The crop has outgrown them.

Yes, the two-tonne rape crop, for so long a dream, is on. Indeed, if you believe him, Mossie had two tonnes of Synergy last year and two tonnes five cwt in one field. With the subsidy that could give a gross output of £600 an acre. That is the way forward.

Even the poor old BSE burgers are doing well.

The market is very depressed but the stock have wintered well, and, with potatoes now at one penny for two kilos, the temptation is to finish them rather than trying the store market. Certainly last year I did a lot better out of the tailenders I took home and finished than with the better sorts I allowed to be stolen at Thainstone.

But there is a snag. I have not enough acres to let me claim subsidies on all the bull calves. The only way is to store them and let others collect. That pushes the price up by about half the unclaimed subsidy. So I guess I'll have to store the bulls and finish the heifers.

I said life wasn't dull. Well the latest is that the Wasting Asset has bought the Salmon Inn. Imagine it. You have a nice cosy spot for a few drinks with the middle-aged lads, and your black sheep son buys it from under you.

Our new publican's apprenticeship has been served as a beach bum on the Mediterranean and the Canaries, the terraces of Europe's football grounds, and the nightclubs of the Toon.

Some see a promise of some of that style coming to the Salmon. The Farmer looks forward in fear. It's the grand opening on Friday so I guess that's another sore head to look forward to.

April 14, 1997

Calving trouble

THE CALVING is going better after a very ropey start.

You could call it bad luck, but it was bad judgement. The best tractor in the world will blow up one day. Then you have plenty of time to get the old one yoked or kid the suppliers into letting you have a few days of a 'demonstrator'.

Even if your tedder disintegrates on the first decent hay day you have an hour or two to get a replacement ... and anyway, it might be another glorious day tomorrow.

But if your calving rope snaps the chances are you have a dead calf.

I don't know how old the

rope we put round the calves' feet to pull them is, but it was here in the days of the great Jimmy Low and he left over 20 years ago.

Old Jimmy used a dreadful set of pulleys. The rope went round two blocks of four rollers and Jimmy told me they gave him the strength of eight men. He had the strength of two men to start with so the whole deal presented the calf with considerable power.

But there was a snag and it wasn't just that all that rope snaking back and fore over the wheels could get into a tangle and that it picked up straw and muck as it worked. The eightfold increase in strength was achieved by using eight times the length of rope. To be sure of getting a calf out you need to be able to pull over four feet so that meant 32 feet of ropes even if the cow didn't get pulled along the ground.

After watching Jimmy pull a Gelbvieh calf half out with this contraption, only to run out of rope, I decided I would calve cows with something better. He spent a good couple of minutes resetting his ropes to give himself a new hold and that was far too long for the calf caught at the heart. The first Gelbvieh calves made £4000 apiece which was a fortune in the early seventies.

Our vet introduced us to the pogo stick. This was T-shaped and made of steel. The top of the T was laid against the cows hips and the calf was pulled out by a ratchet which climbed up the stick as you cranked it. It was a grand idea because as you were pulling against the cow you didn't have the problem of dragging the cow along the byre floor.

The pogo stick was excellent for cows which would have calved themselves anyway, but the vets soon abandoned theirs. If you had a really stiff calving it proved impossible to keep the early pogo sticks in place.

My solution was the American calf-puller. This used Old Jimmy's principle of gearing but with a neat ratchet rather than miles of rope. The first time I saw one it was being used to pull the portal frame for a large tattie shed into place so I knew there would be no shortage of power.

Indeed the trouble with the American calf-puller is that it is too powerful and you can damage your cow and your calf.

Anyway our second cow to calve this year was a Simmental heifer. She wasn't going to manage so I put on the pullers. I had a good bit of pressure on and was trying to turn it round with a metal bar between its legs when Old Jimmy's rope snapped. By the time I had got a makeshift rope together it was

too late. The calf came quite easily and had a heart beat. But I couldn't get it to breathe.

Livestock are rewarding even when they are not paying but deadstock is depressing. It was even more depressing as I knew a careless man would have lost that calving rope many years ago and a wise man would have renewed it.

The next 13 calves came as nature intended ... while The Farmer slept.

Then one presented its feet upside down. It was coming back to front. No problem to the American calf-puller.

But then my equipment let me down again, and again anno domine played a part.

At a time when decent peo-ple are in bed I found this big cow with two feet sticking out. A quick feel revealed a nose attached to a large forehead. She was clearly needing help.

I would have gone for the calf puller but my cow had sat down beside the wall.

You must pull in the direction that would be down if the cow were standing up. The only way I could get my calf puller engaged would be pulling the calf up and it would jam. In the old days when there were six men on the place we'd have turned her right over. I tried to pull the calf manually. It stuck fast, at the chest, a fine fighting red bull. The Farmer reckoned he had two minutes to act.

It was wrong but what else

was there? On went the calf puller. Sure enough, despite great power the calf stuck fast, baaing strongly. It must have been just past the heart or the life would have been crushed out of it by now.

The only hope was to get her away from that wall. Desperately The Farmer wrestled to heave her round. An inch at the head then round and move her tail an inch.

But like old Jimmy's ropes, The Farmer had lost his strength. The calf was strong, though. He was baaing and scrambling with his front legs to win free.

He was still alive after I'd gone for the Ursus. The tractor soon brought her into line. Then with the cow tied to the tractor and the calf to the feed barrier we were ready for some serious pressure.

After another minute or so away he came. Amazingly he shook his head. The Farmer had just enough energy to struggle away to his bed. He had a superb calf in the morning.

But it is not a job for one old man.

April 21, 1997

Bring back Lamont

"BRING BACK Peerie Norrie" (as Norman Lamont used to be called in his native Shetland). That is the cry going up around the watering holes of Aberdeenshire.

You will remember that he was the Chancellor of the Exchequer who earned the grateful praise of Britain's farmers when he took Britain out of the Exchange Rate Mechanism. That was a scheme whereby the pound was more or less pegged to the other European currencies. And it was pegged far too high, which made it cheap for Britain to import food and hard for us to export.

Then on what everyone else called Black Wednesday, Peerie Norrie devalued the pound. Up went the farm gate prices, up went the subsidies and we entered a period of prosperity the likes of which every man should enjoy before retirement. The farmers called it Golden Wednesday.

And what has happened? The Doon Major and the other neeps have made such a mess of running the economy that the pound has risen back to its old

level and undone all Peerie Norrie's good work. Just when The Farmer was looking forward to another good year to pay for the retirement house and add a bit to the retirement fundie, grain which rose to over £110 following Golden Wednesday fell to under £90.

Come back Peerie Norrie. Your farmers need you.

Mind you, help is on the way and it is coming from an unusual quarter. The price of wheat has struggled up to £100 and even barley has made it to about £93. And all because of the drought in England.

It isn't often that Scotland's weather gives us an advantage over our rich friends from the south, but apparently the drought in parts of the bread-basket of England is so bad that light crops are expected. That holds out the hope of the farmer's best friend – shortage.

Indeed it is better than that. For if this does materialise it will be a shortage on the part of our competitors while we may have our heaviest crops ever. No one has ever seen the Northeast looking so lush at this time of year. The winter crops are so far on that a reasonably heavy harvest is more or less assured.

It's just as well, too.

The Younger Investment's decision to get married has brought a smile to her mother's face, and of course The Farmer has been very brave about it, but it is going to make a fair dent in the retirement fundie.

Mind you it could be a smart move.

We went in by the other

side last Sunday. It sounded like the right address – the Garth farm, Forfar. It is among that gorgeous soil which has made the Howe of Strathmore some of the most desired land in the country. It is too good for anything less than potatoes or raspberries, and it costs funny money per acre.

Better than that, Garth is right on Forfar Loch. It can never run dry and it is sure to be needed for development soon.

We had been to a wedding about Perth and had stayed over so that The Breadwinner could have a drink. We had met the other side before, though only the once, and we did expect a fairly enthusiastic welcome. The younger Investment is quite a catch, after all.

But none was forthcoming. The groom's stepfather came to the door and looked rather oddly at us. There was even a hint of menace. We stood and looked back, feeling awkward. Had we done the wrong thing by calling unannounced when the godly are at prayer and not-quite-so-godly feel you should be at prayer rather than knocking at their doors? As we had the Jaggie he surely couldn't think we were tinkers?

After a few hesitant moments The Breadwinner wisely said, "Hallo Jim, we're Susie's parents."

That did the trick. We were welcomed in. He told me later that, with the smart car and The Breadwinner looking so perjink in her wedding gear with the new handbag, he had thought we were Jehovah's Witnesses.

In fact we got on uncommon well. So much so that the other side offered to help pay for the wedding.

The Farmer put up quite a fight. "Oh no, Jim. You know a man likes to put up his daughter's wedding. It's a matter of pride," and a lot of other nonsense.

But The Farmer had seen the new shed as he drove in about to the Garth, and the new digger taking out the foundations for another new shed. He'd seen the split new ten-tonne cart and what looked like a brand new swather ... and harvest still four months away, even in Angus.

Reluctantly, The Farmer agreed that the other side would be allowed to pay for the champagne for the Investment's wedding.

Another smart move. I've to do the ordering and he's to do the paying. How is anyone to know who has paid for the champagne anyway?

That was the end of the debate on whether to have the Asti Spumanti or to go overboard and have the Californian. With the other side paying we'll have the best French champagne even if it doesn't taste better.

Poor Jim. It is just as well he's had such a good year at the Garth. He has no idea how much champagne Mossie, the Red Rooster, Mains and Hilly and the Wasting Assets can drink. I don't know if Penny Washers, the white settler, has tasted Champagne, but when he hears it's free, look out!

April 28, 1997

Elections not what they used to be

SIX WEEKS of boredom on the tele is no way to run an election. The boys are totally turned off. No one has a clue what issues there are for decision apart from the possible advent of a Scottish talking shop.

What a sad, far cry from the days when every village hall had a visit from every candidate and the great issues of what to do about the tied cottages, land nationalisation and featherbedding of farmers were debated with heat and sometimes even with light.

I remember the expectant babble in the Tarves village hall when the great Bob Boothby was overdue to speak.

It was 1945 and my father, John R Allan, had been persuaded to stand as Labour candidate. Though there was no hope for any but a Tory in what was then 'Boothby's Kingdom', it was thought that the old man who had soared from the rank of sapper to that of captain during the war, and so could be presented as a war hero, might put up a reasonable show.

When Boothby arrived there was barely room for him to make his unsteady way (he was often quite tired) between the ranks of his admirers, who mingled quite amicably with his few detractors in the smoke-filled hall.

He reached the stage amid applause which in rural Aberdeenshire would pass for rapturous. I will never forget his opening words. He opened his arms wide as though to embrace his people, "My old friends ... " he said.

He spoke in every village hall during the three weeks and

national politics never touched us. We all loved him.

Meanwhile, Captain Allan was having a stiffer time. He had just as many meetings and those in the towns of Peterhead and Fraserburgh were well filled with supporters.

But supporters were very thin on the ground in the farming communities.

In one such meeting a very earnest young lady school-teacher had agreed to act as chairman. That was a more important job than it sounds, because the meeting had to start at the advertised time and the candidate was always late. That was because he was always asked so many questions at his meetings and also because his Austin Ten was no flier.

On this occasion, the Captain (as he hated to be called) was more than an hour late. The chairman had told the audience all she had known about socialism, which hadn't taken long, and then sung bothy ballads to them until the candidate turned up. I think that exhausted her energy for politics but it was a noble effort.

What a pale event is the election of 1997. Nothing locally, just leaflets through the door and six weeks of boredom on the box.

They tell me things were even livelier before the war. Those were the days when Joe Duncan was trying to organise the farm workers into what became the Scottish Farm Servants' Union.

It was also the time when Sandy Wishart, a great farmer and hard man, is supposed to have welcomed the ending of the high wages caused by the labour shortage during the First War. When the troops came home from France, he is supposed to have said, "Now we'll get the buggers by the throat."

The Liberals, too, had ideas for organising society on better lines. Having founded the welfare state before the first war and having got no thanks for it, many still clung to their older notion that, in a land fit for the heroes of the Somme, every man should be entitled to three acres and a cow.

And that slogan, 'Three acres and a cow', became the basis for one of those bons mots which we farmers in the North-east love so well.

It was at a packed and tense meeting in the market town of Ellon, just ten miles down the Ythan from here, that Joe Duncan was holding a rally. He was telling the workers that if they would just join the union and vote Labour they might have council houses built in the countryside and reserved for farm workers. Then if they lost their jobs they would not be turned out of their houses as

well. It was known that a rowdy crowd of young farmers and perhaps some toughs from Aberdeen were waiting outside for trouble after the meeting.

But it was a Liberal voice inside the meeting that was causing more immediate concern.

"And these houses will have running water and flushing waterclosets," said Duncan. "But what about three acres and a cow?" said the Liberal.

"If you'll stick together we'll make the farmers pay you a living wage like the dockers get."

"Aye but what about three acres and a cow?" insisted the voice.

"And if the land were in public ownership a Labour government could force the farmers to make a right job of it or let someone else in to see what he could do."

"Fair enough, but what about three acres and a cow?"

I only knew Geordie Coutts much later in life, when he was retired and had mellowed. But in those days he was a red hot socialist who believed that if only the workers would listen to Joe Duncan they could have all they deserved.

He was drinking in the words of the great man and was not enjoying the interjections on what he regarded as the inferior concept of three acres and a cow.

In a fury he turned on the Liberal, kicked him precisely between the legs and said, "There's twa acres tae be going on wi'. Now will ye hold yer tongue?"

Ochiltree Show

THE FIRST thing I learned at Ochiltree show is that it isn't Ochiltree at all. It is O'hiltree. I wish they had told me before my speech opening the 150th Annual Cattle Show held by the Ochiltree Farmers Society. The Farmer must have sounded a right chocolate. Almost as bad as the celebrity who comes to Aberdeen and says how grand he thinks it is "to be back in the Highlands".

Ochiltree is just about the smallest show you'll get. It is held in what Big Hamish would call "an erse breadth" of a field, (about three quarters of an acre) just outside the village. But what an excellent event it is.

They don't try to have a poor man's version of a major show. They concentrate on what Ayrshire is famous for, dairy cattle. And there were plenty of them. Thirty-seven classes of as many as nine beasts were lined up in getting on for four hours of judging. All those beasts came from the one parish. Just how local can be seen from the roll of honour which is the list of office bearers – there are five Watsons and five Montgomeries.

It is a magnificent achievement for one parish but I wouldn't have had the judges' jobs for all the cows in the county. For the same cows kept coming round again in different classes.

The great Bob Adam of Newhouse of Glamis is said once to have found his supreme champion in an animal which he had put third in one of its classes. But Jack Rennie of Brocklebank and Robert Steel of Kepculloch seemed to remember the mistakes they had made last time and placed the beasts the same way each time.

The Farmer's role was to dish out the rosettes and to make the opening address.

Both jobs were easy. Even the lack of a microphone wasn't a big handicap with the ring no more that 20 yards across. They say an expert is any fool 100 miles from home and I suppose you could say the same for a celebrity (for as such was The Farmer introduced at Ochiltree). That would have made them laugh at home in Methlick where they would have said, "I kent his faither and he wasna much o' a fairmer either."

But The Farmer was more than 200 miles from home. A celebrity for the day, then, and 100 left over to be an expert.

310

The expert told the good people of Ochiltree that they were at the forefront of a great industry. We can do without computers. We can do without cammy knickers. But no one can do without food.

Therefore we should never apologise if a prudent government decides to give farmers a bit of featherbedding.

I was particularly happy to see the entire contents of Ochiltree school there. They arrived marching in good order behind a piper. It is part of the educative function of the show. They had tried giving the kids the day off but some had decided to watch the tele and some unscrupulous parents had taken the opportunity to visit the in-laws. But the piper was a much better idea. They arrived in time to see their pals showing their calves in the children's classes and I could see some aching to be associated with such a glamourous industry.

Of course all the crowd hadn't been forced to attend. Ochiltree is a day to return and meet old friends.

As John Reid had done. He had been schoolmaster to many of the committee between 1950 and 1960, when he left for Ardrossan. He told me a fine story about past-president Logan Montgomerie of Glenconner.

As headmaster, John had been giving the children their last minute pep-talk before the qualifying exams and telling them that this was the time to be

311

graded into those who were going places and those who were going to be stuck.

Were there any questions? Logan's hand went up and pointed out through the window. "Do you see that bird, sir? Is it a pheasant or a partridge?"

I was also taken by a story from the days when controversy raged about whether hens should be free range, battery or deep litter. A certain Mrs Howat in the village had boasted of keeping her hens on deep skitter.

I enjoyed my day at Ochiltree and so did perhaps a thousand others. But they weren't all guests. The Farmer was entertained to coffee and the most wickedly fattening cakes every hour on the hour by two comfortable ladies, President Sheila Watson and secretary Isabel Montgomerie. There was also a portacabin at the far end of the ground. In the early morning I was entertained to a dram there in a company of three. By midday I was one of ten or so having a refresh. And by half past two there must have been 200 enthusiasts squashed into the clubhouse.

A jolly afternoon, including the show dinner (which I would have preferred to call a late lunch) were in prospect.

But the Jaggie was straining to be off home. We'd had a caesarian calf born at midnight and he wasn't looking that well when I left at five. As I left the little field, to which I am unlikely to return but which I will not forget, the last few of the crowd was trying to get into the heaving clubhouse.

I tried to stop her but the Jaggie was my conscience. I might as well not have bothered. When I got home the calf was dead.

May 12, 1997

Inflation – the grimmer reaper?

INFLATION MAKES fools out of us all. It made a fool of my grandfather when he gave me, on the occasion of my 21st birthday, a ten bob note. He remembered when his father gave him a ha'penny and he was so impressed he took it round to show to all the cotter bairns. Ten shillings would

have been a fortune at Dr Mackie's majority but, for a young man contemplating marriage 37 years ago, it was a meagre reward. And now, ten bob's not nearly enough to buy a half pint at the Salmon Inn.

Inflation made a fool of Sandy Strachan, who bought himself a new bonnet in the early seventies. He was scandalised. "It's nae use," he said. "Four pounds, seven and sixpence for a bonnet, and me without a son to leave it to."

Folks who retire often find inflation stalking them with greater menace than The Grim Reaper. The pension that sees you comfortably off with beer at £1.70 a pint soon disappears if you live long enough to see it up to £5. "The wife and me are doing fine. If we don't live too long we should manage."

But those nightmares are bland compared with what the farmers are enjoying at the moment. I remember my father getting £30 a tonne for his Arran Pilots in the 1940s. He was well pleased with the price but he was not as pleased as the modern farmers would be if they could get as much today. Potatoes on the Thainstone electronic auction fell last week to £2 a tonne.

Housepersons beware! If you go into a greengrocer's and ask for 2lb of potatoes, be sure to make it clear that you don't mean £2 worth. What would you do with a whole tonne of tatties?

What is so unfair is that while I can buy a 20-tonne load to feed to my bulls for £40, the shops are still selling them for as much as 50p a pound.

313

All right, the shop potatoes are washed and some varieties are less abundant than others, but it is a ridiculous multiple. And it fairly puts the farmer's role in food production in a daft perspective if you take manufactured potatoes. The Salmon Inn will give you six bags of crisps, the product of one big potato, for your £2.

I thought Food From Britain was going to secure a bigger share for the farmers? Actually, The Farmer never believed FFB would produce anything but hot air. They had a lot of experts at hot air production but food production and marketing require a lot more than hot air.

And have you seen what has happened to beef? We are back to the prices of 20 years ago.

Having said that, I have a modest success to report. I sold half my bull calves at Thainstone last week and experienced a big increase in price over last year's offering. True, they were on a white CCD, but they were not the tops. They were the ones whose lug numbers were in order. Nowadays you can't send them unless you've got a jumbo tag in place and so many had come out.

At any rate Little Ardo had the top-priced bull of the day at £570 and they averaged 114 pence a kilo whereas last year The Farmer had to suffer the indignity of taking some home which couldn't make 90 pence. The calves were from the same cows but I had used my new bull. It just goes to show how important the choice of bull is.

By skill we have done better but the beef market remains dire. Not so the pigs. The pig boys just don't know where to put their money. They are reaping a huge dividend from the swine fever which is sweeping through Europe and decimating the opposition.

Mossie produces about 6000 baconers a year so you can see that he feels very sorry for the Danish and German farmers who are having to slaughter their sows. He is going to do his best to help by producing as many as he can, and if he has to take bigger prices than necessary, what can he do about it? All he can do to keep prices down is to produce as many as possible.

Beef costs at least £2 a kilo to produce. A good set-up can produce pork for half that. And yet the way things are going the price of pork on the rise could overtake the falling price of beef somewhere around the 165p a kilo mark.

In the meantime Mossie and his piggy pals have developed a new way of getting rid of some of their money. They hire a bus to take them on a 'grub crawl'. I met them at it the other day. They were in the Salmon Inn having a few beers and their starters. Then it was up to the Wasp's Nest for more drink and a delicious sizzler steak washed down with the second best claret. Then over to Tarves for the dessert and liqueurs.

Whatever will they think of next?

Perhaps they've got it going already. There has been a lot of speak about a big charity clay pigeon shoot at the local range and the boys have been training hard for it.

I was having a modest half with Potions when in came the pig boys. "Come on Potions, up to the range and practice for Sunday."

"But I haven't got my gun."

"You winna need your gun," said Mossie with scorn. "The only thing we'll be shootin is the bar."

May 19, 1997

A pill for life

THE FARMER didn't mind being put on the water pills. The change in priorities among men of a certain age, from reproduction to water production, seems quite natural.

There is even a slight cache in being on them – it is a sign of progress on life's journey.

"Aye Willie. They tell me you're nae on the water peels yet? Man, Man! Still, I suppose ye're only 60."

It gives us yet another common interest. Old men on park benches can be seen swopping pills in much the same way as women 20 years ago used to hand round the poke with, "Go on Hen. Have a pheno-barb."

All the same, The Farmer has had a terrible shock, and it came from The Doctor. It was one thing being put on the pill "for the rest of your life", but it was a severe blow to have the prescription cut from 100 at a time to 30.

Mossie showed a touching concern. "By god, Charlie you better nae buy any green bananas. You could easy nae be here when they're ripe." And then when I told him I couldn't stand gossiping any longer because I had a load of Twerpal to put on the barley he was quite surprised: "Are ye bothering?"

Dr Death's vote of no confidence in my waterworks was particularly ironic as I was only in to stock up for my holidays

among those masters of water, the Dutch.

The Breadwinner had been persuaded to take a week off winning bread to go spending some in Holland. She wanted to see the bulb fields in bloom and I wanted to see what on earth the Dutch did with all these windmills and how they managed to keep the parks dry when they are mostly below sea level.

And remember, the Dutch don't only have the sea to keep out. They have to deal with several of Europe's biggest drains. Those come from as far off as the Alps, and collect water from the neighbours before pouring into Holland. They include the Meuse, the Issels and the mighty Rhine rivers.

I used to think windmills were to provide the power which in Scotland was pro-vided by water. I could see it would be difficult for a Dutch farmer to organise a mill dam and a water wheel. That power system depends on water fall-ing, which is just about the last thing the Low Countries need.

And the Dutch would have had problems following us into steam power – their mines would have been awful wet.

To some extent I was right. We saw windmills used to grind flour, to saw planks, and to power a dieworks. But the windmill's main job was to pump water. Without thou-sands of windmills most of Holland would be under water.

Their cunning plan seems to be to build up the river banks to keep the snow from the Alps moving to the sea. The wind-mills pump the water from the farms up into those rivers.

We drain our wet bits down into the streams and rivers but the Dutch have to pump it up from low ditches to higher ones and then to higher ditches still.

Much of that great task is now done by electric pumps but the old windmill can shift a lot of water. They told us that the tips of the blades reach over 100 miles an hour. We saw them at perhaps half that and generating frightening power. It seemed to be lifting the fill of a nine inch pipe about five feet.

If we were impressed by the mills we were less so by the tulip fields. They turned out to be no better than a field of tulips in Kincardineshire. Maybe they are less good. It is many years since Bob Milne of Dykelands in the Howe of the Mearns made his first million selling bulbs to the Dutch.

We slept and ate two meals on a barge, and in between cycled round the country looking at what the farmers were doing. Apart from the bulbs and the pumping that didn't seem to be much. There was a lot of very soggy grazing crisscrossed by ditches. There were a few dairy cattle in the fields, quite a lot of lambs kept in twos and threes in gardens, and very little cultivation. We can't have been where they grow all those potatoes which are such a pest for the British growers.

The fellow cyclists were mostly friendly, middle aged, American fitness fanatics with no eye for the ridiculous and hence no recognisable sense of humour. I heard one professional lady telling another she got up at 4.30 each morning, went to the gymnasium for a good hour then drove to work to be at her desk at 6.30. Pathetic!

There was not a single smoker in the company of 32. That suited us fine but we were shocked and shown up by our companions' drinking habits. Those could be accurately gauged as we had to sign up for our booze.

Despite being the only ones to sneak out to the local pubs after dinner, The Breadwinner and The Farmer ran up a bigger bar bill than the rest of the company put together.

There were few jokes. But there was one piece of all-American wit.

The Americans were not impressed by the cleanliness of the canals. America is clearly a very hygienic place.

It may have been easier for The Farmer, coming from Scotland, to be a good tourist. I kept remarking to them on the things I admired. Including a much cleaner canal. I even exaggerated that I could see a salmon.

"Oh really," said the sour voice of one spoilt by the spotlessness of the Bronx. "Are you sure it's not a salmonella?"

Wasting Asset goes all respectable

THE WASTING Asset, the younger and even more prodigal son, has turned over a new leaf. Indeed he has burned the old book and gotten himself a whole new one. Two years ago he decided that a wife, a family, a business, a positive cash flow and respectability were preferable to all the good things he had been enjoying for the previous 30 years.

He soon found the wife who, as well as being beautiful, had the strength of character to uphold the family and the strength of sinew to batter him as necessary. In his wedding speech the Wasting Asset had the good grace to admit "it was not easy being my parents".

That brought many lumps to the throats of the company and even a tear to the eyes of some who knew the truth.

At the hospital in Glasgow to which we used to take him almost weekly, the staff knew him by name.

When he fell off the school roof at what should have been "play" time, I particularly remember a nice black nurse in casualty saying with the warmest of smiles, "Oh, Davie, you've come back to see us. What was it this time?" He was the only kid on the south side of Glasgow who was sent to school in an American football helmet. (That worked).

There seem to be two main roots of the Wasting Asset's difficulties. When he was just old enough for the Boys Brigade football, he let it be known that he supported Aberdeen. That meant neither the Rangers nor the Celtics would defend him. And that gave him the very odd idea that soccer and fighting were somehow connected.

Then there was the North Sea oil. One week he was at school on the £1 the week that The Farmer gave him, plus what he could earn at a pound an hour acting as a gate or being a go-for on the farm. The next he was an oilman earning more than his teachers, and considerably more than The Farmer.

What may have looked like good fortune made life very difficult for the Waster. It destroyed his understanding of the connection between earning money and spending it. In no time £10,000 a year wasn't nearly enough to keep the 17-year-old.

When The Farmer's pals were blowing that their sons were just finishing at agricultural college and going on to do their PhDs, it was always "And how's your Davie doing?" with a smirk. "He's a Beach Bum in Torremolinos," we had to say and try to smile.

Mind you, he was very good at that. They used to pay him just to go into bars for a drink because he was the Pied Piper.

Everywhere he went, the Wasting Asset was followed by a hoard of adoring girls. Wherever they went, there followed a crowd of thirsty young men.

It was such a waste. The Asset had an eye for stock, the only one of The Farmer's children so gifted, and he could fairly work when he had to. But instead of applying his nose to the grindstone on the land of his fathers, he preferred the life of Champagne Charlie in the sun. Why, I just cannot imagine.

However, we've got him now. He's got the wife, the two teenage stepdaughters, the run-down pub and the mortgage. And now the baby.

The taming of the Wasting Asset is complete. His wife presented him with the bairn screaming out of a purple face: "Here is the son you wanted so desperately. Now he desperately wants you."

The Pied Piper of Torremolinos is now a Modern Man. He shouts "Time Gentleman Please" on the dot with all the gravitas of a Free Kirk minister, and takes his turn of rising in the night to change nappies and administer bottles, a thing The Farmer (to his pride) never did.

"The revenge of the Fathers is visited on the sons even by the third generation."

Retirement house is a stress builder

THE BULL goes in on Saturday. I have been feeding the old dears bucketfuls of a lick which is supposed to aid fertility. Several are impatient for his arrival.

I'm keeping quiet about it, in my usual modest way, but the crops are quite the best I have seen here. And that's important as this should be my last harvest and I need it to be a good one of which I can remind Potions from time to time. The rape is as good as I have seen anywhere.

If height is anything to go by we are in for record yields from the Synergy. Mossie and I have just measured one stem at 7 feet and 2 inches. It could well be a case of all show and no dough but it fairly doesn't look like it. There are pods everywhere.

The news is not all good. Along with the tall Synergy we have sown an equal number of the sturdy variety, Rocket.

The idea is that the Rocket holds its lanky brother up to the light and produces a secondary inflorescence under the Synergy flowers.

That looks like a failure to me. The Synergy is so vigorous that it seems have choked the Rocket out.

Having said that, agriculture has not been dominating The Farmer's life. Indeed it has been squeezed between all the emotion of building our final house and all the panic of putting on a wedding for our Younger Investment.

The house is the worst because the consequences of all the mistakes we make will be with us until we have the mortal coil shaken from us.

It was a ludicrous thing to do but, in order to save money, The Farmer undertook to be his own main contractor and site foreman.

At first it looked like a good move. We put the whole job out to tender but the estimates looked high. The Farmer would put the job out piecemeal to the various trades and choose the cheapest. We would be able to play all those salesmen who want to sell you kitchens and conservatories off against one another.

On that basis we were able to show savings of a good 20%.

Now I'm not going to say what the Death House is costing (it never does to let your neighbours know too much) but 20% of £160,000 is a lot of money.

You will remember that our retirement house is in the shape of an H-plan farm steading. It has a stable and cartsheds at one side and a byre at the other connected by a barn and loft.

The midden at the back is to be the carpark and the farmyard (or 'close' as we call it) at the front, is glassed over for a 'sitooterie'. There the old Farmer and his wife will be able to sit oot among the elements and yet be protected from them.

Oh yes, it was all carefully thought out, right down to the especially wide doors to take any wheelchairs that may one day be necessary and, meantime, to make it easier for The Farmer to get through them at the first attempt after being delayed at the mart by Mossie and the boys.

All went well until we started to take the plans off the paper. The Farmer soon discovered that the main contractor deserves his 10%. As the job nears completion, even 20% is beginning to seem like quite a good investment.

It appears that you can't just assemble all your tradesmen and say, "Right boys? Go!"

The site foreman should dovetail all the bits of work so that each trade follows the other in its logical order. The Farmer had no knowledge of this. He would hassle for weeks to get the slaters to turn up only to be told when they at last arrived, "Oh, na na. We need the joiners to put on the facing boards first."

The sitooterie is being an absolute nightmare.

It seems like conservatory people use up their energy cold-calling in the evenings. We contracted to buy one but had to forego our 10% deposit because they couldn't recommend anyone to erect it and we couldn't get any of the local tradesmen to take it on.

Finally we agreed a price with a firm who would 'supply and erect'.

But how?... and when? And who was responsible for the spouts? and who the lead? and who the slated part of the sitooterie?

As the supervisor who came out to try once more to sort the thing out said to me sadly, "This has been like a job creation scheme."

We are hoping to get it watertight eventually. As Mossie said, "It would be all right for a sparrow to get in between the lead and the glass, but to hell wi jackdaws."

The stress of the wedding is nothing to all that.

June 9, 1997

Gertie's bite was a means to an end

DID YOU see the programme about the intelligence of pigs showing that they could play computer games? Dr This and Professor That were most excited by their discovery that pigs were far more intelligent than dogs and even chimpanzees. As an occasional pig-keeper it came as no surprise to The Farmer. Indeed having seen rugby players at play and Members of Parliament at work, he would put up a good case for the pig being more intelligent than the human being.

What the scientists had done was to set up two pigs with a computer screen with a mouse operated by a joy stick. Every time the pig moved the mouse onto the correct icon it got a sweetie. Even when they changed the icon it was no sweat to Hamlet and Omelette. They mastered the system so well that they were very soon fat and ready for market.

The scientists were bowled over by this sign of porcine genius.

Not so The Farmer. For, in pre-computer days, he had replicated that experimental result many painful times 'in the field', as scientists will say when they don't mean in a field.

It was when he had breeding sows on the Rodenight system. They ran about ploughing a grass park until they pigged and then brought their young to ten weeks old in little corrugated iron huts. It was an idyllic system and the hoards of little piggies charging about were very sweet.

But it was in the feeding arrangements that one sow in particular showed just the intelligence that these computer literate pigs showed.

Each morning The Farmer had to jump the fence with a bag of cobs on his back. His plan was to walk to the centre of the park to spread the cobs where each sow could have a share.

But this old dear discovered that if she bit The Farmer hard on one of his buttocks, he would drop the bag and run. That meant she could have far more than her share, it would be all in one place and she could have it now.

It wasn't that the sow liked the taste of human flesh. She

was just using it – like the joy stick on the computer – as a means to an end. And she only did it when The Farmer had a bag on his shoulder. She never bit strangers. Old Gertie knew which icon would feed her.

The Farmer was impressed, however, by the performance of another intelligent pig shown on the programme. This beast was brought up with working sheepdogs and taught to herd sheep. I don't suppose there were any mirrors about so Streakie probably thought he was a collie.

At any rate, if being able to work sheep is a sign of intelligence, pigs beat dogs hands down, according to this programme. Streakie could cer-tainly gather and turn sheep. If the camera wasn't lying, at the age of perhaps five weeks Streaky was able to shed four from a score of sheep.

You try that with a five-week-old pup. It should be sheepdogs out and sheeppigs in.

And what chance would a five-week-old human have of feeding itself from a menu on a computer screen? Let alone bringing four score sheep down from the hill?

Even the Younger Invest-ment, generally regarded as clever as well as being about as well behaved as you get nowa-days, wasn't much good at five weeks. She is to be married on Saturday.

She's home for a whole week of stress, "helping" us to prepare, dishing out the second best whisky to those who come with presents and working up an appetite for a lifetime of monogamy.

The plan is the village church and then to Haddo House Hall for Mossie's roast beef and the Red Rooster's tatties. As the other side have agreed to pay the champagne but overlooked the question of how much, The Farmer sees no need for other drink. The young man being a musician and all his musical friends coming, we anticipate a hellova ceilidh.

The venue was erected at the turn of the century by the marchioness of Aberdeen as part of her campaign 'Onward and Upward', whose aims included the improvement of the morals of the peasants. So what better place for The Farmer to take his daughter for her wedding breakfast? And what better place for The Farmer to entertain his friends?

I cannot for the life of me see why there has to be such an orgy of preparation. Why do I need to rehearse getting out of a car and walking down the church aisle? Would it be such a big deal if I took a wrong turn and landed in the vestry?

What a fuss about the potatoes. Great lengths were gone to to get Golden Wonders. At this time of year they are a bit wrinkled so when Mossie saw them he refused to come to the wedding unless I bought some of the new tatties with which the Red Rooster is conning the supermarkets.

We're having both. The Farmer is trying to please everyone.

By the way the rape is still growing at an inch per day ... seven feet, nine inches is the record to date.

June 16, 1997

Death of an athlete

THE YOUNGER Investment's wedding not withstanding, the most affecting part of The Farmer's week has been the funeral, in Edinburgh, of a laddie who learned hand-milking on an Island in Loch Lomond, who studied agriculture at Auchencruive and who farmed hill cows and caravans at Aberfoyle. They met 40 years ago when The Farmer

was an apprentice at the Highland Games and Jay Scott was the best all-round athlete Scotland had ever produced.

Fay Lenore, the singer with whom Scott made the couple-of-the-year 39 years ago, asked The Farmer to say something at the funeral about the athletic achievements of his old friend – "and not to be too serious. Give us a laugh."

It wasn't an easy contract but this is roughly what The Farmer said;

When Jay Scott went to the Bahamas to toss the caber in the early sixties, they erected a 20 foot high, full colour cardboard cut-out of him at the entrance to Nassau airport. When the hero emerged from the plane an ex-cited crowd pushed forward. I heard one of the natives say, "I jist gotta see this Jay Scatt. He 20 foot tall."

And you know, the man wasn't disappointed.

For, though he was a mere six foot two, '20 foot tall' was a metaphor for Jay's early life. Everything he did was larger than life, done faster, and cut more corners than was normal. Jay was the sort of person who when he entered a company lifted the whole atmosphere. He quickened the blood wherever he went.

Many people said he should have played the part of Geordie in the film about the Highland games athlete who won the Hammer at the Olympics. But Jay would never have had the patience. Two days to film a minute's action wasn't his way. Had he taken that part I'm sure they wouldn't have reached 'scene one, take 20' before he was wrapping the camera round the producer's neck and looking for somewhere exotic to stick the clapperboard.

In the late 1950s an athlete just back from the Olympics, where he had represented the United States, entered the high jump at Tobermory Games. Jay won. He jumped six feet three and three-quarter inches – no great shakes today. But Jay did that from grass to grass; no tartan run-up and no soft cushion to land on. And he used the old fashioned 'scissors' style where you cross the bar in a sitting position and so lose as much as a foot in height.

But what really makes Jay's achievement so wonderful is that he not only beat this specialist high jumper at his own game but did so while taking prizes in the 100 yards and the 220 yards races, the long jump, hop, step and jump, and pole vault as well as all seven of the heavyweight events.

Indeed, between jumps he put on his kilt to keep his turn in throwing the weights.

There were those in the mainstream of Scottish Athletics who doubted the stories of

Jay's prowess, but they got their proof. A secret contest was arranged between Jay and the best decathlete at the time. We were worried that our man might be beaten as he had never thrown a discus nor run a race further than 440 yards.

We needn't have worried. He was so far ahead after eight events that Jay was victorious without running the mile or throwing the discus.

His achievements went on and on. He was favourite to win the Powderhall sprint one year and that he didn't was typical of Jay's rash determination. He just couldn't hold himself back for the big one as his backers wanted him to and he won a big race at Newtongrange. That cut his handicap and he came second at Powderhall.

I will remember Jay Scott best for his performances at the Aboyne Games. The Chieftain's trophy there is for the best athlete to take at least one prize in the heavyweight and the light events. Jay won that blue riband seven times on the trot.

Jay never patronised an opponent. He never beat you when he could give you a right doing. For, like all great athletes, he had that bit of swagger. The story has been told, retold and exaggerated out of all proportion, but Jay did like to be reminded of the day when he arrived late at Taynuilt Games.

They were just finishing the high jump. The bar stood at the winning height and the winner was claiming his prize. Our hero ran onto the field. He was entering and would attempt a clearance. The officials would have none of it. Jay pointed out, rightly, that there is no law on what stage you have to join the competition. If he wanted to start once everyone else was finished, that was up to him.

He was overruled, but just to show them, without any warm-up or removing his kilt or jacket, or changing his brogues for jumping shoes, he strode up to the bar and sailed over.

Jay thrilled the crowds wherever he appeared, but never more so than at his very first games. At the age of not very much he was to run in the 100 yards at Luss Highland Games on the Banks of Loch Lomond. The youth removed his kilt only to find that in his excitement he had forgotten to put on his shorts. For the first of countless times the young farmer from Inchmurrin got the cheer of the day.

Sadly, perhaps inevitably, Jay was slowed to mortal speed by a knee injury when he was at his peak as a heavyweight athlete. And then when he was in his mid-40s came the tractor accident after which life was something of a struggle for the man who had once moved like a panther.

Jay Scott was the best in the days when athletes looked athletic and athleticism came from the hard work and play in the great outdoors rather than from the gymnasium and the cabinet in the bathroom.

I'll miss him. I miss him already.

June 23, 1997

Wedded blitz

IT IS all a bit of a blur as I look back on it, but the Younger Investment is well and truly wed. There is an anxious queue of cakemakers, caterers, floral artists, organists, hallkeepers, vintners, taxi drivers and musicians at the door to prove it.

They are right to be anxious for it has been a long haul. It was 15 years ago that we started marrying the children off and the retirement fundie has had to pay for four weddings.

I await with mounting dread the arrival of Mossie's

bill for the roast beef, for our guests must have been very hungry. They went through more than a pound per head of best sirloin roast-on-the-bone.

The Farmer was proud of the Investment for insisting that all her new relatives from the south and her Bohemian friends from Edinburgh should be entertained to the right Aberdeenshire beef, hung for a month and then rotated in cooking so that the juices couldn't find a way out.

The Farmer was also pleased to be making a contribution to the market for beef which has been so devastated by the BSE nonsense. But the Investment was quite wrong to think it would be cheap. Just because The Farmer gets less for his beef than he was getting 18 years ago doesn't mean it is cheap in the shops.

Even though his equipment only amounts to a recipe and his converted rotaspreader, you cannot get Mossie to prepare and cook his beef for nothing. I tried to reason with him. "Now Mossie, I know roast beef costs a fortune in a restaurant but you don't have the overheads."

He was furious. "I'm the overheads. You tell me the restaurant that has refreshment bills as big as mine."

At any rate, it was delicious and I can't tell you how many farmers asked me the questions this column has asked before: "Could we not get Mossie to tour the country showing the folk what right beef tastes like? Why haven't the Meat and Livestock Commission got Mossie on their stand at the Highland? Why not scrap the MLC and give the space to Mossie's muckspreader?"

The champagne was good, and paid for by the other side, too. The Breadwinner kept her promise: "I'm going to hit the champagne running," and who was The Farmer to do anything but his best by such generosity? He drank all he could and offered it most freely around the company – all night.

I did notice the other side taking contrary action, however. "Dinna bother wi that stuff. It's nae very good," I heard them say. "Ye're far better wi a dram."

We had a very nice surprise on the morning of the wedding.

The magnificent Adam mansion Haddo House has long since been handed over to the National Trust as not even the Earls of Aberdeen could afford such an overhead towards the end of the 20th century. The Laird, however, retains the wonderful grounds.

Peasants normally have to sneak in by the tradesman's entrance and miss the spectacular front view of the mansion. So we were very pleased

when the Laird phoned and invited us to take the shortcut through his grounds to the hall for the wedding breakfast. It was a nice gesture much appreciated by The Breadwinner and the Younger Investment. The young couple were very grand swishing past Aberdeenshire's historic pile in the Jaggie.

(The Farmer reflected sadly that whereas his first car cost £25 it cost £78 just to valet the Jag for the wedding.)

The Laird might not have been so generous had he known that one of the guests would find an 18th-century bridge, which had been quite big enough when he arrived, was too narrow by the time he was going home.

Nobody knows how the Red Rooster managed it. His new Porsche is quite wide, and the bridge was designed for the Laird's horse and carriage, but the speed limit is 15 miles an hour in the grounds. Yet almost the whole of one side of the bridge landed in the river.

Worse than that, British Telecom had run a cable along that side of the bridge and it was severed. That meant the Haddo Arts Trust, the National Trust for Scotland and the Laird himself were cut off. It was a very small Farmer who sneaked round to the Laird's house with a bottle of the other side's champagne.

And the farm? Well, Potions and I found a rape stem eight feet two inches high and claim it as a world record.

A bridge too near for Red Rooster

AMONG THE many highlights of the Younger Investment's wedding last week was one which will stay with The Farmer until the last day.

The young couple had decided that they would say their vows in a one-er, without any prompting by the minister.

This called for considerable rehearsing. In the case of the groom it was done mostly in the bar of the Salmon Inn on the morning before the do. In church he almost managed it.

But the Younger Investment was word-perfect. Being ever the good girl, she did her rehearsing well in advance. She was practising away in the kitchen one day while The Farmer tried to follow the progress of the British Lions on tele and The Breadwinner was deep in the Financial Times.

"What does 'covenant' really mean?" asked the bride-to-be.

"Oh," said her mother, without raising her eyes from the FT, "if you covenant you get the tax back."

And the aftermath of the great wedding followed us to the Highland Show. Even at Ingliston poor Red Rooster wasn't able to get away from the ignominy of having demolished the Laird's bridge. All the way down he had to listen to the boys patronising him with, "Here's a nice wide bridge now, Rooster, you could hardly miss the opening on it." And "Good strong brig here. A body would be safe enough to hit those parapets."

Big Hamish had a man-sized poster which he paraded about the showground. You may have seen it where it came to rest in the Members' Pavilion. It read, 'P Reg Porsche for sale, Damaged but repairable. Apply, Rooster Farms.'

They might have added; '17th-century bridge breaking for scrap – apply, the Laird.'

The Rooster shouldn't take it so hard. He has given such pleasure to the countryside and his misfortune will continue to make us all happy for many a year. In fact, he should get a grant for it.

We needed something like that to brighten us up. This strong pound is knocking us for six. Food imports are flooding into the country because they are so cheap. When is Mr Blair going to get on with reintroducing socialism so the pound can fall again and give us a chance?

Every day they talk about an even lower price for grain. I even heard of a merchant trying to buy barley at £72 off the combine. He's a chancer, but there now seems to be no hope of getting £80 in August.

At the national average yield, which is still less than three tonnes to the acre, you need a big acreage to make money out of barley at that. There is no problem covering variable costs but, on the croft that is Little Ardo with only 90 acres of grain, there just isn't enough to take a big enough share of the overheads even though we grow more like three and a half tonnes.

We'd be quite lost without the subsidy, but there is a lot of talk about cutting that.

The good news will have to come from the cattle and there the signs are improving. Consumption continues to recover and so does price. In fact the good stuff you serve to your guests at a wedding is selling well. What we need is a breed of cow that is all backend, for it is the forequarter meat that is dragging the market down.

Now comes some good news in the fore end of the market. The trouble has been those damned hamburger joints which stopped buying British beef in response, they said, to consumer fears over BSE. Wimpy have shown the way

331

but now it appears that by far the biggest sellers of grease-burgers, McDonalds, is about to restart buying British.

That could make a big difference. The trouble is that, with the strong pound, it may still pay them to import beef, where the costs of production are also lower in respect of all those hygiene measures which are now taken only in Britain. If there was ever any danger of getting CJD from beef then that is greater from the foreign stuff. Most is still produced without removing the potentially dangerous tissue.

All we can do is plug away. We have to produce what the market calls quality and for that the beef trade now demands a black skin. It isn't that anybody wants to eat the skin. It is just that the Aberdeen Angus bull leaves black calves and Aberdeen Angus is flavour of the year.

Depending on what you cross it with, the Chianina, Romagnola, Marchigiana, and Limousin will give you black calves, but the Aberdeen Angus has an additional advantage which it shares with the Galloways – small calves. Now last year we only had four heifers and we just let the Simmental bull serve them along with their mothers.

It was a disaster. We had two normal calvings and two stuck completely.

Caesarean section was the only hope. We lost both calves. I have just received the cheque for one heifer at the cull and the vet's bill. Guess which is the bigger.

So, despite having been a pioneer of mountainous European breeds, The Farmer has an Aberdeen Angus bull working among his Simmental heifers. He's on loan from the Irishman.

It is true that there is an upside of the strong pound. The imported fertiliser prices are looking very attractive. That will help the farmer of Little Ardo but fortunately that will not be me. By seed time this autumn it will be Potions's turn to try to make cash flow up this hill.

I do not fancy his job.

High and dry on the family ark

I WOULDN'T like you to feel too sorry for me. The stories of flooding in shires of Aberdeen and Moray are all true. The burns are all full and overflowing, and the crops, which promised so much, are a tangled mess in many places.

But The Farmer is all right so far. My grandfather is credited with the observation that Little Ardo would neither 'drought nor droon' and it seems that that is still true.

For though the barley is looking a bit untidy at the endriggs, where the machinery turns and it has too much or too little manure and chemicals, it is still all standing. All that despite an inch of rain a day and wind that chills the bones.

In fact Mossie phoned the other day. He'd got up earlier than usual (at the crack of half past nine) and was quite agitated. "The rape's doon," he said with anguish.

I was surprised as I had followed his instructions and, while our rape is beginning to lean a bit that is hardly a shock, with the Synergy plants going as high as eight feet two inches and looking like a heavy crop. The Rocket we sowed along with it is doing its job. As a short hardy plant, it is there to hold its lanky brother up to the sun – or in this case to the rain.

"No, no. You dinna understand. It's nae lying doon. It's far worse than that. It's doon in price."

Disaaaster!

With the cattle still cheap because of BSE, with the barley £15 a tonne down on the year and now rape down £25 a tonne, things are not looking well for The Farmer's last year in business. The retirement fundie, ravaged by weddings and building the Death House, is suffering. He may not be able to afford to retire after all.

But the news is not all bad. It never is in farming, where one man's misfortune is every other farmer's joy.

Mossie was to be hosting a big do for a lot of crackshot growers from the south. They were to see the crops, shoot some clay doos and eat some barbecued beef and a lamb. As usual Mossie had been very modest about his crops. "It's nae for me to say, but they're just coming to Moss-side to see how it's done. I'm nae telling onybody but my crops are just lookin about the best in the countryside."

But whereas Little Ardo is up on the little hill with gentle southern exposure and plenty of run on its aquifers, Moss-side is so called because it is flat and includes a moss. And it's no use Mossie calling his Moss his "fenland". When we get rain like this the water table rises and Moss-side becomes Lochside.

I was looking forward to hearing our grain baron laying off about how to grow barley in six inches of water. But on Tuesday, the day before the event, our man was struck by one of those things we so cherish when they happen to our

neighbours. Overnight the big field of barley in front of the house and lying down to the main road had succumbed to the waters and gone flat.

Give him his due, Mossie panicked. The farm walk was postponed. I hurried over to savour the damage. It was first rate. Only the tramlines remained standing.

The culprit is a new variety which, thankfully, my adviser was keeping to himself. It's called Muscat – on Tuesday's evidence a name to forget.

"What made you sow this stuff, Moss?" I enquired, as sympathetically as I could.

"Well, they say it's fantastic high-yielding." And then sweeping his eye round the flattened crop, "There was nothing in the brochure about it being fantastic high lodging."

These lads from the south were coming to see barley grown at various heights, particularly Mossie's technique of growing one long-strawed variety and one short, blended together. The idea being that while the tall crop is producing the usual berries at four feet, down at three feet there is another, admittedly much smaller crop, as a bonus.

"Aye, I can fairly show them how to grow barley at different heights. I've some at four feet, some at four inches, and some below the water line." So the walk was postponed till next Wednesday.

But the thing is, how much better off is he going to be next week? The barley isn't going to spring up again.

As the Red Rooster said: "You should just have carried on and told them some teenage travellers had held a folk festival in that field."

July 21, 1997

Staggering across the threshold

WE'RE IN! The Farmer and his wife now live in the house they have built for their retirement.

It was the Elder Investment's Elder Dividend who suggested the doorstep ceremony. "We've to put up a ribbon and Granda Charlie's to carry Granny over the doorstep. Then youse old ones can have some champagne."

The last bit sounded all right but the carrying of your bride over the threshold to a new life is supposed to emphasise male dominance and the role of old fashioned husbands. The Farmer's wife has earned for almost as long (and far more in total) than he has. Systems analysts don't have years when there is no earning at all. The Farmer had a 15-year stretch in the seventies and eighties when the profits only exceeded the losses by an average of £800.

Indeed that was why The Breadwinner is so-called.

Therefore, should she not carry The Farmer over the threshold as an earnest of her willingness to continue to support him in his retirement? After all, the contract was 'until death us do part'.

The weight ratio of two to

335

one in favour of The Farmer decided it. The old man swept the old lady up. It was no bother. Apart for a certain rounding of her edges, it didn't seem that different from when I carried her into our first house 37 years ago.

So we're in.

I swore we wouldn't move in until it was all finished. The paths were all to be laid and the garden landscaped. The Farmer practised waking up on the first day of the rest of his life. He would sweep back the curtains of the picture window they have made of the old cartshed door, to marvel at the views over Formartine to Bennachie.

But when we did move in, after building at the house for a year, there were still no curtains to sweep. The picture window was filled by a digger, and even if it hadn't been there I wouldn't have been able to see Bennachie for our very own mountain of black earth, thrown up when they were clearing the site.

Still, if we can get the drive-way made and the chuckies down to cover some of the mud, and get the roof of the sitooterie to stop leaking, I am sure The Breadwinner and I will be happy here. I am near enough to enjoy the mistakes of the next generation without the expense and I am just far enough away. I didn't feed the bulls last night

and, sure enough, I didn't hear a thing.

It does seem like 53 years since my mother and I walked up the brae to Little Ardo from the village. We had come to make a home for John R Allan who had gone reluctantly to fight Hitler as a sapper in the Royal Engineers and somehow emerged, without killing any Germans, as a captain in the Gordon Highlanders.

My mother wrote an article in the magazine Punch about it. It was called 'Return to my Grandfather's Farm'. It included the story about the crofter who had done well enough and saved hard enough to get the tenancy of a small farm. This required more than just a lease and his savings. The crofter would need the support of the Northern Bank.

Those were the days when bankers knew about business as well as about money, and the next step was for financier and entrepreneur to go and walk the 40 acres of Stoneyhillock.

As they swished through the village in the banker's gig the crofter recognised the end of his well kept secret. "They'll aa' ken noo," he said with quiet satisfaction.

What I remember best is the emptiness of the old house. It was warm but it was empty and every footstep and every word echoed from the wooden floors

to the pine doors. It seemed important to my mother, though at the age of five I don't suppose I had much grasp of what it means to a peasant to move into the farm that her great grandfather first tenanted, and to know that it was her own.

I know now for it was with the greatest of pride and a profound sense of the rightness of it that I moved in with The Breadwinner to the old home. I was the fifth generation of us in the 18th-century listed farmhouse. I stood in the shadow of great men. There was William Yull who won a special gold medal from the Royal Highland and Agricultural Society for drainage work which allowed the breaking in of 55 acres from the moss. Maitland Mackie, who was President of the National Farmers' Union of Scot-

land and who even made money though he thought little of it. And I was succeeding John R Allan, the author of that classic of the North-east, Farmer's Boy.

So what does it feel like, after 20 years, to be leaving such a place for 'a new hoose in the neuk o' a park?' Is that not a comedown?

Strangely, it is not.

The sixth and seventh generations are moving in so that the continuity is not being lost.

And the new house is more truly the work of The Farmer and his Breadwinner. We designed it, we put it out to tender, we hassled the tradesmen, and we paid for it.

Little Ardo was the family farm always. Whinhill will be ours until the last hour of the last day.

Postscript

THE HARVEST was disappointing for most in Aberdeenshire. Prices were very low indeed – far worse than expected, and the weight of the crops was also disappointing. However nature was good to The Farmer and her bounty gave him a very acceptable last harvest. The barley ran 3.501 and the rape 1.675 tonnes to the acre.

Potions didn't want the calves for some reason, so The Farmer had to sell those in the backend sales. The stots averaged £390 and the heifers £250 and we topped the bull calves at Thainstone with a pair of bulls at 137.5 pence a kilo.

Potions took over 40 cows and in-calf heifers and the very last of The Farmer's beasts was taken by the Irishman on the 30th of January, 1998. She was a pure Simmental cow whose great auntie had gone to New Zealand for £10,000. The Irishman gave The Farmer £300 – a fiver more than he would have got from the incinerator.

The Farmer is a happy man.

The Wasting Asset has been elected to the village hall committee – at this rate he'll soon be standing as a Tory candidate for parliament.

His big brother has been breeding again and has four children already. The Young Investment has a daughter.

The retirement house is draught-free and cosy. The sitooterie gives a light and warm view over a huge skelp of Aberdeenshire.

From it The Farmer can see how the Red Rooster, Mossie, Crookie, the Durnos at Uppermill, Maitland Mackie and Waterside are getting on. And he can keep tabs on how Potions is filling The Farmer's boots.

The signs are good. Potions, who wasn't fat to start with, has worked so hard in his first half year that he has lost two stones.

He has fulfilled his dream of stopping making money as a chemist to get on with spending it as a farmer.

In the Investment he has a wife and budget controller who will see that the cash doesn't just flow out.

The Farmer has fulfilled the peasant's duty of care to his land. He has left it in good heart and in good hands.

He has also fulfilled the peasant's duty to his family – that there be a place which is still their place.

Farmer's Diary

Charlie Allan farmed with very middling success from 1973, when he quit his post of Senior Lecturer in Economics at Strathclyde University, until 1986 when his wife Fiona took a three-year aid job in Nairobi, Kenya. They returned to Scotland in 1989. This diary tells how he got the farm going again, tried to keep the banker happy and re-established a place in the small North-east community of Methlick. This volume covers a long year to Christmas 1990. Illustrated by Jim Turnbull. Price £11.95

Volume II

Charlie continues his record of the never-ending battle with the weather and bureaucracy. He recounts the fun had by Mossie, Red Rooster and the other lads of the discussion group which meets at the Salmon Inn on a Sunday night to blow about their crop yields or drown their sorrows when the weather wins. This volume covers 1991 and Jan-Feb 1992. Illustrated by Jim Turnbull. Price £11.95

Volume III

Volume III covers the period from March 1992 to the end of June 1993. Charlie is still trying to grow the four-tonne crop. There are marriages and deaths among the lads of the discussion group; sales and purchases of farms. But the biggest changes are brought in by the EC in the form of set-aside, and the EC commissioner from Ireland, Mr MacSharry, becomes the hero of Volume III. Illustrated by Jim Turnbull. Price £11.95

Volume IV

Volume IV covers June 1993 to October 1994. Mossie grew his sunflowers despite there being only four days of sunshine in the whole growing season, and The Irishman joined the Scottish Farming Community. In 1994 The Farmer had a record harvest but spoiled it by becoming the first and last to sell a heifer with a CCD – only stots are meant to carry those. Illustrated by Jim Turnbull. Price £11.95

All titles available at bookshops
throughout the North-east
or direct from Methlick.
Please add £1 for postage.

**Ardo Publishing Company Ltd.
Methlick, Aberdeenshire AB41 0HR
Tel/Fax 01651 806218**